W9-DIG-741

HAIL AND FAREWELL

HAIL AND FAREWELL

A TRILOGY

HAIL AND FAREWELL

VALE

BY

GEORGE MOORE

PR
5042
H3
1911
v.3

105470

NEW YORK
D. APPLETON AND COMPANY
1914

ST. JOSEPH'S UNIVERSITY
PR5042.H3 1911   v.3   STX
Hail and farewell ... /

RELEASE

3 9353 00127 2770

Copyright, 1914, by
D. APPLETON AND COMPANY

VALE

I

It was about the time of the publication of my letter to the *Irish Times*, mentioned in the last pages of "Salve," that I received from the French Consul an invitation to dinner to meet the Secretary of the Consulate, M. Orange, a young man, a poet, *au moins il a publié un volume de vers chez Lemerre.* The Méaulles, Monsieur et Madame, are among my pleasantest memories of Dublin, and on the night in question, when it was time to bid our host and hostess good-night, I suggested to Orange that we should walk back to Dublin together, thinking that perhaps he might like to talk French poetry with me. As we passed through the garden-gate he muttered: "*Voilà une soirée bien passée.*" He was quite right; we had passed a pleasant evening in pleasant company. But the next time we dined at the Méaulles' the same words were uttered, at the same place; the reiteration attracted my attention, and I began to read into them a hidden meaning: that we were nearer our graves than we had been earlier in the afternoon; and when he repeated the same words some

1

weeks afterward, they suggested still another meaning to me. It seemed to me that he was thinking
that being men of letters we should have done better
to stay at home reading our books under our lamps.
I remembered that books had been abandoned by me
long ago, and as we strode along together I fell to
thinking that I would do well to reacquire the habit
of reading. It did not occur to me that habits are
reacquired with difficulty, and that the temptation
is always by the talker to lay aside his book and go
out to look up a friend. Casual visiting is one of the
pleasures of Dublin life, henceforth it was to be denied to me. Orange's infernal criticism of life left me
no peace, and one evening I begged Teresa, when
she removed the cloth, to tell whoever called that I
was not at home. She promised to be firm with the
possible visitor, and put my coffee on the table.
The moment had come for me to pick out a book
from the shelves. But which?

I should find the large volume containing Shakespeare's plays on the third shelf. "A well of pure
literature undefiled," I said. "Alarums, excursions,
and the blowing of trumpets over the field of Agin-
court, Kings in full armor rushing about crying
for *destriers*—the French word for what we would
call a cob, compact and thick-set. He charges like
a *destrier* in the Henrys, and after the charge re-
tires to a hawthorn-tree and neighs a melodious
plaint of graves and worms and epitaphs. All that
is far away, out of my humor." Balzac appealed
to me for a moment while my eyes ran through the
titles of the edition printed in 1855, a prize brought

2

back from Paris some months ago, but never looked into; treated, alas! like a wife, a sort of matrimonial edition, and only known to me by a long attempt to read "César Birotteau," an adventure that had stopped half-way, so cumbersome was the burly Tourainean in this story, so slow was he, like a cart-horse asleep in the middle of the road, too heavy to struggle to his hooves in less than a hundred pages, getting away at last. "His ends are no doubt fine and thunderous. Turgenev didn't believe in him," and glancing down a line of small volumes I said: "He is neither cob nor dray, but an Arab carrying in every story a lady as romantic as one of Chopin's ballads, especially the third," and I thought of the celebrated phrase. Maupassant seemed to me too much like an intrigue with a housemaid. Goncourt? The fashion of yesterday and to-day older than Herodotus. Pater? His Epicurean? A tide of honeyed words preached by a divine from an ivory pulpit, well worth re-reading, but——

And I returned to my chair frightened, feeling that if I did not learn to read my life would become a burden to me and to others. "Everybody will fly from me, my friends will melt away. Edward wouldn't open to me the other night, he preferred his book to my talk, and he continues to struggle through Ruskin, and John Eglinton toils at 'Don Quixote.' Those fellows can live alone, and Æ . . . ah, well, Æ!"

And then my thoughts left me, and at a quarter to eleven I lit my candle, hoping that in bed some interesting book would come to mind. But when Teresa had removed the cloth the next night and the fated moment had come, I could not conquer a mysterious reluctance to rise out of my arm-chair. It seemed pleasanter to think about Stevenson than to read him, to remember that I had once called him "a young man walking in the Burlington Arcade, the best-dressed young man that ever walked in the Burlington Arcade, but little else." "We writers know how to get the knife under the other fellow's ribs." I raised my head to listen: footsteps sounded in the street, and it seemed as if somebody was coming to see me. . . . The moment grew tense and relaxed, and when the footsteps of the wanderer died away in the distance of Hume Street, I sat limp and miserable, afraid to look round lest somebody were crouching in the corner of the distant room.

But I had come home to read, and read I must, and it seemed to me that what was needed was some long work that would leave a definite impression upon the mind. There was "Tom Jones"; professors of literature declare it to be England's finest novel, but I remembered it merely as a very empty work written in a breezy manner; and there was Richardson that I had not read at all; "Clarissa Harlowe" in how many volumes of letters? And after these writers came Miss Burney, and the name of one of her books floated through my mind, the name of some woman, Emily, Julia—no. There was Sterne's "Sentimental Journey" still unread, and someone had given me a copy saying that no one would ever

4

appreciate Sterne more than I. . . . But my cigar was burning so fragrantly that Sterne was once again postponed, and I lay back in the arm-chair, dozing in the warmth that a huge lump of coal sent out from the grate, and, my brain stupefied in the heat, I said to myself: "Though I may have lost the habit of reading, I have acquired, perhaps more than any other human being, another habit, the habit of thinking. I love my own thoughts; and the past is a wonderful mirror in which I spend hours watching people and places I have known; dim, shadowy and far away they seem, and pathetic are the faces, and still more pathetic is the way everybody follows his little prejudices; however unreasonable they may be we must follow them. The Colonel said the other day that he could accept all that his Church teaches; Transubstantiation, the Immaculate Conception, even the Pope's indulgences did not trouble him; he found it difficult, however, to believe in the immortality of his soul. " 'If Death deprives me of my senses of feeling and seeing, of my intellect, of everything that is me, how can it be said that I exist?' he asked, shielding his face with his hand from the fire. 'How can it be said that I, the personality connoted by the pronoun, exist?' We are all Agnostics at heart." And then it seemed to me that the Colonel and I were engaged in some argument, not about the immortality of the soul, but about a letter that I had written to the *Irish Times* in which he declared that I had libeled him, and then my father seemed to have come back to this world again, and, picking up the letter about which my brother and I were disputing, he declared that he could detect no libel in it but a great many misspellings and mistakes in grammar, and that I must go back to Oscott at once. I was there in a trice, face to face with the headmaster, no other than Sir Thomas More, who was deeply shocked that any descendant of his should use the language as badly as I had done in the bundle of papers which he held in his hand. . . .

The thought of undergoing further school-days awoke me suddenly, and at the same moment the door opened. "Good Heavens, who is it? What is it?"

It was only Teresa bringing in glasses and decanters, and when I had recovered my senses sufficiently I began to think of the two portraits of Sir Thomas More brought from Ashbrook. The heavy monkish jowl and the cocked hat used to awaken a frightened antipathy in me. There must have been a fine strain of Protestant blood flowing in the Moores. But which was the one who discovered himself to be a Protestant? And a keen interest in my ancestors awakening in me, I moved to the writing-table and wrote asking the Colonel for his name.

A few days after Teresa handed me an envelope on which I recognized my brother's handwriting, and making at once for my arm-chair, I read that Sir Thomas More had married twice, begetting a son and three daughters by his first wife. These had remained Papists, and it was not till the second generation that the change came. John had two sons, both called Thomas. The elder founded the

6

line of Barnborough, now extinct; but the younger
Thomas discovered himself to be a Protestant, and
the Colonel reminded me that if I decided to throw
over Sir Thomas More I should also have to throw
over the honor of having a Protestant clergyman
in the family. The clergyman had three sons, of
whom little is known except their names. Two of
them went to live in Essex; the third, another
Thomas, disappeared into Mayo, it is said.

"This tradition," the Colonel wrote, "finds support in the fact that there was a Thomas More in
Mayo in the seventeenth century who had a son
called George, and this George took part in the
Williamite wars in Ireland, and it appears that he
must have conducted himself well at the Battle of
the Boyne, for King William bestowed on him the
title of Vice-Admiral of Connaught, a title which
he held twice, a considerable title still, for its present holder is Lord Lucan. He was buried near
Straid Abbey in Mayo, with this inscription upon
his tomb: 'THIS IS THE BURIAL PLACE OF CAPTAIN
GEORGE MORE AND HIS DESCENDANTS, 1723.' His
son obtained a lease of some property known as
Legaphouca, and from this deed we learn that he
had two sons, George and John, and that John married Miss Jane Lynch Athy of Renville, a Catholic,
and brought her to live with him at Ashbrook. Of
this marriage there were two sons, one died, and the
surviving son, George, seeing that the family fortunes were dwindling, sailed away to Spain and became a Catholic."

"But why doesn't he tell me our great-grand-

father's reasons for going to Rome?" And taking
a cigar out of the box, I lay back in my arm-chair
watching the smoke ascend into the crystals of the
chandelier, tarnishing them and diverting my
thoughts from my great-grandfather, setting me
thinking that the whole chandelier must soon be
taken to pieces and cleaned. "A most provoking
letter." The night of our quarrel, or rather the
following morning, the Colonel told me that our
great-grandfather had married a Miss Kilkelly, a
Spaniard despite her name, if a hundred years of
Spain can turn a Milesian back into a Spaniard.
Wild Geese these Kilkellys were, fled from Ireland
after the siege of Limerick. Her portrait hangs in
Moore Hall between the windows, a handsome woman
in a green silk dress, heavily flounced, her hands on
the keys of a spinet, the kind of woman who would
tempt a man to become a Catholic, a merchant interested above all in his business and only faintly
in religious questions. "It was she that did it. And
he felt no repugnance in being bedded with a Papist
. . . strange."

A little later another explanation emerged as a
wreath of smoke curled upward into the chandelier.
My great-grandfather had changed his religion before setting out for Spain, knowing well that as a
Protestant he could not trade in a country where
the Inquisition was still a going concern. "He became a Catholic as a precautionary measure," I
said, and wrote that very night to the Colonel asking for the date of our grandfather's conversion.
The reply to this question came a few days after-

wards. It was not mentioned in any family paper, but of one thing he was sure, sexual reasons did not determine it, for no religious difficulty in connection with his marriage had arisen. "You must remember," he wrote, "that our great-grandfather's mother was a Catholic, and it was probably the mother's influence."

"How little these Papists understand religion," I said, and walked about the room muttering, "He could not very well ask me to picture the great merchant retiring to his room after business hours to read the Fathers, so he concludes that it was his mother's influence that effected the conversion." Ary Scheffer's picture of St. Augustine and Monica rose up before my eyes, and I vowed that it was kelp that had turned my great-grandfather into a Papist. "Much better it should have been kelp than Kempis," I said; "much better for me." And it amused me to think of the ships laden with seaweed coming round the Bay of Biscay from the Arran Islands to my great-grandfather in Alicante, and the burnt kelp filling the iron chest (still at Moore Hall), and quickly, with ducats, and my great-grandfather returning to Ireland, a sort of mercantile pirate of the Spanish Main. The Colonel's letter told me that it was with two hundred and fifty thousand pounds he returned, on the lookout for investments for his money, and for a site whereon to build the fine Georgian house he had in mind. He would have built it at Ashbrook if there had been a prospect, but there being none, he bought Muckloon, a pleasant green hill overlooking Lough

Carra; and the Colonel mentioned that our great-grandfather used to sit on the steps of Moore Hall, his eyes fixed on the lake. "I have traveled far," he is reported to have said, "but have seen nothing as beautiful as Lough Carra." And he is reported truly, for such simple words are not invented. The phrase evokes a picture: A morning in early May, and an elderly man sitting, his eyes fixed on a lake set among low shores, still as a mirror—a mirror on which somebody has breathed—an elderly man in a wig and a scarlet coat. It is thus that he is appareled in the portrait that hangs in the dining-room, painted when and by whom there is no record. In it he is a man of thirty, and when he was thirty he was in Alicante. It is pleasant to have a portrait of one's ancestor in a wig, and in a vermilion coat with gold lace and buttons, white lace at the collar and cuffs—probably a Spanish coat of the period. The face is long, sheep-like, and distinguished—the true Moore face as it has come down to us. My brother Augustus was the living image of his great-grandfather—the same long face, the same long, delicately shaped nose, without, however, the gay eyes, cloudless as a child's. No face ever told the tale of a happy life more plainly, nor could it be else, everything having succeeded with him. He seemed to have run misfortune clean out of sight, but he had made a little too much running, and was overtaken in the last few years. On awakening one morning he asked his valet why he had not opened the shutters. The servant answered that he had opened them. "But the room is dark."

"No, sir; the room is quite light." "Then I am blind!" he said.

Who has heard of a more horrible discovery than to go blind in one's sleep? Is it to be wondered that his courage died, and that the rest of his life was lived between priest and doctor, in terror of death? for he had become a Catholic. Nor were blindness and fear of death all his misfortunes. His wife wearied of Moore Hall, and her sons bored her. Peter was witless; John, the first President of the Irish Republic, was arrested at Athlone and driven along the roads with other rebels to Castlebar. He died in prison. George, the eldest son, a mild, visionary youth, was interested in literature, and was admired and made much of at Holland House, so the Colonel tells me. And without wife or child the last years of the blind man at Moore Hall must have been very sad and lonely. One room was the same as another to him, and with the disappearance of the lake his thoughts returned to Ashbrook, and the little Protestant cemetery near Straid Abbey. He was the last who thought of Ashbrook with affection. My father did not seem to like to speak of the place; he only went there to collect rents, and the same unsentimental errand took me to Ashbrook when I returned from Paris in 1880. Tom Ruttledge and I had driven through Mayo, visiting all my estates, trying to come to terms with the tenants, and at Ashbrook a crowd had followed the car up a boreen, babbling of the disastrous year they had been through: the potato crop had been a failure; "there was no diet in them."

The phrase caught on my ear, and I remember well the two-storied house standing on a bare hillside. The woods had been felled long ago, all except a few ash-trees left standing in the corner of the field to shelter the cattle from the wind, and the house, having been inhabited by peasants for a long time, presented a sad degradation, a sagging roof, and windows so black that I did not dare to think of the staircase leading to the drawing-room, in which my great-grandmother had stitched that pretty piece of tapestry which is now in the Kensington Museum. Dunne, my tenant, a heavy, surly fellow, whose manners were not engaging (we heard afterwards that he was the leader of a notable conspiracy against us) asked us to step inside, but fearing to meet with chickens in the parlor that perhaps still had the ancient paper on its walls, I pleaded that the day was drawing to a close, and asked him if he would be kind enough to take me to my great-grandfather's grave. He turned aside, and the peasants answering for him said:

"Sure we will, your honor."

"So this is the brook," I thought to myself, and watched the water trickle through masses of weeds and rushes. We crossed some fields and came to a ruined chapel, and my peasants pointed to an incised stone let into the wall, the loneliest grave it seemed to me in all the world; and drowsing in my arm-chair, unable to read, the sadness that I had experienced returned to me, and I felt and saw as I had done thirty years before. I had thought then of the poor old man who had built Moore Hall deciding at last that his ashes were to be carried to Ashbrook. "But the Colonel," I said, "mentions Straid Abbey as the burial-place of Captain George Moore and his descendants. The little ruined chapel that was shown to me can't be Straid Abbey."

A few days afterward another letter came from the Colonel replying to my reproaches that his answers to my questions were vague and insufficient, and from this letter I learnt that my great-grandfather's misfortunes did not cease with his death. He had left instructions in his will that he wished to be buried with his ancestors in the little Protestant cemetery near Straid Abbey. The Colonel had discovered it half a mile down the road, after having searched Straid Abbey vainly for the tomb of Captain George Moore, and his letter told me how he had had some difficulty in pushing his way through a mass of briars and hemlock and in finding the inscription among the ruins of the church; but he had found it.

"So it was there that my great-grandfather had wished to be buried, but he had been buried at Ashbrook in a Catholic chapel. By mistake, the Colonel says in his letter. By mistake!" I cried. "Any breach of faith were better than that he should be laid with his Protestant forbears. The Irish Spaniard, Catholic, back, belly, and sides, would not have hesitated to ignore her husband's instructions. She must have come from London, for George the historian, an Agnostic like his master Gibbon, would have buried his father as the will directed, if he had not been overcome by his mother who, of course,

13

would like to conceal the fact that she had married a man of such doubtful Catholicity that at the last he had chosen to be buried in a Protestant cemetery. I should like to know who was at this funeral, if the historian came over from London to attend it or remained gadding about Holland House, or courting Louisa Browne, whom he afterwards married in spite of the fact that it was her uncle or her brother who secured the conviction of John Moore, the historian's brother. That marriage would have added another grief to the old merchant's many griefs."

A portrait of Louisa hangs in the dining-room, and she appears in it as a voluptuous young woman wrapped in gauze, and by her hangs the portrait of her uncle, Lord Altamont, a copy of the portrait by Reynolds in Westport House. Both are indifferent works, but there is a good picture in the dining-room at Moore Hall, a portrait of my grandfather painted in 1836, certainly not earlier, and therefore not a Raeburn. Nor is it a Catterson Smith, who was painting at that time in Dublin, for his thick, heavy touch is nowhere visible in grandfather's portrait. The drawing is sure, almost unconscious, revealing an old man with white hair growing scantily about a high forehead, and though no books are in the background, we divine a library and a life sheltered from every misfortune. Who could have painted the portrait? Wilkie, perhaps. He was painting about that time. But there are few life-size portraits by Wilkie, and in none that I have seen is the drawing so thoughtful, nor does he show much interest in character except in this portrait.

14

He seems to have said in it all that my grandfather tells us about himself in his preface to the "French Revolution." A very remarkable portrait, no doubt, and for a long time I sat struggling with an idea that would not come into a phrase; that the picture and the preface might be compared to the music and the words, opera and libretto, something like that. But it would not come, and I got up and took the preface out of the drawer.

PREFACE TO MY HISTORICAL MEMOIRS OF THE FRENCH REVOLUTION, TO BE PUBLISHED AFTER MY DEATH.

August 20, 1837.

"I, this day, complete my sixty-fourth year. I have for some time been engaged in a history of the French Revolution. I early in life began collecting books on this subject, and they now fill up an entire side of my very pretty library in this beautiful place. They are most of them bad in style, and worse in spirit and sentiment. There are few of them which I could endure reading were it not for the task I have laid down for myself. This task has the effect of giving interest to the most wretched productions. Any book which offers me a choice of a new fact, or the solution of any difficulty attached to old facts, interests me, and I find amusement in examining it. Amusement and the banishment of what the French call *ennui* are my principal objects. Beautiful as this place is, and much as I love it, I confess I have

not always been able to exclude *ennui* from its pre-
cincts. There are hours in which I have not been
able to keep it away; general vague reading, without any specific object, afforded me no protection
against it, but since I have sat down to my task I
scarcely have known what it is. I have a rough
copy carried on nearly to the present time. To
every written page I have left a blank one, in which
I put down any new facts or reflections or news. I
wish to go on for some time longer in this manner.
But my age, as mentioned at the head of this preface,
admonishes me there is no time to be lost if I wish
the public ever to have an insight into my history.
My rough copy with alternate blank pages it is impossible for anyone to make anything of, and it is
not till after my death I wish my history to appear,
not in the form in which my rough copy exhibits it.

"I have several times published, but never with
any success, so that I am tired of publication in my
lifetime. Besides, as I foresee my history will be
pretty voluminous, I do not like the trouble of super-
intending the proofs. As I am a man of fortune, I
leave by my will five hundred pounds to defray the
expenses of publication. As the publication is in
this manner ordered and appointed by me in my
testamentary deposition, no one who survives me
will be answerable for anything it contains. I foresee many things I say will give offence, but my
objects are truth and my country. As amusement
was my great object in undertaking this task, it may
be said I have already gained my end in never knowing *ennui* since I began it. But having written a

history of the French Revolution, impregnated with
all the feelings and sentiments of an Englishman,
and written in a style, I hope, purely and thoroughly English, I am ambitious it should be read
after me. I have had no celebrity in my life. But
a prospect of this posthumous fame pleases me at
this moment. I may say with Erasmus: *Illud certe
præsagio, de meis lucubrationibus, qualescumque
sunt, candidius judicaturam posteritatem,* though I
cannot add with him: *Tametsi nec de meo seculo
queri possum.* Having missed the applause, and
even notice, of my age, I ought, perhaps, to be indifferent about the opinions of those that follow;
their applause, should I ever gain it, will not reach
me when the grave has closed over me. This is true;
but we are so made that while we are living we think
with pleasure that we shall not be forgotten after
our deaths. The nature of this feeling is beautifully expressed by Fielding in a passage which Gibbon has transcribed in the account of his own life.
What adds to my wish that my history should be
read after my death is that I am convinced no account of the great event of the French Revolution
in all its parts will be fair and impartial coming
from a Frenchman, none certainly will do justice to
my country. I am anxious to have the merits of
the Duke of Wellington duly appreciated as having
done more in war than any captain that ever existed.
He entered on the contest with more disadvantages
on his side, as will be explained in the history. He
had greater difficulties to encounter, and arrived at
more glorious results. Though not a Frenchman,

I am perfectly acquainted with the French language, and there are few Frenchmen better informed with respect to the history, literature, and what are called the statistics of France than I am, so that I conceive myself perfectly well qualified, as much as any Frenchman, for the task I have undertaken. In this improved copy which I am now transcribing, I break the history into chapters, with a view to the grouping of the facts of which it consists. It is this which I call 'grouping' that distinguishes the task of the historian from that of the annotist, and there is no point of greater importance in a history than the manner in which this grouping is executed. The deficiencies of some celebrated historians in this particular may be noticed. . . ."

"How abruptly it breaks off! Some pages must have been mislaid!" and I sought among the litter in the drawer, and finding none, returned to my armchair full of regret that grandfather had not written a biography instead of a history, for such complete sincerity, such engaging simplicity, such humility, I had never met before. Some writers, it is true, have adopted humility as a literary artifice, but grandfather is not aware that he is humble; he dreams, and we hear his dreams. I should like to write like my grandfather; our predecessors often realize us. In speaking of Moore Hall I might have said that it stood on a pleasant green hill, with woods following the winding lake, and attributed the melancholy of the people to their mountains, but my grandfather merely says, "In this beautiful place," and the reader's imagination is free to re-

18

member the place that has seemed to him the most
beautiful. He is able to accept his own failure without attributing it to circumstances, writing that if
he should gain the applause of those that come after
him, it would not matter to him, the grave having
closed over him. "But we are so made that while
we live we think with pleasure that we shall not be
forgotten after our death." This feeling, he adds
modestly, has been beautifully transcribed in Gibbon's account of his own life. For this modesty
and for many other reasons I love my grandfather,
and like to think of his life flowing on uneventfully
for three or four more years in "the pretty library,"
and then his ashes being carried to Kiltome, where
the applause of the world can never reach him. . . .
But by what right do I publish his preface without
his history, perturbing his rest? We are not sure
that the dead cannot hear us. The Colonel, who
has inherited his grandfather's taste for history,
should edit the French Revolution. He began reading it, and finding it entertaining, he gave me the
preface, remarking that our grandfather had managed to escape notice even in his own house, which
was indeed the case. Our mother used to say that
when his wife opened the door of his library to con-
sult him, or to make pretence of consulting him regarding the management of his property, he would
answer, "My dear Louisa, all that you do is right,"
and on these words the old man would drop back
into his meditations.

One's first memory is generally of one's mother,
but my grandmother was the first human being that

came into my consciousness, a crumpled lady of sixty-five, who introduced me to gingerbread nuts, which, however, she did not allow me to eat. This incident may have impressed her upon my mind, but now I come to think of it my second memory is of her; she fell one day as she was coming downstairs, and I remember William Mullowney and Joseph Applely carrying her to her room, and from that day onward she lived in two rooms in the charge of nurses, carried out on fine days in a sort of sedan chair. And isn't it strange that my third memory should be of her? I remember seeing my father sitting at a small table writing letters by the bed on which his dead mother lay. He was weeping bitterly, and his tears were my first experience of grief. He never spoke of her afterward. It seems strange not to speak of those we love, but that was my father's way. He never spoke of his mother or his brother Augustus, whom he loved next to his mother, and when I asked him about what books my grandfather had written, he answered, "Some histories," leaving me in doubt if he had ever read one of them. But he must have looked into the huge manuscript, for five hundred pounds were left for its publication, and he should have edited it. But my father did not appreciate the old gentleman who wrote histories in the room overlooking the lake; he liked his mother, and all the charming letters that he wrote from school were sent to her, and it was to her, and not to his father, that he sent his Latin and English verses, for between sixteen and seventeen he seems to have had literary ambitions.

But as soon as he went to Cambridge he became interested in horses, hounds, and a lady whom he met at Bath. All this the Colonel will write excellently well in his life of our father, for he seems to understand our father's character, though he hardly knew him, and shows a surprising appreciation of the antagonism which arose between mother and son as soon as the son had left school. Our father had inherited his character from her (perhaps that is why he loved her), an obstinate, impetuous character, and he had also inherited from her a taste for letter-writing which followed him through life to the very end, and the letters that mother and son exchanged about the debts the son incurred at Cambridge and about the lady that he wished to marry are very violent, and every quarrel was followed by a violent reconciliation. A time of great storm and stress rolled on until he felt that another quarrel with his mother would be more than he could bear, and he went away to Russia, journeying through the Caucasus, getting to Asia Minor, how, I know not, meditating on the nothingness of things and of suicide as a respite from the torture of existence. His diary breaks off suddenly, to be taken up again two years after; all we know of these two years is that they were spent in the company of a man and his wife . . . no doubt the lady he met in Bath, who married soon after my father's flight, and traveled with her husband in the East.

"The gentlemen of 1830 all had Byronic adventures," I said, and fell to thinking of the illegitimate daughter that was born to him. My mother told my sister that she had seen the lady; my father had pointed her out, saying, "She is my daughter." She married and died childless, an old woman, not very long ago, and it seems a pity, and rather harsh, that we should have never met, for it is quite probable that I might have liked her better than my legitimate relations. There can be no doubt that we should have been great friends, and I fell to thinking of the charm of an illegitimate relation, especially a sister, and then that I did not recognize my father in the avowal he is reported to have made to his wife. A reticent man he was, especially reticent about the dead. He did not speak of his daughter's mother, only of his daughter. But he was not reticent about his journey to the East. . . . It was probably the part of his life that was most real to him.

After dinner Joseph Appely always brought up tea to the summer-room, and my father drank a large cup sitting by a round rose-wood table, on which stood a Moderator lamp; and that he did not eat bread and butter or cake with his tea never ceased altogether to surprise me. After tea my mother read a novel in an arm-chair, and as soon as my toys ceased to interest me I used to clamber on my father's knee and beg him to tell me stories about the desert and the oases where the caravan had rested on its journey from Palestine to Egypt. My father had been obliged to go to Egypt to get permission to measure the Dead Sea and to survey the coasts, and I listened round-eyed to the tale of how the guides, discovering that the Christian dogs

were chalking out the way along the passages inside
the Pyramid, threatened to extinguish the torches.
His voyage down the Nile was a great delight to me,
and between the age of six and seven I was quite
familiar with the Blue Nile and the White Nile, and
had many times mourned the death of a monkey.
The poor little fellow tumbled out of the tree, and
putting his hand to his side had looked up so plain-
tively that my father declared that for nothing in
the world would he shoot another monkey.   The
story that I liked best was the bringing of the boat
from Joppa on the backs of mules to the Dead Sea,
and not satisfied with knowing the story myself, I
wished everybody else to hear it, and very often
embarrassed my father by insisting that he should
tell his visitors that the mules could only totter a
few hundred yards, so heavy was the boat, and then
had to be changed, and that he had let down eighteen
hundred feet of line without touching bottom, the
water being so dense that the lead would not sink
any farther. And I took care that he should not
skip the account of the storm that had arisen and
the great fright of the Arabs at the waves; or the
explanation that on any other sea except the Dead
Sea the boat would certainly have been wrecked.
But the best story of all was of a man whom he met
walking about some world-renowned ruins with a
hammer in his hand. Standing before a statue he
would say, "You've had that nose on your face for
many thousand years, in one second you'll have it
no longer." Whack! and away went the nose. No
sooner had he finished the tale than he had perforce

to tell the story of the merchant who used to go out at nightfall to seek European travelers, and if he saw one who looked as if he had money to spend, he would approach him and whisper in his ear that if he came up a by-street with him he would show him a real Khorassan blade. The celebrated smithies of Damascus had been removed to Khorassan, and the Khorassan blades were being imitated for the European market, and one day the merchant related that he was no longer put to the expense of having new ones made. He had agents in Paris and in London, and whenever these imitation swords came into the market they were purchased for little or nothing, and sent out again to be sold after nightfall for large prices. Nobody but an expert could tell the difference. "And at nightfall," the crafty Persian added. "If you can let me have one of these blades," my father answered, "I should like to take it home." "No," said the crafty Persian, "I have none left, but I have a real Khorassan blade which I should very much like to sell you."

Khorassan or imitation I know not, but many swords, scimitars, and daggers were brought back, and Arab bridles looking like instruments of torture; and these were kept in a great press in my nursery, which I was forbidden to open. But a child cannot be gainsaid on his birthday, and my dearest wish was gratified when I was dressed as a Turk, and rode about the estate flourishing a Khorassan blade above the head of my pony. The success of the ride encouraged me to pursue my inquiries into Eastern costumes and customs, and my father's diaries were examined—not the text, that was too difficult for a child, but the camels with which the text was embellished. His eyes were keen and with a lead pencil, hard and sharp enough to have won all Ruskin's admiration, he followed the long, shaggy, birdlike necks, the tufted and callous hides, and the mobile lips of these bored ruminants, the non-conformists of the four-footed world. The Arab horse never seems to have once tempted his pencil; and it is difficult to find a reason, for he must have had some wonderful horses. He used to tell me of a journey from Jerusalem to Jeddo in a single day; the horse was very tired, but he pricked up his ears and began to trot as soon as he caught sight of the town.

The only portrait of a horse that he ever attempted was a large water-color of Anonymous— a very painstaking piece of work, of which he was a little ashamed, I think, preferring to turn the conversation from the drawing to the race itself. The horse was going very well when he turned a shoe. I wanted him to say that the horse would have won had it not been for the accident, but I could not get him to say that, and remember going to Joseph Applely, a taciturn, clandestine little man whom there is no necessity to describe here, for he is described in "Esther Waters" under the name of John Randal, to find out the truth—whether Anonymous would have won the Liverpool if he had not turned a shoe. He had done some riding himself, and was disposed to be critical, and he thought—well, it is difficult to remember exactly his criticism of my father's riding, for he had a habit of dropping his voice and muttering to himself in his shirt-collar, mumbling and turning suddenly to his press, that wonderful press in which all things could be found. It was out of that press that "Esther Waters" came, out of the stable-yard and out of my own heart.

Oscott College had demonstrated to the satisfaction of my unhappy parent that it was impossible to teach me to write a clean, intelligible letter, and in despair he allowed me to apply myself to the study of life. At Moore Hall there was no life except the life of the stable-yard, and to it I went with the same appetite as I went to the life of the studio afterward; if I had remained at Moore Hall I certainly should have ridden many steeplechases, and perhaps succeeded in doing what my father had failed to do. A pretty indulgence it would be for me now, sitting here, surrounded by Impressionist pictures, to look back upon the day at Liverpool when the flag fell and we raced for the bit of hard ground, numbers of us coming down at the first fence, myself, however, escaping a fall, and then away off into the country . . . three miles, over how many fences? And then the jump into the race-course and the three-quarters of a mile over hurdles. A pretty memory all that long way would have been for a man who has written a line of books, and I should certainly have had some such memory to play with if my father could have restrained himself from asking the electors of Mayo to send him to Parliament to ride for Repeal of the Union. They answered that they would; the horses were

sold, and my dream of doing on Slievecarn what
my father had hoped to do on Anonymous died in
South Kensington, where we had taken a small house
at the corner of Alfred Place, opposite South Kensington Station, a pleasant suburb then, thinly popu-
lated.

The Exhibition Road was building, and it was at
the corner of Prince's Gardens that we met Jim
Browne, the painter of the "Crucifixion" that hangs
in Carnacun Chapel, in the roof high above the
altar. I can remember him painting in the break-
fast-room, and Tom Kelly coming to stand for the
figure of Christ. The angels on either side of the
cross Jim had painted no doubt out of his head; I
had often wondered how he had been able to paint
them, and the great picture that my father used to
describe to me in the summer-room, the great picture entitled the "Death of an Indian Chief," a
tribe of Indians reining up their horses at the edge
of the precipice over which the horse bearing the
dead chieftain springs madly into space. The day
we met him in the Exhibition Road Jim told my
father that he and his sisters were living in Prince's
Gardens; he invited us to come and see his pictures
on the following Sunday, and during the interven-
ing days I could neither think nor speak of anything
but Jim Browne, asking my father all the while why
Jim was not the greatest painter in the world since
he had painted a tribe of Indians; how many? fifty,
sixty, a hundred? He did not think they were so
many. Twenty, thirty, forty? And if he could
paint so many, why will not the Academy hang his

pictures? Are the pictures he paints now not as good as the "Death of an Indian Chief"? My father suggested that Jim did not finish his pictures sufficiently for the Academy, and tried to explain to me that Jim's drawing was defective. But it was difficult for me then to understand that a man might paint a tribe of Indians reining up their horses at the edge of a precipice and yet not be able to draw, and in bed at night I lay awake thinking, waiting for the day to come.

"Father, where is Prince's Gardens? Is it the first turning or the second? Do you think you will be able to persuade Jim Browne to use models? And if he does, will the Academy accept his picture in May?"

II

Myself, an elderly man, lying in an arm-chair listening to the fire, is a far better symbol of reverie than the young girl that a painter would place on a stone bench under sunlit trees; myself trying to remember if it were on our way back from Prince's Gardens or a few days afterward that I begged money from my father to buy drawing materials, remembering everything but the dates—that a pencil was never out of my hand, and that as soon as family criticism was exhausted, professional criticism was called in. Jim was invited to dinner. But a bad cold kept me in bed, terrified lest my drawings should be forgotten. As he descended the staircase voices reached me, and when the front-door closed I listened, expecting somebody to come up to tell me what Jim had said. But nobody came, and when I went shyly to my mother next morning her news was bad; after dinner my sketches had been shown to him, but he did not seem to think much of them, and on my pressing my mother to tell me more I dragged the truth from her that he considered girls riding bicycles showing a great deal of stocking a low form of art.

"He only likes Raphael, Michael Angelo, and Rubens," my father said, and he invited me to come

29

to the National Gallery, and I followed him from masterpiece to masterpiece, humble and contrite, but resolute in my persuasions that he must come with me to Drury Lane and buy some plaster casts. He seemed to look upon the money thus expended as wasted, and when he came to the bedroom that I had converted into a studio he glanced round the walls shocked at my crude attempts to draw the Venus de Milo, the Discobolus, and some busts.

The next step in my artistic education was the South Kensington Museum. He sent me to the evening classes, but he sent my brother with me, and this jarred a little, for I looked upon my wish to learn drawing as a thing peculiar to myself, and my brother was so subaltern to me and seemed so utterly unlikely to understand a work of art that I looked pityingly over his shoulder until one day the thought glided into my mind that his drawing was as good as mine, if not better. And if that were so, what hope was there for me to become an artist, an exhibitor in the Royal Academy? an exhibitor of pictures like Jim's Julius Cæsar overturning the altars of the Druids? For even if I did learn to draw and to stipple, it did not seem to me that I should ever be able to imagine figures in all positions as Jim did, and I despaired.

Youth is a very unhappy time, Art and sex driving us mad, and our parents looking upon us with stupid unconscious eyes. My father must have been ashamed of his queer, erratic son, and could have entertained little hope that eventually I would drift into a respectable and commonplace end. We all want our children to be respectable, though we may not wish to be respectable ourselves, and as he walked to the House of Commons, a short, thick-set man with a long, determined mouth set in a fixed expression, his hands moving in little gestures to his thoughts, he must have often asked himself what new caprice would awaken in me. Would I tell him that I had decided to take up literature or music as a profession? There was no knowing which would be my next choice, and either was equally ridiculous, for in me at that time there was as little idea of a tune as there was of a sentence. It was impossible for me to grasp the different parts of speech or the use of the full-stop, to say nothing of the erudite colon. As he turned me over in his mind he must have remembered his own brilliant school-days, coming sadly to the conclusion that I must go into the Army, if he could get me into the Army, that very sympathetic asylum for booby sons. But that our soldiers may not be altogether too booby, the War Office has decreed a certain amount of ordinary spelling and arithmetic and history to be essential, and to get such as I through examinations there are specialists. Somebody must have exalted Jurles above all men, for my father came home one evening with the news that Jurles had pushed men through who other tutors had said would never be able to pass any examination, and would never get their livings except with the labor of their hands. The record of this thaumaturgist was seventeen hundred and fifty-three, and my father reflected that if there were miracles that even Jurles could not per-

form, he would at least redeem Alfred Place from
the annoyance of seeing me trick-riding on a bicycle
up and down the street. And Jurles would also
save me from the Egertons, and daughters of a small
tradesman living in Hammersmith, whither some
other wastrels and myself were wont to go to sup on
Sundays. Alma and Kate were on the stage, and
photographs of Alma in tights and Kate in short
skirts were left about the house, and disgraceful
letters turned up in the blotting-book in the drawing-room; he was a man of action rather than words,
and putting a season-ticket into my hand he bade
me away to Jurles's in the Marylebone Road, to
one of the little houses lying back from the main
road.

As I passed up the strip of garden under the
aspens I used to catch sight of Jurles's old withered
face blotted against the bow window, and very often
met his wife, a tall and not ill-looking woman about
thirty; she seemed to be always going up and down
that pathway, and at that time almost anything was
enough to waken an erotic suggestion, and I began
to wonder if she kept trysts with any of the young
men sitting on either side of the long mahogany
tables bent over their books and slates. It seemed
to me that there was warrant for the supposition,
for as soon as old Jurles finished a lesson he went
to the window and stood there, his bald head pre-
senting an irresistible attraction for flies, a dangerous attraction, for Jurles was quick with his hands.
It is probable that Mrs. Jurles's trysts were with
the butcher, baker, and grocer, for besides the half-

dozen young men who arrived at ten o'clock every morning, Jurles took in several boarders, and there were never less than ten men sitting down to the midday meal, among them Dick Jurles. We all respected old Jurles, a distant, reserved gentleman and knowledgeable beyond the limits of his craft, but we laughed at Dick for his long red whiskers and mustaches, and his vulgar and familiar manners. We used to charge him in private, on what foundation I know not, probably none, with being a money-lender's tout, and no one cared to take a lesson from him, feeling him to be "a fake," one who had acquired just enough education to overlook our sums or to construe a Latin text with us, feeling that if he were to ask a question we might place him in a quandary. The seventeen hundred and fifty-three young men that Messrs. Jurles had passed into the Army owed their success to the diligence of his brother and to the solemn Swiss who taught modern languages in the back room. Out of it he came every hour, a red handkerchief hanging out of his tail pocket: "I will trable you now," and, my chair tilted, I used to watch him, wondering the while what kind of death each one of his pupils would meet on the battle-field, worried by the thought that my lot might be to die in defence of my country, or be wounded in her defence, which was worse still. It seemed to me that myself was my country, but having no alternative to propose to my father I accepted the Army. All professions were equally repugnant to me; I could not see myself as a doctor or as a barrister, or anything except perhaps a gentleman rider. I did not dare to tell my father that I would not go into the Army; it did not occur to me to say to him: "You went to the East for five years, and when you returned home did little else but ride steeplechases." In many little ways I lacked courage and preferred procrastination to truth. I could not be put into the Army unless I passed the examination, and I realized that to miss passing no more was necessary than to read the *Sportsman* under the table, and spend most of the afternoon at the tobacconist's round the corner —an affable man with a long flowing mustache like Dick Jurles's, and some knowledge of betting, enough to have a book on the big races, laying the odds in shillings with his customers, cabbies from the rank; and while he teased out the half-ounces of shag we discussed the weights, the speed, and the stamina of the horses; we laid the odds and took them, and at the end of the half-year I had won five or six pounds. One day Lord Charlemont mentioned a horse as certain to win the Derby—Pretender, wasn't it? The tobacconist bet in shillings, half-crowns, and dollars, but he would take me round to the public-house and introduce me to the great bookmaker who came there to meet his customers on Thursdays and Fridays. Pretender won, and the Monday after the race the great bookie invited me behind the urinal and took ten five-pound notes out of his pocket, fifty pounds, a sum of money that enabled me to eat, drink, and smoke on terms of equality with Colville and Belfort, two young men who were fast becoming my friends—Belfort, a handsome, high-class, little fellow, bright brows and brown hair, a high-bridged nose, the mouth a little pinched, the chin a little too forward, sharp teeth, a pale complexion, and a high voice. He was going into the cavalry, and lived with his mother and sister at the top of the Albert Road, and as I lived at the bottom of the Exhibition Road it made very little difference whether I took Exhibition Road or Albert Road; there was a short cut at the end round by some cottages with thatched roofs, which have long ago disappeared. We made friends in this walk, and he asked me to dine with him, and we went to the theater; later he introduced me to his mother and sister, and a very distinct picture these two women have left upon my mind: the mother frail, reserved, and dignified, with fair hair, about to turn gray, parted in the middle and brushed on either side of her thin temples. She must have worn a long gold chain, and she was always in black. The daughter had her brother's high-bridged nose, and her manner was showy—the opposite of her mother's—and I used to find them sitting on either side of the fireplace after dinner. Now Colville was quite different from Belfort, a south Saxon if ever there was one, his ancestors having been on the land probably since Hengist and Horsa came; a man of medium height, of good trim figure and military bearing, for his thoughts were always on the army, and his talk was of tunics and of buttons and epaulets, and very proud he was of his great military mustache which he stroked pensively with his little crabbed hand. He was often at Truefitt's getting his hair shampooed and cut closely about his small well-turned head and narrow temples, and from Truefitt's he often walked to his tailor's; he had thirty-six pairs of trousers when I first knew him, and his charm was his cheerful disposition and his somewhat empty but merry laugh.

He was the first man I had ever met who kept a woman, but that was a secret, and Belfort used to wonder how he did it on five hundred a year; he told us that he gave Minnie Granville three, reserving two for himself, and if he ran short he returned to Buckingham and lived free of cost till his next quarter's allowance allowed him to return to the clandestine little home in St. John's Wood. We envied him his lady, and on fine afternoons used to leave the confectioner's shop where we had luncheon and go forth to St. John's Wood for an hour before returning to Jurles, and the two of us would loiter, admiring the greensward shelving down to the canal's edge, wondering if Minnie Granville were true to Colville; we wished Colville well, but we remembered that if she remained faithful to him she would never become a celebrated light-o'-love, and we should be deprived of the honor of having known her in her early days. We had heard that Mabel Grey lived in Lodge Road, and turned into it wondering which house was hers, and, not daring to inquire, we searched South Bank and North Bank, and, talking of her ponies, we gazed at the pretty balconies, hoping to catch a sight of her or her great rival, Baby Thornhill. Everybody knew these two ladies by sight, for photographs of Baby

Thornhill and Mabel Grey were everywhere, in every album; and many other beautiful women were famous. Lizzie Western, "the sheep," as she was called—a tall woman with gold hair and a long mild face—and Kate Cook, too, was as famous perhaps as any, Mabel Grey always excepted; Kitty Carew, Margaret Gilray, and Sally Giles her cousin, lived in South Bank, and were often on their balconies tending their birds, giving their canaries and finches seed and water; a favorite bird was a mule gold-finch and canary, a green-brown bird that used to take seed from his mistress's pretty tongue. Belfort brought opera-glasses one day and that day we were happy boys; the pony carriage was at the door. "We shall see them get into it if we wait." Belfort wanted to get back to Jurles; and I should not have been able to persuade him to remain if the ponies had not presented a peculiar attraction—fiery chestnut mares, foaming at the bits, and swishing their long tails, a dangerous pair for ladies' hands to drive through crowded streets, and the longer they were kept waiting the more restive they became, rearing over against the little groom, or striking out with their hind legs. And as soon as the ladies stepped into the carriage, before Sally was seated, they bounded forward, overthrowing the groom, and what disaster might not have happened if we had not rushed forward to their heads it is impossible to say.

"The ponies have not been sufficiently exercised, that is all, Miss Gilray," and I begged Belfort to soothe Miss Giles, who was very much frightened.

It would have been splendid to offer to drive the
ponies into Regent's Park and bring back Spark
and Twinkle chastened, but Belfort said that we
must be getting back to Jurles, and we regretfully
bade them good-bye. It seemed to us the merest
politeness to call next day to inquire, and we were
received by the cousins, platonically, of course. But
even boys get their chances, and the idea came to
Sally Giles to invite Belfort and me to supper, and
to come to Jurles's herself with the invitation, stopping the ponies before Jurles's establishment and
sending her little groom up the pathway with the
note. I was at the window, and how my heart beat
at the sight of him! Wearing the livery of his
mistress proudly, he stopped Mrs. Jurles, who was
coming down the pathway at that moment with her
white Pomeranian dog, and after a talk with her,
old Jurles called me aside and began his lecture: he
could no longer consent to waste my father's money,
and felt constrained to inform him of the company
I kept.

"But, Mr. Jurles, the ponies were kicking, my
father would never have spoken to me again if I
had not gone to their heads, and Miss Giles was so
frightened."

Old Jurles seemed to accept my excuse as valid,
and, although it was quite out of the question that
such ladies should send their grooms with notes to
his front door, still the incident might be overlooked
were it not that I showed no disposition to learn
anything since I came. He reminded me that he
had frequently to take the *Sportsman* out of my

hand, and that there was no chance of my passing
for the Army.

"But you won't tell my father that, Mr. Jurles?"

Jurles in his quiet way promised me that I should
have another chance. "You must mend your ways,"
he added. But it were only by reading the *Sportsman* under the table that I could escape from the
horrid red tunic with buttons down the front and
the belt, and if I were caught with it again Jurles
would write to my father, and every day I expected
to see him coming toward me with threatening
brow, and to hear him say, "I have received a very
bad account of you from Jurles." There was some
justification for my fears, for he wore a troubled
look, and I caught him in whispered talk with my
mother frequently; they ceased talking or spoke of
indifferent things suddenly, and one night after dinner I heard him say that he was going to Ireland
by the Mail. The reason of this sudden departure
was not mentioned, and my mother was so often agi-
tated that her fluttered voice caused me no alarm;
my father's sudden return from the front door to
give me a sovereign did not awaken a suspicion; it
seemed, however, to strike my mother's imagination,
and a few days later a wire came from her brother
summoning us to Moore Hall.

"Something dreadful must have happened!" she
kept repeating to herself, and her talk was full of
allusions to a letter she had received from my father.
At last she confided to me that he had written to
her saying if she did not get a wire from him on a
certain day she was to come at once; and her dis-

tress was acute that she had not obeyed the summons. I wish I could remember what ordinary circumstance of life had detained her in London, but I can only recall my repeated assurances that if father had been shot from behind a wall his death would have been published in the evening papers. We got the morning papers coming off the boat, and there was nothing about him in them, but the absence of news was not enough to reassure her, and I felt there was something on her mind of which she did not dare to speak. The journey across Ireland is forgotten, and she does not appear again till I see her and myself at Balla outside the gate. Her brother was waiting, and he took her aside, and I heard him say, "Mary, prepare for the worst; George is dead."

We climbed on the side-car—Joe and my mother on one side, the driver sat on the dickey, and I remember his back showing all the way against a gray sky and my mother wrapped in a brown shawl. Joe Blake is not so distinct to me, only his yellow mackintosh. Every now and again I heard the wail of my mother's voice, and I sobbed too, thinking of my father whom I should never speak to again. At the same time I was conscious, and this was a source of great grief to me, that my life had taken a new and unexpected turn. In the midst of my grief I could not help remembering that my father's death had redeemed me from the Army, from Jurles, and that I should now be able to live as I pleased. That I should think of myself at such a moment shocked me, and I remember how frightened I was at my

own selfish wickedness, and a voice that I could not
restrain, for it was the voice of the soul, asked me
all the way to Moore Hall if I could get my father
back would I bring him back and give up painting
and return to Jurles? I tried hard to assure myself
that I was capable of this sacrifice, but without
much success, and I tried to grieve like my mother.
But I could not.

We never grieve for anybody, parent or friend,
as we should like to grieve, and are always shocked
by our absent-mindedness; at one moment weeping
for the dead, at another talking of indifferent things
or asking casual questions as to how the dead man
died. We only remember certain moments, and at
will I can see myself and Joseph Applely in my
father's bedroom standing by the great bureau at
which he wrote, and in which he kept his letters, in
front of the empty bed. He had been removed to
the next room, or perhaps he had died in the marriage bed; however this may be, it was in his own
room that Joseph Applely told me that when he
had come to call the master, he was lying on his
back breathing heavily, and thinking that it would
be better not to disturb him he had gone away, closing the door quietly, and when he returned an hour
later the master was lying just as he had left him,
only he could catch no sound of breathing. So
much do I remember precisely, and somewhat less
precisely, that Joseph Applely told me he had sent
for the doctor. A dim thought hangs about in my
memory that the doctor was in the neighborhood;
be this as it may, the reason assigned for death was

41

apoplexy. Two, three, or four days went by and I remember nothing till somebody came into the summer-room to tell my mother that if she wished to see him again she must come at once, for they were about to put him into his coffin, and catching me by the hand, she said, "We must say a prayer together."

The dead man lay on the very bed in which I was born, his face covered with a handkerchief, and as my mother was about to lift it from his face the person who had brought us thither warned her from the other side of the white dimity curtains not to do so.

"He is changed."

"I don't care," she cried, and snatched away the handkerchief revealing to me the face all changed. And it is this changed face that lives unchanged in my memory and three moments of the next day: the moment when Lord John Browne bade me good-bye on the way from Carnacun (the body had been brought there for High Mass and was being carried back to Kiltoome, a cold March wind was blowing over the fields, and he feared the journey round the lake); the moment when Father Lavelle called upon the people to hoist him on to the tomb for him to speak his panegyric; and the moment when the mason's mallets were heard closing the vault where the dead man would remain with his ancestors, one would like to say for centuries, but nothing endures in this world, not even our graves. I cannot remember who spoke after Lavelle, and afterwards the multitude began to disperse through the woods and

along the shores of the lake, a great many lingering
on the old stone bridge to admire the view. Of
course I was very principal, and as I passed up the
road I felt many eyes fixed upon me, and conjec-
tured that they were all wondering how much of my
father's talent I had inherited, and if I would take
up the running at the point where he had dropped
out of the race. Among the hundreds of unknown
there was here and there a known face; our car-
penters, sawyers, gardeners, and stable men—all
our servants came from Derrinanny and Ballyholly,
the villages beyond the domain over the hill along
the lake's edge. And of course, I did not escape the
inquisitive gaze of the men that used to row me
about the islands when Lough Carra was my adventure, and they were probably thinking what I
would do for them when I came to live in Moore
Hall; and after these men were other faces known
to me, but not so well known, the beaters whom I
had seen rousing the woodcock out of the covers of
Derrinrush, and it seems that when I turned from
the Dark Road and walked up the lawn some
of the old tenants spoke to me. I have some recollection of being spoken to at the sun dial, and I
think their questioning eyes reminded me that the
house on the hill was mine, and they who spoke to
me and those who did not dare to speak were mine
to do with as I pleased. Until the seventies Ireland
was feudal, and we looked upon our tenants as animals that lived in hovels round the bogs, whence they
came twice a year with their rents; and I can remember that once when my father was his own agent,

a great concourse of strange fellows came to Moore Hall in tall hats and knee-breeches, jabbering to each other in Irish. An old man here and there could speak a little English, and I remember one of them saying: "Sure they're only mountaineymen, yer honor, and have no English; but they have the goicks," he added with unction. And out of the tall hats came rolls of bank-notes, so dirty that my father grumbled, telling the tenant that he must bring cleaner notes; and afraid lest he should be sent off on a long trudge to the bank, the old fellow thrust the notes into his hand and began jabbering again. "He's asking for his docket, yer honor," the interpreter explained. My father's clerk wrote out a receipt, and the old fellow went away, leaving me laughing at him, and the interpreter repeating: "Sure, he's a mountaineyman, yer honor." And if they failed to pay their rents, the cabins they had built with their own hands were thrown down, for there was no pity for a man who failed to pay his rent. And if we thought that bullocks would pay us better we ridded our lands of them; "cleaned our lands of tenants," is an expression I once heard, and I remember how they used to go away by train from Claremorris in great batches bawling like animals. There is no denying that we looked upon our tenants as animals, and that they looked on us as kings; in all the old stories the landlord is a king. The men took off their hats to us and the women rushed out of their cabins dropping curtsies to us until the seventies. Their cry "Long life to yer honor" rings still in my ears; and the seignioral rights flourished in Mayo and Galway in those days, and soon after my father's funeral I saw the last of this custom: a middle-aged woman and her daughter and a small gray ass laden with two creels of young chickens were waiting at my door, the woman curt-seying, the girl drawing her shawl about her face shyly. She was not an ugly girl, but I had been to Lodge Road and had seen Jim Browne's pictures.

Everything was beginning for me, and everything was declining for my mother. She would have liked to linger by her husband's grave a little while, but I gave her no peace, urging the fact upon her that sooner or later we should have to go back to Lon-don. "Why delay, mother? We cannot spend our lives here going to Kiltoome with flowers."

An atrocious boy as I relate him, but an engaging manner transforms reality as a mist or a ray of light transforms a landscape, and my mother died believing me to have been the best of sons, though I never sacrificed my convenience to hers. It will be admitted that that is the end we should all strive for. But the means? Ah, the means! An ancient saw this of ends and means which it will be well to leave to others to disentangle. . . .

Awaking from a long reverie, I asked myself where I had left off, like an absent-minded old woman telling a child a story. At the part when every day spent in Moore Hall after my father's death was like a great lump of lead on my shoulders. My mother's grief increased day by day; and if her health were to break down we might be kept at Moore Hall for months. It was important to get

her back to London, and I think it must have been
in the train that she heard the Army had never
appealed to me; I had only consented to accept the
Army because I had nothing else to propose to my
father; it was painting that interested me, and a
studio was sought as soon as I arrived in London.
My aspiration did not reach as high as a private
studio; the naked was my desire, and a drawing-
class would provide me with that. No examination
was required at Limerston Street. Barthe, a Frenchman, ran the show. Whistler was one of the attractions of it. A lock of white hair showed over a
drawing-board, and as soon as the model rested I
picked my way through the easels and stood at the
edge of the crowd that had collected round the
celebrated artist. His drawings on brown-paper
slips seemed to me to be very empty and casual, altogether lacking in that attitude of mind which interested me so much in Rossetti. His jokes were
disagreeable to me; he did not seem to take art seriously, but I must have disguised my feelings very
well for he asked me to come to see him; any Sunday
morning, he said, I should find him at 96, Cheyn
Walk. The very next Sunday I went there, but only
to find him surrounded by friends talking noisily.
There were few pictures in the studio, and I was
left to look upon the melancholy portrait of his
mother which he had just completed, but could
gather nothing from it, and turned instead to another picture, a girl in a white dress dreaming by
the chimney-piece, her almost Rossetti-like face reflected in the mirror, azaleas breaking the blacklead

46

stove. Swinburne had translated her languor into verses; these were printed round the frame; and while I read them Whistler discoursed to his friends on the beauty of Oriental art, and his praise sent me to the Japanese screen, but I could discover no correct drawing in it, and begged one of the visitors to tell me how faces represented by two or three lines and a couple of dots could be considered to be well drawn. He gave me a hurried explanation, and returned to Whistler, who was laughing boisterously and rattling iced drinks from glass to glass; and I think that I despised and hated him when he capped my somewhat foolish enthusiasm for the pre-Raphaelite painters with a comic anecdote. I left his house irritated, and it does not seem to me that after that morning I cared to see him again, and I somewhat ostentatiously neglected him at the class, allying myself openly and defiantly to the next celebrity, for our class boasted of another, Oliver Madox Brown, son of the great Ford Madox Brown, a boy that came from Fitzroy Square, bringing with him such a reputation for genius that he paid no attention whatever to Whistler—a strange boy, stranger even than I: a long fat body buttoned in an old overcoat reaching to his knees, odd enough when upright, but odder still when crouching on the ground in front of his drawing-board, his right hand sketching rapidly, his left throwing black locks of hair from his face, of which little was seen but the great hooked nose. I could not keep him out of my thoughts, for he seemed to me even more unfortunate than myself, less likely to win a woman's

47

love. At last my passion to know him overcame me, and I dared to speak to him. He engaged immediately in conversation just as if he wished to become my friend, and agreed to walk back to South Kensington with me. I remember the care with which I picked my words during this walk, and my object being to win him it seemed to me to be perfectly safe to ask if he were in the life-room in the Academy, the stint of my ambitions at that time. My surprise was therefore great when he answered that he had no time to spare for the Academy, all his mornings being employed upon his six-foot canvas, the "Deformed Transformed," and wondering how he managed to give visible shape to an idea so essentially literary, I asked if he could explain his composition to me. He said that he would prefer to show me his picture, and I promised to call at Fitzroy Square, but delayed going there from day to day lest too much desire to see him and his picture might wean him from the willingness he had shown for my acquaintance; and it was not till he asked me why I had not been to see him that I summoned sufficient courage to take the train to Gower Street. Before me on the doorstep was a handsome middle-aged man, somewhat thick-set, with graying hair and beard, who said to me, "You have come to see Oliver, haven't you?" divining one of Oliver's friends in me.

"We met at the class in the Fulham Road, and he asked me to come and see his picture. And you are Oliver's father?" I added, "the great painter." For I recognized Oliver in the handsome and kindly eyes.

48

"Yes, yes," and he turned on the landing to ask me if I would care to come into his studio before going to see Oliver. "Does he, then, think so much of Oliver?" I asked myself while he pulled the easels forward and showed me his pictures. "If I may make a remark," I said aloud.

"Pray do," he said.

"Your hands always seem a little heavy, but perhaps that is your style, as long necks are Rossetti's."

He laughed in his beard, and we ascended the great sloping staircase, and Oliver seemed glad to see me as soon as he recovered from his surprise.

"He paints in the morning and writes in the evening when he doesn't go to the class." A volume of poems was mentioned, and I asked the admiring parent if the manuscript had gone to the publisher. "Oliver hesitates about sending it. Swinburne and Rossetti are publishing poetry, and all the literature of the pre-Raphaelite movement has hitherto gone into verse." He drawled on telling me that Oliver had finished a prose romance of about three hundred and fifty pages and was about to begin another, and somehow a volume of short stories got into the conversation, and I learnt that these had been abandoned. "Oliver, you have your six-foot canvas in the morning and your novels and poems in the evening. Don't waste your time on short stories."

I was too overwhelmed to give any answer, and Oliver paid no heed to his fond parent's admonishment. He seemed to take it for granted that he was not like other men, and I understood that he had heard himself so often referred to as a genius he had accepted the fact of his genius as he had come to accept the fact that he could speak and hear and walk. But I, who had been brought up in the belief that I was very stupid, was astonished at my extraordinary good fortune at having met Oliver and won his good opinion. After all, come what may, this wonderful father and still more wonderful son had thought me worth speaking to for a while, and then, remembering that Oliver was writing a novel, I begged him to read me some of it if he weren't too busy. He hesitated and might have been tempted if his father had not reminded him that luncheon would be ready in a few minutes. Father and son were condescending enough to ask me to stay to lunch, but I did not dare to say yes, and descended the stairs regretting my shyness. On the doorstep, while trying to summon up courage to say, "On second thoughts I'll come back to lunch," I besought Oliver to bring his manuscript down to the class and read it to us during the rests. He promised to do so, and the following day when Mary Lewis left the pose and wrapped herself in a shawl (a shapely little girl she was, Whistler's model; she used to go over and talk to him during the rests), Oliver began to read, and Mary sat like one entranced, her shawl slipping from her, and I remember her listening at last quite naked. And when the quarter of an hour had gone by we begged Oliver to go on reading, forgetful of Whistler, who sat in a corner looking as cross as an armful of cats. At last, M. Barthe was obliged to intervene, and Mary resumed the pose.

"*Après tout, je ne veux pas que mon atelier devienne un cours de littérature,*" he muttered.

But we were thinking of the story, and begged Oliver to take up the reading again at the end of the sitting, and Whistler went away in high dudgeon, for Mary stopped behind to hear how the story ended. . . .

A few months later we crowded together, forgetful of the model, telling how typhoid had robbed England of a great genius; and after Oliver's death my interest in the class declined.

III

Our advancements are broken or delayed by un-expected returnings to our beginnings, and my story is that a young man whom I had known at Jurles's asked me to visit him for the hunting season, and that I met a man at his house who had a horse running at Croydon but was without a jockey. So it was natural to me to propose myself, and rely on Joseph Applely's promptitude to send me my father's racing breeches and boots, which he did; and the farce was gone through of taking them down to Croydon, though the owner had written saying that he intended, or half-intended, to scratch the horse, his warning serving no purpose, for we are all mummers, and life being but a mumming, it was pleasant to think of myself taking all the jumps, the water-jump especially, in front of the stand. But to do this it was necessary to go down prepared, the breeches and boots in a brown-paper parcel under my arm, the parcel helping me to realize myself as a steeplechase jockey. No doubt that with some luck I should have got the horse round the course as well as another, but the owner having scratched the horse, and the day being wet and the Ring a couple of inches deep in mud, the result of

that Croydon meeting was for me a severe cold that
prevented me from taking my driving-lesson from
Ward, one of the great coachmen of that time, a
lesson that I sorely needed, for I had engaged to
drive a coach down to Epsom.

All the same, on four lessons this feat was accomplished, the horses meeting with no serious accident,
and, encouraged by my luck, a few weeks afterwards
the same party was invited by me to a great gala
dinner at Richmond, and while the coach was being
led over several hillocks through the furze bushes
on to the dusty road, for in the darkness we had
wandered into Wandsworth Common, one of my
guests said to me: "You mustn't think of giving up
driving; your luck will never desert you." "But
four horses galloping on Wandsworth Common in
the middle of the night!" Margaret Gilray whispered to her cousin, Sally Giles. "I wish we were
safely at home."

These excursions passed the summer away, and
in August Sally and Margaret were bidden good-
bye. Belfort's brother, who was going to be married and wished to make a splash before doing so,
had hired a lodge in Ross-shire. He had invited
his brother, and his brother had been allowed to
invite me; a great event this was, and hours were
spent at the tailors' considering different patterns;
at the hosiers' turning over scarves, neck-ties, and
shirts of many descriptions, frilled and plain; and
when my mother said that I could not have a dressing-case costing fifty pounds and a pair of guns, I
decided to have the dressing-case and to send to

Moore Hall for my father's muzzle loaders, and though forty years have gone by, I can still smile at the astonishment that the guns had inspired in the Ross-shire shooting-lodge. And when it was noticed that the locks were noiseless, Captain H——, who had been told off as my companion on the morrow, was soon busily interested in them, and spent most of the evening with a tooth-brush trying to clean them, succeeding at last in producing a faint clicking, but not enough to convince him that he would be safe while shooting with me. It were better, he thought, to lend me one of his guns, and the breech-loader, the first that I held in my hands, was held fairly straight, and my bag was numerous for a boy of my appearance and conversation. Captain H—— had begun to feel that if by chance my bag were the bigger, he would be wickedly chaffed, and this misfortune might have happened to him if the boots that had won my fancy in the Sloane Street shop-window had not begun to break up, the pretty clasps and buckles being unable to resist the tough Ross-shire heather.

"I can't think how you ever came by such boots. Where did you get them? They are as wonderful as your guns! How do you contrive to hit off the extraordinary?"

And I told him that it was not until the last moment, between six and seven in the evening, that I remembered I had forgotten to order any shooting boots. "My feet, you see, being as small as a woman's, the ready-made shooting boots in the Brompton Road were too large for me; all the shops were shutting, I was getting frantic when I saw a line of boots in a shop-window in Sloane Street marked 'Ladies' Boots for the Highlands'! 'They'll fit me,' I said to myself. You see they do, only——"

"I shall have to take you round to-morrow to the local cobbler."

The noiseless locks, the ladies' boots, and the admission that I was always in love supplied the Ross-shire shooting-lodge with matter for humorous conversation, and as I sat before my fire in Ely Place, I heard my nickname, "Mr. Perpetual." To be ridiculous has always been *mon petit luxe,* but can anyone be said to be ridiculous if he know that he is ridiculous? Not very well. It is the pompous that are truly ridiculous. A random thought carried me out of Ely Place across the years to Lodge Road, and I can see myself and the company and the room: a round table on which are beef and salad, Cheshire cheese and beer, the supper provided by the fair cousins. Canaries are shrilling in their cages, and the bow-window is hung with rep curtains, and the sofa, too, is rep. There is wax fruit on the sideboard, and Sally and Margaret wear the tight bum-revealing dresses that succeeded the pious crinoline. Side-whiskers have not disappeared altogether; Belfort and myself, Humphries and Norton—two cavalry officers—are shaved only to mid-cheek. Incident after incident rises up and floats away like cigarette smoke, one incident retaining my attention a little longer than the others—the evening that Belfort refused to smoke one of my cigars, saying that he preferred to smoke one of

his own manillas. He lighted one, and it was just
beginning to draw when, impertinently, I tore it out
of his teeth and flung it into the fire. A joke it had
seemed to me, but he rushed for the poker and would
have brained me with it if I had not slipped round
the table and seized Colville's sword and, unsheath-
ing it in a moment, warded off the blow aimed at
my head, and seeing another coming, it occurred to
me that the best way to save myself would be to
run Belfort through, and he would have received a
thrust that might have done for him if one of the
cavalry officers had not armed himself with a chair.
The sword sank in the upholstery, and by that time
Belfort had recovered his temper, and a few minutes
after he was smoking one of my cigars in token of
reconciliation. One of the cavalry officers asleep
on the sofa is another memory that Time has not
rubbed away, and Margaret coming to sit on my
knees, perhaps because she had been warned not to
inflame "Mr. Perpetual." Her dressmaker had
brought home a beautiful blue tea-gown that evening; she was wearing it for the first time, and its
folds of corded silk floated over my knees. The
very weight and shape of her are remembered, and
our inquietude whether the officer was shamming
sleep or was asleep. The tea-gown had seemed to
me the very painting robe that I needed, for art
was never altogether out of my mind, and I had
been thinking for some time of Saturn sitting in the
shady sadness of a vale as a subject for a picture
that my poor dead Oliver would have liked to paint.
It would have been of no avail to offer it to Jim

Browne, for he could not draw from Nature. A few months later I discovered another which he would have carried out if he had lived: the Witch of Atlas calls to Hermaphroditus, and I could see his wings catching the fainting airs bearing the boat up the shadowy stream to the austral waters beyond the fabulous Thamondacona, without, however, being able to arrange the figures so that they filled the canvas—the sinuous back of the witch, her arm upon the helm, looking up at Hermaphroditus; and one day Jim Browne was implored to say what was wrong with the composition.

"Give me your palette and go upstairs and dress yourself. Take off that ridiculous garment," he added, thereby humiliating me, for Margaret Gilray's tea-gown had seemed an excellent painting robe, an advance on the smock which Jim wore in his own studio. But it would be henceforth discarded, for Jim was now my mentor, my hero, my boon companion. It was my pride to be seen in Piccadilly with this fine Victorian gentleman whom I recall best on a wintry day; he never wore an overcoat, but buttoned his braided coat tightly about him and swung a big stick. Long flaxen locks fell thick over the collar, and his peg-tops blew about in the wind; he was known to everybody as "Piccadilly Jim" or "Piccadilly Browne," I have forgotten which. We met everybody between Hyde Park Corner and St. James's Street, and Jim saluted his acquaintances with a "How are you?" never a "How do you do?" He very rarely stopped to speak to any, but strode on quickly, mentioning

the name of the passer-by, and I could but try to
fix in my memory the appearance of the notable,
regretting that Jim did not stop, that I had not
been introduced. He liked to quiz me, and sometimes
there was plenty of reason for mockery, and sometimes there was none, but in either case he quizzed
me, turning some simple phrase into ridicule, as
when I mentioned, regretfully—perhaps it was the
note of regret in my voice that caused him to
laugh at me—that my hair was yellower than
his. How he used to drag out the word "yellow,"
making me feel dreadfully ashamed of myself, until
at last summoning up courage, I asked him if there
was anything foolish in what I had said, and to my
surprise he answered no. Then why had he been
laughing at me all this while? and I listened to Jim
again, for he was now asking, out of politeness—
he always decided these questions—whether it would
be more amusing to dine at the St. James's or at
Kettners' or at the Café de la Regence. It did not
matter which. In whichever he might choose I could
learn his taste in food, and my hope was that with
practice I might acquire it; his taste in everything
seemed essential, especially in women, and to make
myself more perfectly acquainted with it, I drew his
attention to the ladies dining at the distant tables,
never daring, however, to hazard an opinion unless
one seemed to realize all the ideals of beauty set
forth in his pictures, and if he deigned to approve of
any woman's face and figure at Cremorne Gardens
or in the Argyle Rooms, I used to mark her down
for future study. My mistakes were numerous,

and I was ashamed if he caught me talking to a woman whom he did not admire, and very proud if my choice met his approval, as it happened to do one day in the Park. I had stopped to speak to Kitty Carew, letting him walk on in front, and on overtaking him half-way down the pathway, he said: "Yes, indeed, a very pretty woman. You were in luck, George, when you picked her up."

Jim's satellite I was, but given to wandering out of my orbit. There were other companions whom Jim looked upon contemptuously—the Maitlands— and Jim's contempt was shared by my gaunt Irish servant, William Mullowney, who used to enrage me when he came into the drawing-room with his "Sor, Mr. Dhurty Maitland has called to see you." It was quite true that Sydenham presented a somewhat neglected appearance, but that was no reason why . . . my indignation used to deprive me of words, and when he left the room to ask Sydenham to come upstairs, I used to mutter, "This Derrinanny savage shall be sent back to Moore Hall."

Sydenham Maitland and Jim Browne were the beginning of my life in London. When we arrived from Mayo we had gone to live in Thurloe Square, in the house of a very genteel lady who did not let lodgings but who might be persuaded, so the house agent had said, to let us have her drawing-room floor and some bedrooms for five or six guineas a week. She used to ask me into her parlor and talk to me about her connections and the neighborhood, and, seeing I was a sort of loose end without companions, inspired by some association of ideas,

she said one day she would introduce me to the
Maitland boys, the sons of a retired stipendary
magistrate from Athlone. The mother was a wonderful pianist, the boys were all clever, the three
younger sons had a room to themselves at the bottom of the house where they painted scenery, wrote
verses, and composed music. William and Dick,
the two older brothers, had taken the Lyceum
Theater, and were going to produce "Chilperic," a
comic opera by Hervé. She tapped at the window
and Sydenham came in, and his news was that a
letter had arrived that morning from Hervé. He
was coming over to play the title-rôle himself.
Everything is relative, and at that moment of my life
it was very wonderful for me to go to the Maitlands'
house and to hear the scores of "Chilperic" played
by Sydenham and his mother. We received boxes and
stalls from the Maitlands, and after a run of nearly
six months, "Chilperic" was taken off to make way
for the composer's later opera, "Le Petit Faust."
But it did not please as much as its predecessor, and
the theater had to be closed. Dick had, however, managed to escape bankruptcy; half a success guaran-
tees that another door shall be opened to the retiring manager, and in the seventies, a few months
after my father's death, he brought over the entire
company from Les Folies Dramatiques to play in
French, "Chilperic," "L'Œil Crevé," "Le Canard à
Trois Becs," and possibly "Le Petit Faust."

He sent me seats whenever I asked him, and I
used to sit in the stalls learning all the little choruses
and couplets night after night, admiring Paola Ma-

riée, a pretty and plump brunette, who sang enchantingly as she tripped across the stage, and Blanche d'Antigny, a tall fair woman who played the part of a young shepherd. She wore a white sheepskin about her loins, and looked as if she had walked out of Jim's pictures. I learnt from Dick that she was a great light-o'-love, sharing the Kingdom of Desire with Hortense Schneider and Léonie Leblanc.

It was well to sit in the stalls as Dick's guest, and it would have been wonderful to accompany him through the stage door on to the stage, and be introduced to the French actresses to whom he spoke in French every night. But I could not speak French, and I vowed to learn the language of these women, who disappeared suddenly like the swallows, leaving me meditating what lives they lived in Paris, until Dick's new theatrical venture, a translation of Offenbach's "Brigands," put them out of my head.

He had collected in the Globe Theater the most beautiful women in London to form the corps of the *gendarmerie* that always arrived an hour too late to arrest the brigands; and one of the attractions of the piece was Mademoiselle d'Anka, a beautiful Hungarian, who sang Offenbach's little ditties bewitchingly, and a song that Arthur Sullivan had written for her, "Looking Back." Madame Debreux, a pretty brunette whom Dick had brought over, for he loved her, was in the cast, and Nelly Bromley, who was loved by the Duke of Beaufort, was in it too. A lovelier garland was never wreathed, and there was no lovelier flower in it than Marie de Grey, who never kissed anyone except for her pleasure, and yet managed to live at the rate of three or four thousand a year. There was a woman who wore a green dress in the second act; her nose was too large, but her thighs were beautiful, and there was a pretty, tall, fair woman, whom I ran across in Covent Garden on her way to the theater, and whom I took to lunch. She would have loved me if my heart had not been engaged elsewhere, but, as usual, I abandoned the prey for the shadow. And the shadow was the stately Annie Temple, who dared not listen to my courtship for dread of the rage of her fierce cavalry officer, a stupid fellow who snarled at me once so threateningly at the stage door that Annie must fain refuse me her photograph. Dot Robins' mother sold me one for a sovereign, and from it I painted many portraits. Jim painted one from memory, mentioning again and again while he painted it that Annie was as tall as Mademoiselle d'Anka, whose acquaintance he had made on her arrival in London, before the theater opened. It was he who introduced me to her, and he was glad now that I was able to get free seats at the Globe, and disappointed that Dick would not allow me to bring him behind the scenes. I should have liked to chaperon him, but it was a feather in my cap to leave him sitting in his box and skip away to the dressing-rooms, and when I returned we would lay our heads together trying to discover which was the handsomer woman, Annie Temple or Marie de Grey. Annie, in his opinion, was the finer woman, being as big, in fact, as Alice Harford, and he confided to me then and there that he used to meet Alice in a

most romantic nook at the end of a little paved
alley off the Fulham Road. He believed her to be
in keeping and unfaithful only with him; all the
same, she proposed one night at Cremorne to meet
me at the nook; and, delighted with my success, I
could not refrain from telling Jim all about it, just
to take him down a peg. But the result of this indiscretion was that Alice did not come to the nook
at the time appointed, and I walked down the paved
alley meditating that once again I had missed the
prey for the shadow. And, as if my punishment
were not enough, Jim continued to talk of her beauty,
telling that her legs were shapelier than Mademoiselle d'Anka's; they did not go in at the knee, and
this great beauty, or this great fault, formed the
theme of many conversations in the studio in Prince's
Gardens; Boucher's women did not go in at the
knee, but Rubens's did, and laying his palette aside,
Jim would throw himself on the sofa and tell me for
the hundredth time that the only women worth lov-
ing were tall women with abundant bosom and flaxen
hair, the only women that men with a sense of the
beautiful could admire.

But long before this my guardian, Lord Sligo,
wrote Jim a letter which brought him round to Alfred Place, and sitting on the edge of the table he
read it to my mother, saying that if she agreed with
Sligo's strictures, there would be nothing for him
to do but to refuse to see George any more, and if
she didn't agree with Sligo, the best thing would
be to write to him saying that she thought he was
mistaken. Foreseeing that Lord Sligo would read

any such letter from her as "Please mind your own business," my mother hesitated, but I insisted, feeling that Jim's friendship was necessary to me. All the same, Lord Sligo's letter was not without avail. It stimulated Jim to moralize, and when I called in the afternoon to ask him if he would come up to Piccadilly to dine somewhere, and go on to the Argyle Rooms, he would read me a long lecture on the dangers of women.

The strong and healthy man refrains from women, and when I asked him if he always refrained from them himself he said he refrained as long as he could, and advocated a strong and energetic life to me. He said he would like to see me shoulder a gun and go away; not to Scotland to shoot grouse, but to Africa. Every young man should go forth and lead a natural life. Abyssinia was often mentioned, and to discover the source of the Nile was held up to me as an ambition suitable to my health and my fortunes. I should come back a far finer man than I went out. Alice Harford and Annie Temple were probably given to us so that we might resist their seductions, which were very trivial to a man who had got anything in him. And if Abyssinia and the source of the Nile appeared too slight an adventure, there remained the Sahara and the Mountains of the Moon and Timbuctoo, where no European had been, but which a determined man might reach, and in his imagination Jim would roam through the great equatorial forests, filled, he said, with cities, relics of a civilization that had passed away, now inhabited only by lions, and to encourage me to accept an African adventure he would pull out a picture of a troop of elephants plunging through some reeds into a river while a gorilla disported himself on the branches of a dead tree. This led us to consider the exploits of Du Chaillu, who had shot the first gorilla. The animal had approached thumping his breasts with his fists, and the sound that he produced was that of a big drum. Du Chaillu had, however, knelt unmoved, saying to himself, "Not yet." The gorilla approached another ten steps and Du Chaillu said, "Not yet," and again the gorilla approached, and Du Chaillu said, "Fire!" and the gorilla rolled over dead at Du Chaillu's feet after twisting the rifle as if it were a bit of wire. Jim admired such nerve as this, and it recalled to him an excellent shot he had made years ago when he was staying at Moore Hall. He had said he would like to shoot a marten, and had taken a rifle with him; martens were rare even at that time, but he had caught sight of one at the end of a branch, and had shot it, and the incident had inspired him to think that he would like to wait for a lion in the moonlight at the foot of a tree. "A moment like that is worth living for!" And exalted by the thought he would seize his palette and paint Cain amid the rocks by the sea under a darkening sky, his arm thrown about his sleeping sister, a spear within his right arm; and as if the terrific lion stealing down upon him were not sufficient terror, Jim would sketch a lioness and her whelps in the background. As all the beasts in the picture were roaring, Jim roared in accompaniment, while whirling a mass of vermilion and white upon his palette; and then, uttering a deep growl, he would rush forward and a red tongue would appear; and when he had mixed emerald green with white he would advance some paces, cat-like, and then, snarling, would leap forward, and a moment after a great green eye started out of the darkness.

He retreated to watch the effect of his work, and in the frenzy of creation, soliloquized, explaining to himself, and to me, the reason why his pictures were refused by the Academy. The art that the Academicians catered for was a meanly realistic art, and for them to accept his picture of Cain defending his wife from wild beasts, the lion's mane would have to be painted from the bearskin rug, every hair put in; and the dove that Jim's memory of Alice Harford had rescued from Cupid and clasped to her bosom, would have to be studied from a dead pigeon sent round from the poulterer's.

Alice's great blonde body was finely conceived, and the movement of her shoulders bending over the eager boy was well enough, somewhat rudimentary, but better in a way than the frigid sophistications that pass for art in Burlington House. If he had nothing else he had the sense of the noble and the beautiful, but was he speaking the whole truth when he said that the Academicians would hang the picture if every feather were imitated from real feathers? Did he believe it to be as well painted as the Correggio in the National Gallery? Was the modeling of that shoulder altogether faultless? Was it not emptier than the Correggio? Was not the

VALE

Correggio more real? At that moment it became
clear to me that the feet were not as beautiful as
those in the bright picture of the Italian master,
and that Jim could not make them as beautiful, for
he had not learned to draw and to paint from
Nature. If he had gone to the Academy schools and
subjected his genius to discipline, he might have
been the great painter of modern times; but I could
not see Jim attending the Academy schools, drawing
patiently from the model, working out the shadows
with a stump. My thoughts must have stopped
there if they ever got quite so far; and now the
explanation of the enigma seems to me that Jim was
one born before due time and out of due place, in
Mayo in 1830. For his talent to have ripened fully
he should have been born in Venice in 1660. His
mentality was of that period, and his appearance
coincided with his talent—splendid shoulders, fine
head upreared, an over-modeled brow, a short aqui-
line nose, proud nostrils, long languid hands. But
why enumerate? A portrait by Van Dyke.

"Get out of my way," he cried, and squeezing out
the best part of a tube of raw umber on his palette
and breaking it with a little black, he whisked in
the lion's tail, and with another brush sought out
the yellow ochre and the Naples yellow, and Cain's
wife received such a dower of tresses that I was
thrilled. It was my sense of the voluptuous and
romantic that drew me to Jim and his pictures, and
I remember him crossing the room one day and
seeking among the canvases and returning with
a small one, six feet by four, in which a brown satyr

67

overtook a nymph at the corner of a wood. My eyes dilated and I licked my lips.

"The best thing you have ever painted in your life, Jim. Why do you turn it away to the wall?"

He murmured something about his sisters who sometimes came into the room unexpectedly, and throwing himself on the sofa melted into another of those long soliloquies very dear to me at that time —a flow of talk of Michael Angelo, Rubens, and Raphael; and mixed with his remembrances of the pictures he had seen in Italy were remembrances of pictures and statues that he had modeled and painted himself, the colossal statue of Caractacus that he had exhibited in London when he was seventeen, and the great picture of the Battle of Arbela, forty feet wide by twenty feet high, containing several life-size elephants. At that time he had painted and modeled in the same studio, leaving the picture for the statue and the statue for the picture, and, my admiration roused, I begged him to tell me where were these pictures and this statue; but without answering my question he broke into a criticism of Ary Scheffer's picture of the Devil offering Christ the Kingdom of Earth if he would cast himself down and worship him. Christ raises his hand and the gesture portrays the famous words, "Thou shalt not tempt the Lord thy God," while the Devil points downward.

"The two men are speaking at the same time."

"And in your picture, Jim?"

"Christ listens while the Devil offers him the earth," he answered, and he did not speak again for a long time so that I might better appreciate his genius. An intense moment of appreciation was when he said that no gallery in the world afforded so many beautiful pictures to his sight as did a dirty ceiling. He had only to half close his eyes to see Last Judgments finer than Michael Angelo's, and if he closed his eyes a little he could rediscover his Battle of Arbela.

"The lost picture," I said. "But, Jim, the satyr overturning the nymph; is he visible in the ceiling above your head?"

Jim laughed.

"Perhaps not in this ceiling, but in the ceiling above the little sofa at Alice Harford's."

These lapses of humor jarred a little, and I was glad when he lowered his eyes from the ceiling and remained quite still considering the picture of the nymph and the satyr, and I thrilled again when he said, "That picture has all the beauties of Raphael and other beauties besides." In youth one likes exaggeration, and in response to my cry for Art Jim said: "If you want to learn painting you must go to France."

His words were like "all ashore"; the vessel moves away but so slowly that one does not feel it is moving, and three weeks after my arrival in Paris I wrote to Jim from the Hôtel Voltaire, Quai Voltaire, asking him if he would come over and stay with me; I had a room which I did not use and he was welcome to it. But he wrote saying that he could not come over to Paris at present; and I was very much hurt by his ironical thanks for the room "which I could

69

not use." "But it is the room that one does not use
one offers a friend, not one's own bedroom," I said,
and continued to consider his rude letter, wondering
what had provoked it, without being able to discover
any reason. Some months later he wrote again, this
time in French, and to prove to *mes camarades d'atelier* that it was possible for an Englishman to write
French I took the letter out of my pocket, and while
they scanned it, picking out the English locutions,
it struck me that if Jim were mistaken about his
French he might well be mistaken about his pictures.
And to convince myself of their worth I described
the compositions to Julian—"Julius Cæsar Overturning the Altar of the Druids," "The Bridal of Tria-
maine," "Cain Shielding his Wife from Wild Beasts"
—and Julian listened indulgently over many cups of
coffee. He was becoming my intimate friend, allowing me to take him out to dinner and to treat him
to the theater; I was a little personage in his circle
when a tall young man came into the studio late one
afternoon—Lewis Ponsonby Marshall it was—and
as we went with him to the café to drink a bowl of
punch (the custom of the studio was that every
new-comer should stand a bowl of punch), he turned
and spoke to me in English, asking me, after a few
remarks, if we had not met in Jim Browne's studio.

In a moment I was back again in Prince's Gardens
and Jim was introducing me to a tall young man
whom I did not altogether like, so dissipated did he
look, and so contemptuous was he of Jim's genius,
and of me as soon as I invited him to come forward
and tell me what he thought of "Cain Shielding his

to, and the carriage drew up at the door of the house in which he was living.

"You won't have to go up many stairs. I am on the *entre-sol,*" he said. And his studio was a large room with an immense fireplace, in which he had hung an iron pot on a chain. The fireplace had cost seven hundred and fifty francs; seven hundred and fifty francs represented no actual sum of money to me; it was a pitiful thing to have to turn francs into pounds and to have asked whether any cooking was done in the pot. Of course I should have known that the pot and chain were decorative effect, as were the Turkish lamps and draperies, as indeed everything in the room was, including Lewis himself, especially when he took a fiddle from the wall and began playing.

"Stradella's 'Chant d'Eglise'—do you know it?"

Alas! I didn't, and after hearing it my wonderment increased, for Lewis said that he did not know a note of music, but had met a vagrant once and had picked up some knowledge of the fiddle in half an hour. He played by ear on most instruments, and going to a small organ he strummed snatches of Verdi's "Requiem," until a young girl entered the room out of breath.

"Lewis!"

She stopped suddenly on seeing me, and turning his head he introduced me to as beautiful a girl as I had ever seen; the reader knows that I had seen very beautiful ones at the Globe Theater during Dick's management, and Alice Howard was as fair as any. She was in the first bloom of her beauty, a girl of seventeen or eighteen, tall, five feet six or seven, with brown eyes, fair hair, and a voice that was already a little hard and scornful. She had come to fetch Lewis to dinner, and it occurred to me that she might be disappointed at finding me with Lewis. But he assured me they would be glad of my company if I didn't mind dining at Alphonsine's. Not the least. But who was Alphonsine? And I learnt that she was a light-o'-love of yesterday, who gathered all her old friends around her *table d'hôte*, at three francs and a half, he said. His supercilious style delighted me, and he left me talking to Alice while he crossed the street to order some coals at the *charbonnerie*, and he looked such a fine fellow, as he stepped from one paving-stone to the other, that Alice could not restrain her admiration.

"What a toff he is!"

A toff he was, not a tailor's toff, but one of Nature's toffs, a tall, thin young man and yet powerful, his long arms could no doubt deal a swinging blow on occasions, and in a race his long legs would have carried him past many a competitor. The shoulders were square, but not unduly square, and the neck was long; the head small and covered with dark brown curls, a small face, not in the least spoilt by the broken nose. He must have told me how his nose was broken; I have forgotten; but I remember that it gave character to the face, going well with the soft violet eyes. He might have looked a little girlish if his nose had not been broken . . . his chin would have been too prominent. The breaking of the nose was without doubt advantageous to his appearance, an appearance which absorbed and interested me all the evening, my eyes returning to him again and again. He leaned across the table talking and telling stories in fluent French, delighting everybody, the men and women assembled under the awning. Alice could not speak French even as well as I could; all the same she paid little attention to me, so absorbed was she in Lewis, and so jealous was she of the interest that he evoked in Marie Pellegrin, a beautiful girl with an ivory complexion and hair as glossy as a blackbird's wings.

"What is he saying?" she asked. I could not tell her, alas! "He thinks he is such a fine man that all he would have to do would be to strip himself naked and walk into a woman's room for her to fall down and adore him."

I begged her to tell me about Marie Pellegrin.

"You admire her, don't you? Well, she'll cost you a thousand francs; but if you were a *voyou*——"

"What's a *voyou?*"

"A cad—you could have her for nothing."

"And if she is rich why does she come here? Are all the women here worth a thousand francs?"

Alice laughed scornfully and broke off the conversation, and applied herself to trying to understand what Lewis was saying.

"I wonder why she came here. She must have left the Grand Duke."

"What Grand Duke?"

"All dukes are the same. Do hold your tongue."

Lewis told me afterward that Marie had been to Russia and had had hundreds of thousands of francs from the Grand Duke, but she liked *les voyous du quartier* better, and returned to them when she was bored. She had just come back from Russia and was spending her earnings in the Rue Breda, and, intoxicated with the romance of the story, I begged of Lewis to tell me more about her. But he had told me all he knew, and Alice sat very much annoyed, for she was just as pretty a girl as Marie Pellegrin, and if she had had the luck to be introduced to Grand Dukes she would know how to put her money to better use.

We were in a victoria, for Lewis had proposed an excursion to Bullier, and a train of cabs crossed Paris, over the bridge down the Rue du Bac and round the Luxembourg. But I cannot write with the same insight and sympathy of the Bal Bullier as I did of the Elysée Montmartre, in the story entitled "The End of Marie Pellegrin." I am of Montmartre kin, and Bullier, unhallowed by memories, rises up a mere externality, a crowd pushing through the tables and chairs set under trees, sweating waiters doing their best, and the band under cover, a sort of exaggerated shed into which one walked from the garden. I never danced at Bullier, and it matters little to me that the finest can-can dancers assembled there; polkas and waltzes were looked upon as a kind of waste of time, but the moment the band struck up a quadrille, a crowd formed in dense rings, and the merits of the kickers were discussed as eagerly as the toreadors in Madrid and Seville. The grisettes of the quarter advanced kicking furiously, and about one in the morning the company separated through the Latin quarter, the Montmartians returning by themselves. Nothing was more rare than for a Montmartian to bring a grisette back with him; the girls are faithful to their quarter.

Lewis and Alice dropped me at the Hôtel de Russie, going on themselves for another half hour to the Rue St. Denis, somewhere between the Boulevard Sebastopol and the Gare du Nord . . . I think. My last words to him were, "You'll be sure to be at the studio to-morrow." I was anxious that Julian should see my cousin's picture, and I can see myself still bringing him round to Lewis's easel. An instinctive fellow Julian was, divining at once a useful ally in Lewis, and, to make sure of him, Julian proposed a few weeks later that we—Lewis, myself, Julian, Renouf, Boutet de Monvel, and a few others —should take the first boat next Sunday morning to Bas Meudon. The landscape painters, he said, would find some pretty *motifs* along the banks of the Seine; the others could go for a walk, and I remember that Renouf and Boutet de Monvel went off together, and returned an hour later saying that they had found nothing that tempted them. Whereas Lewis had been immediately struck by the picturesque ascension of the staircase leading up from the river to the village. Was it jealousy that stayed them from admiring his facility? I asked myself, for they did not seem to admire the picture that Lewis had nearly completed on a panel; bestowing only a casual glance at it, they began to talk about breakfast; but Lewis could not be persuaded to lay aside his palette overflowing with bitumen and cadmium yellow; he continued to add bits of drawing, and I to admire the perspective and to wonder how he did it; Alice watched him from under her sunshade, and Julian caught my serious attention when he said: "All that facility will go for nothing if he doesn't come to work at the studio." We found the others waiting for us at the door of the restaurant, very impatient, and to my delight our table was laid under a trellis, and the green leaves and the white table appealed to my imagination, and the cutlets and the omelettes linger in my memory, and the races that we ran in the evening when the bats came out, Lewis beating me a little in one race, for his legs were longer, but only just beating me, whereupon one whose name I cannot recall challenged me to race him for a bottle of champagne, and Lewis whispered, "Take him on; you'll run away from him." And to my surprise Lewis's judgment turned out right; my competitor gave up after a few yards, we drank his champagne, and the boat took us back to Paris, all a little conscious that the last lights of a happy day were dying—a day that I felt I should never forget. "We shall be thinking of this day when we are old men," I said to Lewis, and was ashamed for a moment of my emotion. He had not heard, he was talking to Alice. The night gathered about the green banks of the Seine, and the dim poplars struck through the last bar of light which seemed as if it could not die, the month being June; it lingered between gray clouds till the boat had passed under the first bridge. . . .

And then, bridge after bridge, the landing, the

separations, each one returning to his bed, his mind filled with remembrances of blue air, and flowing water, and swaying trees. But did Lewis bring Alice with him? I think so. She was certainly with us a few weeks later, for Lewis had caught sight of a picturesque corner, and was full of scorn of Renouf and Boutet de Monvel who had missed it, and we three returned to Bas Meudon for Lewis to paint it. But the Seine was so sunny the morning we arrived that a swim suggested itself to Lewis, and a boat was hired, and a boatman rowed us to the hither side of an island. Alice, who could not swim at all, remained in the shallows with me, who could only swim a little, and splashing about together we watched Lewis disporting himself in mid-stream, breasting the current, head upreared, turning over on his side and rushing through the water like some great fish. We admired him until he passed behind the island; and then Alice would have me teach her to swim. We were getting on nicely when, just for some fun, I threatened to duck her. She screamed to me to let her go, and as soon as I lost hold of her she went under, coming up unconscious, though she had not been under the water for more than a few seconds. The boatman came to my assistance quickly, and Lewis came swimming by, and together we got her into the boat. "Good God, Lewis, try to bring her to," I cried, falling on my knees beside her, terribly frightened, for Lewis was so angry with me that I could not doubt that he would have pitched me into the river if he had failed to revive her. At last she opened her eyes, and after a tender scene between her and Lewis, we rowed back to the inn where her beauty inspired much commiseration.

"A day has been wasted," Lewis said, for his mind was fixed upon the corner he had selected, and he went away next morning without me, the boat not being large enough to hold two painters. "You don't want to paint. You had better remain and talk to Alice." But it was impossible to persuade Alice out of her bed, and feeling, I suppose, that I was as negligible a quantity in love as in art she invited me, after some hesitation, into her room; and we used to gossip there every morning when Lewis went away to paint until gossip busied itself with us, and one day he told us that he was return-ing to Paris next day. We could see that some-thing had gone wrong, and at last we got the truth out of him. People at the inn had begun to notice that I went into Alice's room as soon as he went out painting. Alice began to grow angry, and I pro-tested, and Lewis said: "Of course I know she wouldn't have anything to do with you; all the same, I don't wish to pass for a cuckold." A very rude answer I felt this to be, but held my tongue, and we returned to Paris next day, all three rather angry and disappointed, and Lewis discouraged, for his picture had not turned out well; it had, indeed, turned out so badly that landscape painting was not mentioned again that summer. It was not until the autumn that he began to speak of Cernay, a beautiful country celebrated among painters, not more than fifty or sixty kilometers from Paris. His suggestion was that we might go there for a week,

and I consented, for I wanted to see the inn whose
walls had been decorated by every painter that had
stayed there—by every man of talent—for this inn-
keeper would not hand over his walls to be daubed
by me and my like. And wondering if Lewis were
trying to fool me, or if it were really true that Cernay was a relic of the Middle Ages that had escaped
civilization, I asked him if he proposed to pay his
bill with a picture, and if the inn-keeper would accept poems from me in exchange for what I owed him.
"Here are five rondels, two sonnets, and a villanelle;
enough for two days' board and lodging. Some
change in ordinary specie you will be able to give
me."

"You see now I have told you the truth," he
said as soon as we entered the inn, and I looked
round the rooms seeing every subject that had
ever been treated dashed here and there: seascapes,
horses ploughing, battle pieces, ravens, parrots, ladies in their shifts amid pillows, swine on the hillside,
and herds of cattle winding through fields, a birchen
wood showing aloft on a hillside which Lewis said
was worth all the other pictures put together, and
he mentioned the name of the painter of a large
flowerpiece, and we should have admired his peonies
longer if the inn-keeper had not been at our heels
waiting for us to choose our rooms.

The empty inn afforded a liberal choice, but for
reasons that my memory does not seem to have kept
any record of, we elected to sleep in the same room.
It may have been that the inn was in process of
transformation, and the inn-keeper had only one

room to offer us. Hardly that, for in the seventies the inns of France were as they had ever been, without bath-rooms and without water-closets; inconvenient omissions, especially on that occasion, for I was awakened in the middle of the night by Lewis trying to find matches to light a candle, saying that he was going into the backyard. A dog began to bark, and Alice sat up quaking, beseeching me to go to Lewis's help and save him from being devoured. It seemed to me that I had better waken the inn-keeper, and, while standing in the middle of the floor wondering what had better be done, Lewis returned. The dog had rushed at him, but fortunately he was on a chain.

"But, Lewis, if you had been within reach, or if the chain had snapped!"

And the depth of her passion may be judged from the discussion that arose between her and me as to what one would do if one had to eat something incredibly nasty or drink a cup of poison. Alice's point was that it mattered a great deal from whence the nastiness came; if it came from Lewis she would sooner eat a pound than a pinch if it came from me, and she woke up Lewis to ask him if he would not return her the compliment, and was very angry when he said that nastiness was the same all the world over, and he would prefer to swallow a pinch rather than a pound, no matter who owned it.

We certainly pigged it together, pigs no doubt, but aspiring pigs, however, who went out in the morning to the borders of the lake to paint, Lewis able to get down a large willow-tree in the foreground, retaining some parts of the view, rejecting others, myself quite uninterested in trying to arrange the lake as Corot might have arranged it, but unable to express myself, fumbling with the beautiful outline of the shore, which I could not fit into the canvas till Alice, who had not risen so early as we, came to meet us and joined in Lewis's criticism of my abortive drawings, giggling under her parasol and echoing Lewis's opinions.

"Of course there must be a willow-tree and a man in a boat to make a picture. Give me your charcoal," and he began to recompose, bringing the edge of the wood into my canvas. "Don't you see?"

"No, Lewis, I don't see; the edge of the wood doesn't come into my vision."

"It should come in to make a picture"; and he strove hard vulgarizing what I had done, and doing this so successfully that in the end he had to hand me back my pencil, saying he was sorry, that perhaps it was better the way I had it. Alice did not think so, and we strolled over to admire Lewis's work, which captured all her admiration. "I think that is how Corot would have seen it," he said, and we watched the slate-colored lake amid its autumn tints and sedges, and returned to Paris a few days afterward without a picture, to continue——

"Good heavens! it is twelve o'clock, and I have been sitting here dreaming since ten!" And my eyes went to the large fat volume on the table, not one line of which I had read.

IV

As soon as Teresa had removed the tablecloth my
eyes went to a bulky volume, "The Brothers Kara-
masov," and, determined to break the back of the
story, I threw myself into an arm-chair, saying: "If
I read fifty pages every evening I shall soon get
through it." And I read on and on through the fifty
pages that my conscience had stipulated for, and
might have read to a hundred if the endless corridors down which I had been wandering and the
great halls through which I had passed had not
suddenly seemed to dissolve into vapor. "A talent,"
I said, "that appeals to the young men of to-day.
The pigmy admires the giant, however loosely his
frame may be put together, and our young writers
lift their pale etiolated faces to Dostoievsky. 'We've
had enough of Art,' is their cry, 'give us Nature,'
and this book fulfills all their aspirations. It is
impersonal and vague as Nature," I said, returning
to the consideration of the book, finding myself
obliged to admit that I could detect a dribble of
outline in Aloysha, as much as may be detected in
the ikons on the walls. A man of genius without
doubt, on a different plane from our miserable
writers of fiction, but inferior to his own country-
men, to one at least, Turgenev, and on the whole

inferior to Balzac. Some rough spots there may be in Balzac, some rocks, but rocks are better than marsh, and my thoughts went to the philosophical studies, to "Louis Lambert," "Seraphita," "Jesus Christ in Flanders." These books affected me in times past, but to read them again would be to run the risk of a great disillusion. So why read them? As I took a cigar from the box my thought returned to Paris, and I remembered that in about a year I had begun to pine for London, for the English language, English food, for my mother's house in Alfred Place. Close by it I had rented a studio, in Cromwell Mews, and Millais used to come to see me there, and Jim of course came and talked to me of his compositions; but his influence was a declining one, for in London Lewis was always by me in spirit controlling me, exciting in me a desire to be loved for myself, prompting the conviction that for a young man to go to Cremorne Gardens or the Argyle Rooms, armed with a couple of sovereigns, was merely to procure for himself a sensual gratification hardly on a higher level than that which schoolboys indulge in. But if he go there with only a few cab fares in his pocket he will be obliged to reconsider himself physically, and those negligences in dress which were the despair of his parents will vanish, his boots will begin to improve in shape and quality, a pin will appear in his necktie, or maybe he will wear his scarf in a ring, his shoulders will take a finer turn, and his head will be upreared above them proudly. And if he would be loved for himself he must cultivate an interesting attitude of mind, he must be able to slough himself at will (his outer skin, I should have said), and take part in wider humanity, in dreams, hopes, aspirations and ideals not strictly his own, only his through sympathy with the lives of others.

The only one who knew me in the days of the Cremorne and Argyle Rooms is dear Edward, and it always interests me to hear him say that I began myself out of nothing, developing from the mere sponge to the vertebræ and upward. I should have liked another simile, for Nature has never interested me as much as Art, perhaps I should never have paid any attention to Nature if it hadn't been for Art. I would have preferred Edward to have said that I was at once the sculptor and the block of marble of my own destiny, and that every failure to win a mistress in the Cremorne Gardens was a chipping away of the vague material that concealed the statue. But the simile would perhaps not have been so correct, for to say that one is at once the sculptor and the block of marble means that one is a conscious artist, and I was not that in those days; I worked unconsciously. Yes, Edward is right; I developed upward from the sponge, returning to Paris about eighteen months later a sort of minor Lewis, having not only imbibed a good deal of his mind, but even fashioned myself so closely to his likeness that Julian, who caught sight of me on the boulevard soon after my return, thought for a moment that I was Lewis.

On arriving at the Gare du Nord, the first thing to do was to find Lewis, for without him the evening

would never wear away; but the concierge told me
that Monsieur Marshall had left, and that he did
not know his present address. . . . Julian took his
coffee every evening at the Café Vivienne, but never
came before eight; I waited till half-past, and then
bethought myself of Alphonsine's. Monsieur Marshall and Madame Alice had not dined there for
some weeks. Alphonsine did not know their address;
the dinner seemed worse than usual, and the chatter
of the women more tedious. At last somebody said
that she thought Marie Pellegrin knew Madame
Alice's address, but Marie was not at Alphonsine's
that evening. . . . She came in, however, a little
later, and told me that Madame Alice was living in
the Rue Duphot, No. 14, an *appartment au rez de
chaussée*, and away I went. Madame was at home,
but she had a gentleman dining with her.

"Monsieur Marshall."

"Yes," the servant answered timidly, and I burst
in.

Lewis was glad to see me, and Alice welcomed me
with hard empty laughter. Was she glad to see
me back again? Or did she fear that painting would
distract Lewis's attention from her? However this
may be, she welcomed me, and was certainly pleased
at my admiration of the fine suite of apartments
that I found her in. "Yes, I have been going
ahead," she said, leading me through the windows
into a strip of garden where tall trees were trained
up a high wall. She liked my question, "Who is the
fellow who pays for all this?" and I heard the name
of Phillipar for the first time, a great name it was

87

then in the Parisian financial world. After going bankrupt for a dozen millions or more, he bought an Island in the Mediterranean, and it was he or one of his associates that kept Alice, never coming to see her oftener than once a week, and then only in the afternoon.

"So when you hear the servant whisper, '*Monsieur est ici*,' you'll just skip round to the café and wait."

"And I shall find Lewis there," I added.

The remark did not please him, for he was trying to carry off the life he was leading with great airs; and when I went to him a few days after, seriously alarmed for his artistic future, saying that I had heard in the studio that he had not been there for months, he answered that I had a fixed income, but he had only four hundred francs a month from his mother, and it was not easy to abstract Julian's fees, one hundred francs a month, from four. He had counted upon selling the landscape which we were looking at—a flowering glade in the woods of Ville d'Avray; but the customer had been called away to South America suddenly. He would come back, but in the meantime. . . . The picture was not finished; he would like to have done some more to it, but he was so hard up he could not afford the train fare; and my heart melting at the thought of so much genius wasted for the sake of a train fare, I went away with him to Ville d'Avray, and we found *motifs* and painters in the woods, and strayed under flowering boughs, and returned with two pictures in time for dinner in the Rue Duphot, and a great

deal of art talk that was continued during and after
dinner till Alice said:

"I don't see where I come in. You two have been
away all day in the woods, and have no doubt had a
very pleasant time, and you come back here merely
to talk painting." She flounced out of the room, and
we wondered at her ill temper and how long she
would remain away. She appeared in the doorway
ten minutes after, and turning on her heel, said,
"I don't know what you two are going to do; I am
going to the Bois."

We were both a little tired, but Lewis did not dare
tell her that we would prefer to spend the evening
lounging in her drawing-room, and we had to accompany her to the Cascade and sit with her in
the café till midnight watching the celebrated cour-
tesans arriving and departing in their carriages, our
art talk constantly interrupted by her remarks.
"So-and-so is now with So-and-so; he gives her a
hundred thousand francs a year *et elle le trompe
tout le temps avec le petit chose.*" She was interested in these details, and not unnaturally, for she
was now very nearly in the front rank, and to keep
her there we had to take her out every evening. If
we did not go to a theater we went to a music-hall;
the Folies Bergères was coming into fashion at that
time, and we were often there till it was time to
go to the Mabile. A tedious place of amusement
the Mabile always was to my thinking, and the dinner that had cost over eighty francs, and the box
at the Folies Bergères which had broken into a
second hundred-franc note, did not cause me as

many pangs of conscience as the five-franc entrance-fee. Ladies entered the Mabile free, and Alice sometimes paid for Lewis, but very often before she had time to slip five francs into his hand some friends engaged her in conversation, and then he would beseech me to lend him the money, and I used to see him fling the coin down with the air of *un grand seigneur*. We did not remain in the garden for more than half an hour, and as we walked round the estrade in silence, I often thought of my poor Ballintubber tenants.

"I wonder how much longer Alice intends to keep me waiting?"

Sometimes she joined us, sometimes she went away with her aristocratic connections, and as we walked home Lewis would rail against her, swearing that he would never see her again, turning a deaf ear to my pleading. It amused me to plead for her, and to soothe him I agreed that she should not have left his arm as abruptly as she had done; but her position was a difficult one, torn between love and necessity. He would answer that he wasn't going to be made a fool of before all Paris, and it delighted me to see him put on the grand air, though if I had been Alice's *amant de cœur* I should like to have been treated frankly as a ponce, one that has to make way for the *miché qui happe le pot*, as in Villon's ballade. To be an *amant de cœur* as Lewis was, *en cachette*, would have filled me with shame, my instinct being always to be ashamed of nothing but to be ashamed, and it was from the day that Lewis confessed himself ashamed of the rôle he was playing

held one in my hand with a famous passage marked
for her to read. I can still hear her talk. "I have
been offered three hundred thousand francs to go
to Russia." "But you're not going? If you go I
shall never see you again." "I don't know whether I
shall go or not. I don't know what's going to happen to me," were the last words of *la belle Hollan-
daise*, the last words she addressed to me. She
passed out of my life forever, and if I relate the incident of our meeting it is because I would pay trib-
ute to her who revealed sensuality to me. On that
memorable night Alice and Lewis seemed but perfunctory lovers, and a few evenings later he offered
Alice to me, and she was willing to accept me, for
they had outlived their love for each other, and were
now seeking to maintain it in excess and orgy.

Of the psychology of love I knew nothing at the
time, and did not read in the incident the instinct of
every woman to turn to him who has witnessed her
love as soon as she wearies of her lover. There was
no more and no less in it than an eternal instinct,
and we may acquit Alice of any deep plan to ruin me
when one day on my calling to ask her to come out
to dinner, she answered that she would, but she
wasn't dressed. Would I mind her taking a bath
before me? Few men turn away from a beautiful
woman, and she was more beautiful than any of the
models that had posed in Julian's studio. If her
breasts were large they were perfectly well formed
and firm, and during her toilet we talked of indifferent things, myself maintaining an attitude of reserve,
admiring her as if she were a model, for, truth to

93

tell, Lewis was very clever at hiding himself, and had told me many tales of how he had crept under a sofa, or ensconced himself between the tester and the ceiling. It was one thing to offer Alice to me in a moment of satiety, and another to discover her giving herself to me for her pleasure. I refrained, and perhaps wisely, but there are things that one never knows, and it was not very long afterward that he announced that he had left her.

" 'You couldn't leave such a pretty pair of breasts,' was her idiotic answer," he said; and a few days later he told me that her carriage and herself in it had passed him in the Champs Elysées. But she had looked the other way, a great scorn upon her face, and he vowed that he would prove to her that in losing her he had not lost everything, and that very night he went to Alphonsine's in search of some woman whom he could set up as a rival. A few days after he introduced me to a pretty blonde Swede, a woman who was well thought of, but with hardly a tithe of Alice's reputation, and after three months he left her. According to her account he was sent away because she found a *voiture de remise indispensable*.

"*Les voitures de remise et les amants de cœur sont la ruine des femmes*," she said one day, stepping into her carriage, and, letting down the glass, she added: "*et comme combinaison, c'est aux pommes*."

And the wisdom of this second-rate light-o'-love, begotten no doubt of many experiences, called my thoughts back to Alice, who, since she had thrown out her *amant de cœur*, was rapidly becoming one

94

of the celebrated *demi-mondaines* in Paris. And all
the while Lewis was sinking lower, attaching himself to women who could barely afford him three
hundred francs a month, the price of a grisette in
the Quartier Latin, the occasional bank-note that his
mother used to send him she could afford no longer;
his niece was a great expense, and he came to me
one day to tell me that he had decided to earn his
own living.

"Vanderkirko, you know whom I mean," he said,
"has a small china factory, and he has agreed to
take me as an apprentice. I am going to live with
him in the Avenue d'Italie *près de la barrière*."

"But you'll see nobody. You'll be exiled."

"I am weary of the life I have been leading; and
you'll come and see me sometimes, though it is a
long way off."

"I'll come every Sunday," I answered, and a few
Sundays later I found him and Vanderkirko building
a wall.

"So you've come at last!" and he took me into
the house and showed me some of his first attempts
at painting china, and interested me in the manufac-
ture, in *la cuisson au petit et au grand feu*. Vanderkirko was an ex-Communist, and Lewis told me
how he had only just escaped with his life. At the
moment when escape seemed impossible, a door
opened, and he had rushed through it, and through
the house beyond. He was now married *et très
rangé*, and that was why he had refused my invitation to dine and to go to Constant's afterward.
Lewis advised me that the restaurants in the quar-

ter *n'étaient pas trop fameux*, but we could get some
simple food *au coin de la rue de la Gaieté*, and afterward at Constant's he would introduce me to some
very dangerous criminals, and he talked to me of
the thieves he knew and the robberies they planned
and were planning; he talked to me about their mistresses, exciting my imagination, for their nicknames
were odd and picturesque. "If he be not the lover
of a great *demi-mondaine*, he likes to live among
thieves and ponces," I thought; "one extreme or the
other of society for him. A somewhat unreal person. Now, why is one person more unreal than another?" I asked myself, deciding that a man without a point of view always conveys the impression
of unreality. The long street that we used to walk
up together rose in my vision, and Lewis growing
more confidential from lamp-post to lamp-post,
telling me that it was not idleness, as I supposed,
that had kept him out of Julian's studio, nor was it
because he had no money to pay the fees—Julian
would have let him work for nothing—but he could
not accept favors from Julian. The tone of his voice
in which he said this surprised me, and then becoming
still more confidential he said that he could not go to
Julian's studio because his niece was Julian's mistress. I don't know why I should have been so surprised, but I was surprised that such a thing should
have happened and that he should have told me, and
very much concerned, I begged of him to tell me how
it had all come about. Apparently in the simplest
way. He had introduced her to Julian, and—my
memory has dropped a stitch, something and some-

thing. He had called at her hotel, and the concierge had told him that Madame had gone away to the country, and the next time they met he asked her where she had been; she answered that she had been to the country with Julian. "But you didn't come back that night. Where did you sleep?" "With Fatty," she had answered coolly. He did not think it right, and he did not think it wrong, that his niece should live as it pleased her; he was always *un peu veule de nature*, without a point of view; and returning from the coal-box, for the fire had sunk very low, I picked up the thread of my thoughts again. He had told me that it was on account of debts he had given up work at the studio; he had mentioned some of his debts to me, and I remembered that he had said he owed Renouf one hundred francs, that Julian had lent him fifty, he had had a bit off Chadwick, he had borrowed from Julian's *bonne*, and it was this last debt that had convinced him that sooner or later he would have to earn his own living. My heart warmed toward this handsome fellow who could take the rough with the smooth, and was as light-hearted in the Avenue d'Italie as in the Rue Duphot, and I praised him to Julian as we drank our coffee at the corner table, until one night, after listening in silence, Julian asked if it had not occurred to me that in losing Lewis Art had suffered a great loss. Lewis's defection from the studio had never struck me in quite so serious a light before, and I asked Julian if he thought that a great genius was being wasted at the Barrière d'Italie. As if he did not hear me, Julian said that casual loans of

money were no use, and that it would be better for
me not to see Lewis any more unless I could do
something definite for him.

"Why shouldn't you invite him to live with you
for a year, eighteen months?—two years will be sufficient."

"But I live in the Hotel de Russie."

"The proper thing for you to do is to take an
appartement, give him a room and let him be certain
of his breakfast and his dinner, and pay for his
washing. His mother will send him a little pocket-
money, and he can work at my studio."

"But the studio fees?"

"Of course I couldn't take your money."

Julian had caught me, and feeling that I lacked
courage to say "No," and bear the blame of allowing a great genius to wither unknown down by the
Barrière d'Italie I wrote to Lewis telling him of
Julian's proposal to me, and next day he came up to
thank me and to assure me that he would try to
justify the confidence that we placed in him. He
did not give me time to consider the wisdom of the
sacrifice I was making, and very wisely, but set out
at once to find an *appartement* that would suit us,
coming next day to me with the joyful tidings that
he had seen one in the Passage des Panoramas in
the Galerie Feydeau. "But I don't think I could
live in the Passage des Panoramas," and I begged
him to look out for another *appartement*.

"But this one is on the first floor," he urged;
"we shan't have to go up many stairs, and we shall
only have to run round the galleries to Julian's

studio. That will save us getting up half an hour earlier in the morning and walking through the wet streets."

"We shall never see the sky nor feel the wind blowing," and I looked up at the glass roofing through which trickled a dim sordid twilight.

"The sky and wind are well enough out of doors, but once we are within doors the more we are within the better. I have seen other *appartements,* but nothing as suitable to our convenience. You are going to work, aren't you? And if you are, nothing else matters."

It was with such specious argument that I was inveigled into my prison, and more or less feebly I agreed to forego light and air for eighteen months or two years.

V

We had been working together in the studio for
three months when it became plain to me that I
could never hope to be an artist. The first week
my drawing was no worse than Lewis's; indeed, it
was rather better, but the second week he had out-
stripped me, and whatever talent I had the long
hours in the studio wore it away rapidly, and one
day, horrified at the black thing in front of me, I
laid down my pencil: saying to myself, "I will never
take up pencil or brush again," and slunk away out
of the studio home to the Galerie Feydeau to the
room above the umbrella shop, to my bed, my *armoire à glace*, my half-dozen chairs; and on that bed
under its green curtains I lay all night weeping,
saying to myself: "My life is ended and done. There
is no hope for me. All I wanted was Art, and Art
has been taken from me. *Je suis fichu, fichu, fichu,*"
I repeated, and the steps of the occasional passer-
by echoed mournfully under the glass roofing.

The Galerie Feydeau had never seemed a cheerful
place to live in; it was now as hateful to me as a
prison, and Lewis was my gaoler. He went away
every morning at eight o'clock, and I met him at
breakfast in the little restaurant at the end of the

Galerie Feydeau. After breakfast he returned to
the studio, and I was free to wander about the streets
or to sit in my room reading Shelley. He came home
about five, and we went for a walk, and he told me
what was happening in the studio. Everything that
happened seemed to be for his greater honor and
glory. He had won the medal and the hundred
francs that Julian offered every month for the best
drawing—an innovation this was to attract custom
—and a little spree had to be given to commemorate
his triumph. He organized the spree very well; of
course it was my money that paid for it; and the
best part of the studio came to the Galerie Feydeau
one evening, and we sang and smoked and drank
punch and played the piano. Lewis played the violin, and Julian, drawing his chair up to mine, told
me that in ten years hence Lewis would be *hors con-
cours* in the Salon, and living in a great hotel in
the Champs Elysées painting pictures at thirty
thousand francs apiece. *Les grandes tartines* we
used to call the pictures that went to the Salon, or
les grandes machines: I am forgetting my studio
slang. Julian had a difficult part to play. If he
were to depreciate Lewis's talent I might throw up
the sponge and go away; he thought it safer to assure me that my sacrifices were not made in vain;
but man is such a selfish and jealous animal that it
had begun to seem to me I would prefer a great
failure for Lewis to a great success. "Not a great
failure," I said to myself; "for if he fail I shall never
get rid of him. There will be no escape from the
Galerie Feydeau for me, so I must hope for his suc-

cess. He will leave me when he begins to make money. When will that be?" and the cruel thought crossed my mind that he was laughing at me all the while, looking upon me as the springboard where-from he would jump into great Salon success. It seemed to me that I could see us both in the years ahead—myself humble and obscure, he great and glorious, looking down upon me somewhat kindly, as the lion looks upon the mouse that has gnawed the cords that bound him. I think I was as unhappy in the Galerie Feydeau as I had been in Oscott College. I seemed to have lost everybody in the world except the one person I wished to lose, Lewis. I was a stranger in the studio, where I went seldom, for everyone there knew of my failure; even the models I feared to invite to my rooms lest they should tell tales afterward. At last I remembered that one of my sister's school friends lived in Paris, and at her home I met people that knew nothing of Julian and L'Ecole des Beaux Arts, and at a public dinner I was introduced to John O'Leary and his Parisian circle, and all these people were interested in me on account of my father. One can always pick one's way into Society, and three months later I was moving in American and English Society about the Place Wagram and the Boulevard Males-herbe, returning home in the early morning, awaking Lewis frequently to describe the party to him, awak-ing him one morning to tell him that a lady whose boots I was buttoning in the vestibule had leaned over me and whispered that I could go to the very top button . . . if I liked. A very pretty answer it had seemed to Lewis, and it was clear that he was affected by it, though he resisted for a long time my efforts to persuade him to allow me to introduce him to my friends. I had only intended an outing, an exhibition of my cousin, after which he was to return to his kennel. But I had interrupted his life, and fatally; invitations came to him from every side; he accepted them all, and we started to learn the Boston before the *armoire à glace*. He learnt it quicker than I did, and when he returned from Barbizon, whither he had gone to meet the wife of an American millionaire, I told him I could live no longer in the Galerie Feydeau and was going away to Boulogne to meet some people whom I had met at Madame Ratazzi's, into whose circle I had happily not introduced him, and wishing to take him down a peg I mentioned that I had acted with her in "La Dame aux Camélias." He flew into a violent rage. I was going away with swagger friends to enjoy myself, careless whether he ate or starved. He was right from his point of view. I was breaking my promise to him. But is there anybody who would be able to say he would not have broken his in the same circumstances? It was at once a shameful and a natural act; he was my friend; it was shameful, it was horrible, but there are shameful and horrible things in other lives beside mine. His presence had become unendurable. But why excuse myself further? Let the facts speak for themselves and let me be judged by them. They have already been published in "The Confessions of a Young Man," but I wonder now if I told in that book sufficiently of the surprise that I experienced on finding him still in the *appartement* in the Galerie Feydeau when I returned from Boulogne? It was difficult to understand his indecency. . . . He should have moved out of my rooms after the quarrel, but instead of that he had converted the sitting-room into a workshop, and his designs for lace curtains occupied one entire wall. "He'll go to-morrow, of course," I said, but he did not go on the morrow or the day after, and at the end of the week he was still there annoying me by whistling as he worked on his design. At last, unable to bear it any longer, I opened the door of my bedroom and begged him to cease, and it is to this day a marvel how he restrained himself from strangling me. He looked as if he were going to rush at me, and on the threshold of my room indulged in the most fearful vituperation and abuse, to which I felt it would be wiser not to attempt an answer, for his arms were long and his fists were heavy; he was always talking about striking out, and it is foolish to engage in a combat when one knows one is going to get the worst of it, so I just let him shout on until he retired to his lace curtains and resolved to give notice.

"He can't stay after quarter-day."

But the quarter was a long way off, and every day I used to see him in the Passage des Panoramas among my friends flowing away in a new ulster past the jet ornaments and the fans; a splendid fellow he certainly was with his broken nose and his grand eyes, and the ulster suited him so well that I began

to regret a quarrel which prevented me from asking
him questions about it. He came and went as he
pleased, passing me on the staircase and in the
rooms, his splendid indifference compelling the conclusion that however lacking in character a reconciliation would prove me to be, I could no longer
forego one, and after many hesitations I called after
him and begged that he would allow bygones to be
bygones. I think that he said this was impossible;
he must have been counting on my weakness; however this may be, he played with me very prettily,
forcing me to plead, practically to ask his forgive-
ness, and when we were friends again he related that
he was looking out for a studio, and in the effusion
of reconciliation I very foolishly asked him to tell
me if he should happen upon an *appartement* that
he thought would suit me, for live another quarter
in the Galerie Feydeau I couldn't. He promised
that he would not fail to keep his eyes open, and a
few days after he mentioned that he had seen a
charming *appartement* in the Rue de la Tour des
Dames—the very thing that would suit me. As
there was not nearly sufficient furniture in the Galerie Feydeau to fill it, he entered into negotiations
with an upholsterer, and dazzled me with a scheme
of decoration which would cost very little to carry
out, and which would give me as pretty an *appartement* as any in Paris. He was kind enough to relieve me of all the details of *un déménagement*, and
what could I do in return except to invite him to
stay with me until he had painted a picture? We
had a friend at that time who painted little naked

women very badly and sold them very well, and it occurred to Lewis that if Faléro could sell his pictures there was no reason why he should not, so he borrowed a hundred francs from me to hire a model and painted a nymph; but though much better drawn than Faléro's, she went round from shop to shop, never finding a purchaser.

Her failure to please, however, did not matter much, for Lewis began at this time to please a rich widow who lived in Rue Jean Goujon, and he spent most of his time with her. She was not, however, very generous, refusing *de le mettre dans ses meubles,* and he continued to live with me, wearing my hats and neckties, borrowing small sums of money, and what was still more annoying, beginning to cultivate a taste for literature, appropriating my one literary friend, Bernard de Lopez, a Parisian despite his name—Parisian in this much, that he had written a hundred French plays and nearly all were written in collaboration with all the great men of letters of his time, including Dumas, Banville, and Gautier. He was my first Parisian friend. I had picked him up in the Hotel de Russie very soon after my arrival in Paris. He dined there every Monday, an old habit (the origin of this habit he never told me, or I have forgotten)—a strange habit, it seemed, for anything less literary than the Hôtel de Russie . . . for the matter of that anything less literary than Bernard de Lopez's appearance it is impossible to imagine: two piggy little eyes set on either side of a large, well-shaped nose; two little stunted legs that toddled quickly forward to meet me, and two little warm, fat hands that often held mine too long for comfort. So small a man never had before so large a head, a great bald head with a ring of hair round it, and his chin was difficult to discover under his mustaches; roll after roll of flesh descended into his bosom. I remember his round shoulders, and, by God! I can still see his little brown eyes watching me just like a pig, suspiciously, though why he should have been suspicious of me it is impossible even to conjecture, unless, indeed, he suspected that I doubted the existence of the plays he said he had written in collaboration, a thing which I frequently did; but he was telling the truth. He had collaborated with Gautier, Dumas, and Banville, and having assured myself of this by the *brochures*, I began to think that he could not have been always so trite and commonplace. Men decline like the day, and he was in the evening of his life when I met him, garrulous about the days gone by, and in the Café Madrid, whither I invited him to come with me after dinner at the Hôtel de Russie, he told me that Scribe had always said he would like to rewrite "La Dame Blanche." "Rewrite a piece that has been acted a thousand times," Lopez would gurgle, and then he told me about *la scène à faire.* The morning he had brought Dumas the manuscript of "Le Fils de la Nuit" he had said to him: *"Nous aurons des larmes."* He used to speak about a writer called Saint-George, whose rooms were always heavily scented, and scent gave the little man *des maux de tête.* There was another man whose name I cannot recall, with whom he had written many

107

plays, and who had an engagement book like a doctor or a dentist, *qui ne l'empêche pas d'avoir beaucoup d'esprit.* It pleased me to recall Lopez's very words; they brought back that time to me, and my own thoughts of that time—the intellectual atmosphere in which these men lived, going about their business with comedies and plays in their heads—an appointment at ten to consider the first act of a vaudeville; after breakfast another appointment, perhaps at the other end of Paris, to discover a plot for a drama; a talk about an opera in the café at five, and perhaps somebody would call in the evening. But they wrote in the evening, on into the night, tumbling into bed at three or four in the morning. How wonderful! Of that wonderful time Lopez was *le dernier rejeton;* and talking about "Le Fils de la Nuit," the first play that had ever run two hundred nights, we strolled back to his lodging in the Place Pigalle—a large room on the second floor overlooking the Place with a *cabinet de toilette.* There was some little mystery in his life. He had been married, and it is probable that he received from his wife the few thousand francs a year on which he lived, and the Empire bed with chairs and a toilet-table to match must have come from her; he would not have thought of buying them, and still less the two portraits by Angelica Kauffman on either side of the fireplace. The world is full of such little odds and oddments as Bernard de Lopez —"men that have outlived their day," so the phrase runs, a superficial phrase, for none can say when a man has outlived his day. He had not outlived his when the managers ceased to produce his plays, for he drew my attention to literature, and it was pleasant to remember the day that I hurried down to Galignani's to buy a play. One evening while we talked in the Café Madrid it had occurred to me that with a little arrangement Lewis and Alice would supply me with the subject of a comedy. But never having read a play I did not know how one looked upon paper. Congreve, Wycherley, Farquhar, and Vanbrugh (Leigh Hunt's edition) were my first dramatic authors, and my first comedy, in imitation of these writers, was composed and written and copied out and read to Bernard de Lopez within six weeks of its inception. His criticism of it was, "I thought at first we were going to have a very strong play, a man that marries his mistress to his friend. But you don't pursue the subject." And I understood at once that the subject had been frittered away in endless dialogue after the manner of my exemplars, and it was as likely as not in the hope of getting all this dialogue acted that I returned to England, remaining there some time, writing and painting by turns, writing a long comedy which Lopez did not like. And then drama was abandoned for poetry. Lopez encouraged me to tell him of my poems, advising me as we ascended the Rue Notre Dame de Lorette or the Rue des Martyrs to choose subjects that would astonish the British public by their originality—for instance, if instead of inditing a sonnet to my mistress's eyebrows I were to tell the passion of a toad for a rose.

109

"Not that, of course not that, but poems on violent subjects."

"A young man's love for a beautiful corpse," I interjected. "What do you think?"

He was my first introduction into French poetry and French literature; through him I read a great deal that I might not have heard of, and wrote a great deal that I might never have written; and it was to him that I brought my first copy of my first book, "Flowers of Passion," together with the articles that had appeared in the London papers.

The World, a paper then at the very height of its popularity, published an article entitled, "A Bestial Bard," and the article began: "The author of these poems should be whipped at the cart's tail, while the book was being burnt in the market-place by the common hangman." It filled the greater part of a column, and was from the pen of the late Mr. Edmund Yates, a mere piece of blatant journalism written to sell the paper. My poor little book did not deserve such violent notice, perhaps no notice at all. The note struck by Edmund Yates was taken up by other critics, and, much impressed by the violence of their language, Lopez said:

"They seem to have exhausted the vocabulary of abuse." And he began to sound me regarding the possibility of an English and a French author writing a play together for the English stage. Martin Luther seemed to us a character that would suit Irving, then at the height of his fame.

"But shall we present both sides of the question

110

impartially like Goethe? Or shall we write as ardent Protestants?"

. "As ardent Protestants," I answered without a moment's hesitation; and the composition brought Lopez round very often to the Rue de la Tour des Dames, and we used to sit talking of the Diet of Worms unsuspicious that Lewis was much more interested in our conversation than in his own painting. It had never occurred to me that he took the least interest in literature, and I should have laughed if anybody had told me that he was writing sonnets. He was doing so all the time, and one day when I called to discuss a certain scene between Catherine Bora and Luther, I caught him reading his sonnets to Bernard de Lopez. He had had the impertinence to take his manuscript round to the Place Pigalle.

"*Mon cher monsieur, ce n'est pas pour vous contrarier, mais 'd'où suintent d'étranges pleurs' est un vers de sept; suintent n'a que deux syllabes.*"

"*C'est ma mauvaise prononciation flamande,*" Lewis said, and he bundled up his papers. "You have come to talk Martin Luther, so I'll leave you."

"Leave us! But what right has he to come——"

"He only came to show me a sonnet."

"But what the devil does he want to write sonnets for? Isn't it enough that he should paint bad pictures?"

"He merely came to inquire out the prosody of a certain line," Lopez answered, and he tried to calm me.

"No, there's no use, Lopez. I can't fix my thoughts on Martin Luther. Let us go out and dine somewhere. What do you say to the Rat Mort?"

He raised no objection to the Rat Mort, and the moment we entered the café he rushed up to a disheveled and wild-eyed fellow. "Let me introduce you," he said, "to Villiers de l'Isle Adam." And Lewis was forgotten in the excitement of dining with a real man of letters, in the pleasure of confiding to Villiers the scene that I had come to talk to Lopez about. I had imagined Catherine Bora walking with another nun in a wood, and, seeing a monk reading his breviary, she conceives the idea of confessing the sin that preyed upon her mind to him.

"And it is to Martin Luther himself," I said, "whom she has never seen, that she confesses her love of Martin Luther."

"I must introduce you to Mallarmé"; and Villiers wrote a note on the edge of the table. "You'll find him at home on Tuesday evenings."

It is always amusing to recall the stages of one's life. Mallarmé spoke to me of Manet, who used to go every night to the Nouvelle Athènes, and he must have spoken to Manet about me, for one night in the Nouvelle Athènes Manet asked me if the conversation distracted my attention from my proofs. "Come and see me in my studio in the Rue d'Amsterdam." And not very many evenings later Mendès was introduced to me between one and two in the morning. He asked me to the Rue Mansard, where he lived with Mademoiselle Holmès. I was launched on Parisian literary and artistic society and six months afterwards I knew everybody.

"There is no Frenchman in England who occupies the position you do in Paris," Manet said.

"Perhaps there isn't," I answered mechanically, my thoughts turning to Lewis, "who," I said to myself as I went home, "seems to be sinking. If I am going up in the world, he is certainly going down, and I should have done better to have left him in the Mont Rouge to get his living as a workman. He'll never be able to scrape together any sort of living as a painter." He seemed to feel that was so himself, for he no longer took round his sketches to the dealers; he had given up all hope of doing anything that would sell, and was now writing ridiculous sonnets, "and he not knowing either French or English," I said, and my spirits rose mountains high against him. "An old man from the sea whom I cannot shake off. But why should I be forced to live with him always? To keep him in my apartment?" But the courage of flinging him into the street was lacking, and I continued to bear with him day after day, hoping that he would leave me of his own accord. He was well enough in Julian's studio or in the Beaux Arts or in English and American society, but he would seem shallow and superficial in the Nouvelle Athènes, and I always avoided taking him there; but one night he asked me to tell him where I was dining, and I had to tell him at the Nouvelle Athènes. He pleaded to be allowed to accompany me, and I will admit to some vanity on my part; or was it curiosity that prompted me to introduce him to Degas, who very graciously invited us to sit at his table and talked to us of his art, addressing himself as often to Lewis as he did to me. He opened his whole mind to us, beguiled by Lewis's excellent listening, until the waiter brought him a dish of almonds and raisins. Then a lull came, and Lewis said, leaning across the table:

"I think, Monsieur Degas, you will agree with me that, more than any other artist among us, Jules Lefevre sums up all the qualities that an artist should possess."

I thought I should have died of shame, and Degas's laughter did not console me, nor his words whispered in my ear as he left:

"*Votre ami est très fort.* . . . *Il m'a fait monter l'échelle comme personne.*" And a few days afterwards in the Rue Pigalle he said:

"*Comment va votre ami? Ah! celui-là est d'une force.*"

"*Mais, cher ami, le pauvre garçon n'a jamais su se dégager——*"

"*Pas du tout; il est très fort.*"

"*Son esprit n'a jamais su dépasser certaines bornes . . . la Rue Bonaparte.*"

But no explanation pleased Degas as much as his own: "*Il m'a tiré les vers du nez . . . et comme personne.*" I resisted this explanation till, feeling that I was beginning to show myself in a stupid light, I accepted it outwardly, though convinced inly that Lewis had been guilty of the unpardonable sin—lack of comprehension. He must go and at once, and as soon as I returned home I begged him to leave me. "At the end of the month, when my mother sends me my money," he answered, and my heart sank at the thought of having him with me so long. I think I must have answered, "For God's sake go!" and a few days afterwards the concierge mentioned to my great surprise that Monsieur Marshall had left, and had paid her the few francs he owed her. A good trait on his part, I thought, and my heart softened toward him suddenly, and continued soft until a lady with whom I was on intimate terms told me that Monsieur Marshall had been to see her and had borrowed a hundred francs from her.

"I didn't dare refuse," she said, "but I thought it rather mean of him to come to ask me for the money."

We sat looking at each other, the lady thinking no doubt that I should not have told Lewis I was her lover, and myself thinking that I had at length caught Lewis in deliberate blackmail; and, going round to the studio in which he had settled himself, I said, before looking round the walls to admire the sketches:

"I have just come from Miss ——, and she tells me you borrowed a hundred francs from her."

"If I did, you borrowed from Alice Howard, my mistress," he answered.

I had forgotten, and sat dumbfounded, and he giggling at me. But why had I borrowed this money? I never wanted for money. Perhaps to put Alice to the test, or to get back some of my own, for she had borrowed often from me, and finding her in affluent circumstances. . . . She asked

115

me some days after to repay her, and I gave her the
money that was in my pockets—a hundred francs;
the other hundred I forgot all about until one evening at Alphonsine's I saw her rise up from her place
and walk toward me, a vindictive look round her
mouth and eyes.

"Have you come," she said, "to pay me the money
that you owe me?"

To admit that I had borrowed money from Alice
at Alphonsine's was impossible; lies happen very
seldom in my life, but they have happened, and this
was an occasion when a lie was necessary. But I lied
badly from lack of habit, and Lewis had heard from
the women there that I had not stood up to Alice;
and now to pass off the matter on which I had come
to speak to him, I asked him how I should have
answered Alice.

"You should have answered her ironically: *'Toi,
tu m'as prêté de l'argent? Où ça? Quand tu venais
me trouver à l'hôtel de toutes les Russies et que tu
pleurais pour un déjeuner? Quand tu n'avais pas
deux mètres d'indienne à te coller sur les fesses?
Non, mais vrai: y avait-il une maquerelle rue de
Provence qui voulait de ta peau? Tu dis que tu
m'as prêté de l'argent? C'est-il quand ton tôlier te
reprenait ta clé tous les matins, ou quand tu de-
mandais aux michés cinquante centimes pour aller
aux chiottes?'*"

"Splendid!" I cried.

"*Faut pas se laisser marcher sur le pied, dis. Je
ne lui aurais pas parlé autrement.*"

"You have *l'esprit prime-sautier*, but any wit I

116

have is *l'esprit de l'escalier . . . et de la dernière marche.*"

"*Je ne lui aurais pas parlé autrement.*"

"You seem to be doing a good deal of work," I said, looking round the studio, and the thought crossed my mind how vain were all my sacrifices, for here was Lewis living just as comfortably now as he had ever lived with me. The work he was doing seemed to be snatches of color and line, random sketches difficult to dispose of through the ordinary channels. But he had discovered a patron, and relishing exceedingly the story he was telling me, he described an old man living in a barred house in a distant suburb, who never opened his door except to a certain ring—an old man in gold-rimmed spectacles who would buy any drawing that Lewis brought him at a price. "He pays thirty francs for a flower in a vase, for an apple, a pear, for a street corner, for a head sketched in ten minutes; anything will do. It is like cashing a cheque, and he has been buying pictures in this way for years and years; the house is filled with them."

A strange, fantastic story, but I had heard the like many times before from Lewis, and hoped for his sake that it was all true, and that the old man who lived in the barred house in the distant suburbs, and looked at all the drawings that Lewis brought him through gold-rimmed spectacles, and paid for them at thirty francs apiece, would live for many a year. But if he existed outside of Lewis's imagination, he would have to die some day, and when he died, what would happen to Lewis? I often asked

myself, for I could think of nothing else except
Lewis again borrowing money from me. But nothing happens twice the same; life is full of many odd
little turns; months, if not years, passed away without my seeing Lewis, and when we met it was at
Barbizon, whither he had gone intent upon investing all his savings on a Salon picture. An old graveyard full of the lush of June seemed to him an appropriate subject, and he made a variety of sketches;
but what was sufficient in the sketches seemed empty
when transferred to a large canvas. He was sure
he had hit on a good subject, but the picture did
not begin to take shape until somebody suggested
that two children looking at a gravestone would
balance the composition; and later, another critic
said that a yellow cat coming from the cottages
along the wall would complete it. He was right, and
nothing now remained for Lewis but to paint the
picture. But a picture does not exist in the composition or in the drawing, but in the touch, and
his picture would have remained very "tinny" if
Stott of Oldham had not appeared at Barbizon suddenly.

"You mustn't rub the paint like that. See here";
and taking the brush from Lewis's hand he mixed
a tone and drew the brush slowly from right to left.
Almost at once the paint began to look less like
linoleum, and Lewis said, "I think I understand,"
and he was able to imitate Stott sufficiently well to
produce a picture which Bouguereau said would attract attention in the Salon if the title were changed
to "Les Deux Orphelins."

" 'L'Amour Renait de ses Cendres' is not a title that will appeal to the general public."

Lewis tried to explain that what he meant was that the love of the parents is born again in their children; but he allowed Bouguereau's good sense to prevail, and the picture drew from Albert Wolf an enthusiastic notice of nearly half a column in the *Figaro*, after which it became the fashion to go to the Salon to see "Les Deux Orphelins" and Monsieur Marshall, *un jeune peintre anglais de beaucoup de talent*, for Lewis could not separate himself from his picture, and every day he grew bolder, receiving his friends in front of it and explaining to them, and to all and sundry, the second title, "L'Amour Renait de ses Cendres." His conduct was not very dignified, but he had been waiting so long for recognition of his talent that he could not restrain himself. He sold "Les Orphelins" for ten thousand francs, and next year the Salon was filled with imitations of it, and there was a moment when it seemed that Julian's prophecy was going to come true. The hotel in the Champs Elysées was being sought for when Lewis's first patron, the old man to whom he had sold his sketches for twenty-five or thirty francs apiece, died suddenly; and for nearly two years Ponsonby Marshalls were being knocked down at the Hôtel de Vente for fifty and a hundred francs apiece.

"Fifteen hundred or two thousand pictures thrown upon the market was no doubt a misfortune," I said as I stirred the fire, "but if Lewis had been a man of healthy talent he would have painted other pictures. But his talent was the talent of *un dé-*

traqué," and a recollection of a naked man looking at a naked woman through a mask shot up in my mind. "The hereditary taint was always there," I said, and I began to turn over in my mind all that Lewis had told me about his father. I remembered his saying: "My father left mamma some three or four years after their marriage. I think I was twenty before I ever saw him. I was given an address of a lodging-house in St. James's, and found my father in a small back room, sitting on a bed playing the flute. 'Oh, is that you, Lewis? Just a moment.'" And he had gone on playing to the end of the piece, astonishing Lewis by the brilliancy of his playing and by his likeness to himself. He had heard many stories of his father's eccentricities, and he had had an opportunity of verifying these in the first few minutes, for when the elder Marshall laid aside his flute and engaged in perfunctory conversation with his son he allowed a fly to crawl over his face. Every moment Lewis expected his father to brush the insect away. It had been round one eye several times, and had descended the nose, and was about to go up the eye once again when Lewis, who could contain himself no longer, cried out:

"Father, that fly!"

"Pray don't disturb it, I like the sensation," he had answered. My thoughts passed from Lewis to Jim, and I sat for a long time asking myself if Jim would have succeeded better than Lewis if he had gone to Paris in the fifties. He had more talent than Lewis, but his talent seemed still less capable of cultivation . . . there is a lot of talent in Ireland, but whether any of it is capable of cultivation is a question one can ponder for days, and my thoughts breaking away suddenly I remembered how, soon after my return from Ireland when I had settled in Cecil Street in the Strand, and was trying to make my living by writing for the papers, the desire to see Jim again in the old studio in Prince's Gardens had come upon me, and I had gone away one night in a cab to Kensington; but the appearance of the footman that opened the door surprised me, and I asked myself if Jim had sold some pictures, or had let the house. He had sold the house, and any letters that came for him were sent to Arthur's Club, where I could obtain news of him. The porter told me that any letter would be forwarded, but I wanted to see Jim that very night, and addressing myself to the secretary of the club, who happened to be passing through the hall at that moment, I begged of him to authorize the porter to give me Mr. Browne's address, which he did: and I went away in the cab certain that the end of the drive would bring me face to face with my old boon companion. "He was the beginning of me," I said. The cab turned out of Baker Street and we were soon in Park Road driving between Regent's Park and a high wall with doors let into it. Before one of these the hansom stopped and I saw a two-storied house standing in the midst of a square plot. A maid-servant took me up a paved pathway, mentioning that Mr. Browne was on the drawing-room floor, and I found him waiting expectant in his smock, a palette and a sheaf of brushes

121

in his left hand, the thumb of his right hand in his leather belt.

"My dear Jim, I've been to Prince's Gardens."

"We've sold the house and Pinkie and Ada have gone to live with friends and relations."

There was a feeling in the room that nobody had called to see him for many a month, and I noticed that a good deal of color had died out of the thick locks of flaxen hair and that his throat was wrinkled.

"And all your pictures, Jim?"

"Your mother was kind enough to hang them up in Alfred Place when we left Prince's Gardens, and when she left the house at the end of her lease the pictures were taken away."

"And you didn't make any inquiries?"

"Well, you see, I haven't room here for many canvases."

The moment had come when I must show some interest in his pictures, and turning from the one on the easel I picked one out of the rows, hoping that the design might inspire a few words of praise.

"It is like lead. You must have painted a dozen or twenty times upon it. I don't know how you can work over such a surface, a thick coagulated scum. Why don't you scrape? Manet always scrapes before painting, and he never loses the freshness; his paint is like cream after twenty repaintings."

Jim did not know anything about Manet, nor was he very interested to hear about Monet, Sisley, Renoir, the Nouvelle Athènes and its litterati. He knew nothing of Banville's versification and had not read Goncourt's novels, so I told him that Catulle had thought well of my French sonnet, for having written a drama on the subject of Luther it was necessary to write a French dedicatory sonnet, and I recited it to Jim to revenge myself upon him for his having told me that he knew French as well as English. Other people's illusions are always irritating to me.

"My landlady's daughter," he said, pointing to a small portrait on the wall, and some time afterwards a young girl was heard singing on the stairs. "There she is. Shall I ask her in?"

I begged of him to do so, and a somewhat pretty girl with round eyes and a vivacious voice, came into the room and chattered with us; but her interest in the fact that Jim was my cousin was a little high-pitched, and it was obvious that she took no interest in his pictures, or indeed in any pictures; and it was a relief when she turned to Jim to ask him if he was staying in to dinner.

"Let us go out together and dine somewhere," I said.

"Yes, ask him out to dinner. It will do him good. He hasn't been beyond the garden for weeks."

"Yes, Jim; we will go up town and dine together."

"I have no money."

"But father will lend you any money you want. It will go down in the . . . you can settle with father when you like."

She left the room and Jim spoke of the people in whose house he was lodging, a dancing master and his wife, and he gave me a mildly sarcastic account of Mrs. —— coming up to see him in the morning to tell him that he might have the use of the parlor for ten shillings extra; my ears retain his voice still saying something about coals and gas not being included, and what tickled his fancy was the way the old lady used to linger about the drawing-room trying to draw the conversation on to his sisters, where was Miss Ada living now, and was Miss Pinkie still living with Lady Shaftesbury? He continued talking, moving the canvases about, and I was willing to appreciate the designs if he would only say that he would come out to dinner. At last he said:

"You see, I haven't been to my tailor's for a long time, and my wardrobe is in a ragged and stained condition. I dare say they'll be able to find some cold beef or cold mutton or a sausage or two in the larder. You don't mind?"

Of course I did not mind. It was for a talk about old times that I had come, and after the cold meats we returned to the drawing-room. Jim showed me all his latest designs and we discussed them together, mingling our memories of the women we had known. The names of Alice Harford, Annie Temple, and Mademoiselle d'Anka, came into the conversation; I told him about Alice Howard, hoping he would ask me if she were as big as Alice Harford, and then determined to rouse him I said the great love affair of my life was a small, thin woman. Still he did not answer.

"If a woman be sensual——"

"Beauty is better than bumping," he answered with a laugh, and it seemed that we were to have one of our erstwhile conversations about Art and that Jim would draw forth a canvas and say, "This has all the beauties of Raphael and other beauties besides"; but he seemed to have lost nearly all his interest in painting, allowing me, however, to search round the room and discover behind the sofa a new version of "Cain Shielding His Wife from Wild Beasts," and I spoke of the design and the conception and the movement of the man about to hurl a spear at a great lion approaching from behind a rock. He took up his palette but forgot to roar like a lion, and when he laid it aside he did not sing *Il Balen* or *A che la morte,* nor did he tell me that Pinkie had a more beautiful voice than Jenny Lind, and when we walked across the garden and he bade me good-bye at the gate, I felt that he had worn out himself as well as his clothes—his hopes, his talent, his enthusiasm for life, all were gone, an echo remained, an echo which I did not try to reawaken. I never saw him again; he was for me but an occasional thought, until one day I found myself sitting next a showily dressed woman at luncheon. I recognized her as the young girl I had met in Park Road, the daughter of Jim's landlady, and she told me that Jim had died about two years back in Park Road. He had become quite a hermit in the later years of his life, never leaving the house except for a stroll round the garden.

"Painting always," I said.

A perplexed look came into her face which I attributed to the fact that she did not know whether the pictures were works of art or nothing at all, and I asked myself suddenly what Jim's death might have been, for a man so individual as Jim should die an individual death. But my imagination did not succeed in conjuring up any worthy death for him. Perhaps Turgenev might have failed too, though indeed Jim's death is very like a Turgenev death, only a little more wonderful. Nature often invents better than we, better even than Turgenev, who would have seen that Jim must be killed by a lion; but even Turgenev could not have seen how this could be managed without sending him out to Africa to hunt lions, which would be an invention only one degree more stupid than the supposition that the keeper had left one of the lion's cages open in the Zoological Gardens, and that the animal had escaped and climbed over the wall of Park Road, killing Jim, after tearing a hole through a large canvas of "Cain Shielding His Wife from Wild Beasts," behind which the painter had hidden himself. Turgenev would not have thought of a snow lion, but Nature did, and one day when the snow was lying several feet deep round the house, she inspired Jim to make good his theory that a lion always lies with one paw tucked under him, never with the fore-paws stretched out like Landseer's lions in Trafalgar Square. He had always been saying that this was so, but his landlord and landlady did not wish him to start sculpture in the house. But now there was snow at the very door, and he began to pile it up, and when all the snow in the garden was exhausted the neighbors sent their snow in wheelbarrows and he continued to pile up hundredweight upon hundred-weight until his lion assumed almost Egyptian proportions, rising above the surrounding walls, attracting the eyes of the hansom cabmen who drew up their horses to admire and to suggest that the lion should be sent to the British Museum. "Perhaps the Governor might have a refrigerator built for him," was a remark which caused some amusement to the dancing master, his wife and daughter, and to Jim. But it was not thought worth while writing to the Governor of the Museum on the subject. The suggestion "Why don't you 'ave him photographed?" coming next day from the top of an omnibus seemed more practical, and the maid-servant was asked to run round to the photographer, and the evening was spent counting the number of copies that would be required; each neighbor who had sent his snow must get one, and before bedtime it was noticed that the brightness of the stars predicted a fine day. But during the night clouds gathered, and in the morning the garden was enveloped in a white mist. A message came from the photographer to say he could do nothing that day, and the following day he failed to keep his appointment, and in a drizzle of rain Jim set to work to patch up his melting masterpiece. The next day the photographer arrived and got what he hoped would prove a very good impression; but everybody wanted a half-plate; he had to send round for some and Jim worked on among the wet snow, Florence begging of him to put on an overcoat and a stronger pair of boots. But he tramped about in shoes, and next day he was crouching over the fire, and when the doctor heard the story of the lion he threw up his hands.

"How a man of his age could be foolish enough to risk his life for such nonsense! And you tell me he always goes out without an overcoat? I'll call to-morrow and give him oxygen if required."

The thaw continued during the night. Jim and his lion dissolved together. "My first friend," I muttered, "the springboard from whence I jumped into life and Art." And going to my Monet, I asked myself if Jim would have been able to discern better than Æ the beauty of the evanescent willows rising out of and vanishing into the mist. He was a clever man, and knew a great deal more than anybody gave him credit for knowing. He talked nonsense about his own genius, but he knew he was talking nonsense, and his nonsense helped him to disguise his failure from himself for a moment. "He should have been born in Venice about the year 1680; his talent would have come to fruition in those years, and Van Dyke would have painted his portrait." Just then the servant opened the door to ask me if I were at home to Mr. Hugh Lane.

"Yes."

And a moment after there came into the room a tall, thin young man, talking so fast that I gathered with difficulty there must be a great many pictures in Irish country houses that nobody had seen, and that he would like to exhibit them in Dublin.

"If anybody cared for pictures," I contrived to interject, and he sat twisting and untwisting his legs, linking and unlinking his hands, his talk beginning to bore me a little, for I could not detect any æstheticism in him, only a nervous desire to run a show. "Your brother," I said, "called here a few days ago to prepare me for your visit. He said that you were going to revive Irish painting. I came here to revive the Irish language; it existed once upon a time, but Irish painting——"

Lane interrupted me, admitting that the men who had painted in Ireland at the end of the eighteenth century were merely reflections of Sir Joshua and Romney.

"But your brother——"

Without noticing my interruption he continued telling me that, for the last fortnight, he had been traveling through Ireland, visiting all the country houses, and had obtained promises from many people to lend their pictures.

"Now, your name among the list of patrons at the exhibition——"

"But why are you giving yourself all this trouble? What is your object?"

"Well, you see, I am Lady Gregory's nephew, and must be doing something for Ireland."

"Striking a blow," I said.

A bewildered look, quickly repressed, however, revealed to me that he did not understand my remark. "You don't speak with a brogue. Your brother said you didn't. How is that?"

He produced his little hysterical laugh, and without stopping to explain why it was that he had no brogue, looked round the room in search of pictures worth borrowing, and having decided upon two, a portrait of Rachel by Couture and a small Constable, he said he hoped I would try to influence Sir Thorn-

ley Stoker in his favor; he would like to print Sir
Thornley's name among the patrons of the forth-
coming exhibition, an exhibition designed for the
advancement of Art in Ireland. I gave Lane my
promise that he should be invited to "the palace,"
our nickname for Sir Thornley's house, so full was
it of beautiful things. But Sir Thornley could not
be persuaded, and my natural affection for him was
strained to the uttermost by his persistent speaking
of Lane as a London picture-dealer who had come
to Ireland to see what he could pick up.

"Or perhaps he's on the look-out for a post in the
Museum."

"I have told you, Sir Thornley, that he is Lady
Gregory's nephew, and would like to do something
for Ireland. That should be sufficient." He growled
and muttered that Lane might tell us he was a great
expert, but what proof had we of it? And the old
doctor grew as grumpy as if I had been speaking of
a bone-setter. "My dear Thornley, we do not learn
anything that we did not know before"; and I
sketched out the life-history of a chef who before
discovering his vocation had wandered from one
trade to another, trying all, until one night in the
kitchen two ducks were roasting before the fire, the
gravy running out of their backsides, and deeply
moved, he had stood immersed in a great joy.

"But what has that got to do with Lane?"

"Lane is Lady Gregory's nephew."

"You have told me that before; you have said that
before."

"Of course, if you interrupt me. I was going to

130

tell you that Lady Gregory told me herself that the family had thought of all kinds of professions suitable for Hugh, but his heart was not in any of them, and they were beginning to feel a little anxious, when one day, as they were sitting down to lunch ——"

"Was there a duck for luncheon?"

"No. He caught sight of the fold of Lady Gregory's dress, a tailor-made from Paris; it is always a pleasure to a woman to hear her gown admired; but there was a seriousness in Hugh's appreciation of the hang of the skirt, and a studied regard in his eyes which caused her a moment's perplexity, and when they rose from table he stood watching her as she crossed the room. Of course, the skirt fitted rather nicely, but . . . In the same afternoon she had occasion to go to her bedroom, and to her surprise found her wardrobe open and Hugh trying on her skirts before the glass. 'Hugh!' 'Doesn't it seem to you, Aunt Augusta, that this skirt is a little too full?' During the evening he spoke of some premises in Conduit Street; but tailoring was only a passing thought, and the next thing they heard of Hugh was that he had gone into Colnaghi's shop to learn the business of picture-dealing.

"Nature is always unexpected, Thornley, bounding about like a monkey, and it may be that Lane sprang from tailor-mades right into Salvator Rosa, and up again to Georgione and Titian. But if I had to choose Lane as the hero of a novel or play, I should proceed more regularly, a transition would be necessary, a little shop in St. James's, down some court long ago swept away by an enterprising builder. In my novel there certainly would be a little shop with a window full of old fans and bits of silver, just the kind of shop that you would hang about every afternoon when you came back from the hospital, and I should place Lane in a little den out of which he would come to show you some paste—old paste. I have it, Thornley; cameos and old paste would be the steps whereby Lane mounted from tailor-mades to Salvator Rosa and then on to— whom did I say, Thornley?"

"Georgione," the old doctor muttered, laughing in his beard. "Two years is not long enough. I was five years walking the hospitals."

"It was long enough for Lane. When he left Colnaghi's shop and took a lodging in Bury Street, he was able to buy and sell pictures so successfully that in two years he had put together, I think he told me, ten thousand pounds."

"Yet you say he is not a dealer"; and the old doctor continued to growl by the fireside.

"He is a collector who weeds out his collection. Let us call him a 'weeder'; and let us never speak of the lavatory but of the cloak-room or the toilet-room. And let us avoid the word 'lodger,' for he is extinct, or, like the phœnix, he has risen from his ashes and become a paying-guest. Petticoat-bodice is taboo; and bodice—even bodice—one of the beautifullest words in the language, has yielded to the detestable 'corsage'; and the journalist speaks of a woman as *petite*, thinking that *petite* suggests refinement. 'Naked' is a word that nobody of taste

132

would think of using—'unclothed' or 'undraped'; no
reasonable man or woman would object to meeting
this sentence in a novel: 'I would give all my worldly
wealth to see Venus walk undraped from her bath';
the novelist might even write: 'I would give all my
worldly wealth to see Elizabeth Hawkins walk undraped from her bath'; but if he were to write: 'I
would give all my worldly wealth to see Elizabeth
Hawkins walk naked from her bath,' he would be
dubbed a very gross writer by the newspapers,
though it is difficult to say how morality gains by the
substitution of 'unclothed' or 'undraped' for 'naked,'
and easy to see that literature dies in these substi-
tutions. Who would ever think of asking a lady for
the bill-of-fare? Even in the second-class restaurants the word 'bill-of-fare' has been dropped, we
read now the 'menu.' So you see, Lane is quite in
the fashion when he calls himself a collector. If
you would only meet him you would be converted,
not to euphuisms, but to Lane. He has got such
pretty ways. When you ask him if he is going to
sell a picture he will say: 'Don't talk to me about
selling; I can't bear to part with my pictures. One
of these days I shall have a house and shall want
pictures'; and immediately the conversation will
slide away, and you'll find yourself listening to a
long tale of a collection of pictures which he intends
to present at cost price to some provincial gallery.
He is all for Art, and you, who have been talking
Art and buying beautiful things all your life, now
repudiate the one man who comes to Ireland to revive the art of painting."

"It never existed in Ireland."

"Never mind. It will be revived all the same."

"He's a dealer. He has made, according to you, ten thousand pounds in two years, and a dealer never will miss the chance of picking up something, and you'll find that he will pick up something."

"There's no use talking any more. I've spent a very pleasant evening. Good-night, Thornley, good-night."

"Well, you'll see," were his last words, and he was very sarcastic when it became known that Lane had bought a large Lancret from Sir Algernon Coote at the close of the exhibition, and whenever I went in to smoke a cigar with him he referred to this deal with extraordinary bitterness. I could not see what ground of complaint he had against Lane. "Sir Algernon Coote," I often said, "was glad to get seven or eight hundred, perhaps a thousand for his picture. What concern is it of yours the price the picture fetches afterward?" He growled in his arm-chair, averring that Lane had no right to ask Sir Algernon Coote to lend him a picture and then to buy it from him. "A most extraordinary proposition," I said. "If nobody is to make a profit, there can be no buying or selling. Yourself made a profit upon your sale of Wedgwood."

Sir Thornley did not think that this was quite the same thing, and I said, "Pooh, pooh."

We had just begun to forget Lane when we heard that he had run across to Tiepolo at Ostend, and had picked up another picture in Antwerp, and for these pictures and Sir Algernon Coote's Lancret he

134

had been paid seventeen thousand pounds by Durand Ruel. He had not taken it all out in cash; Lane's genius lies in swopping. It is a bold man that dares to swop with Durand Ruel, but Lane dares everything, and he got Manet's portrait of Mademoiselle Gonzales probably cheaper than a private buyer could have gotten it, on the plea that it was going into a permanent exhibition. It came over with a number of Impressionist pictures, lent by different people—Monet, Pissaro, Renoir, Sisley, Berthe Morisot—all the Impressionist school.

"And for what object?" Sir Thornley cried.

"To found a Gallery of Modern Art." Again I set myself to explain Lane to Sir Thornley without arriving at any results whatever. He would not, or he could not, understand that though it is Lane's instinct to make money it is also his instinct to spend the money that he makes upon Art. "Nobody that I have ever met, Thornley, desires Art as purely as Lane. I have known many people who make money out of Art, but it is generally spent on motorcars, women, cooks, and valets. But Lane spends hardly anything upon himself. His whole life is absorbed in Art, and he would not be able to gratify his passion if he did not make money. Why will you not be reconciled to him? Why will you not accept him for what he is?" I said again and again. But he remained grumpy, doggedly refusing to become a member of the committee, consenting, however, to visit the exhibition, not being able to resist my descriptions of the portrait of Mademoiselle

Gonzales, the "Itinerant Musician," and the other pictures.

A wonderful exhibition it was, organized by Lane who rushed about Dublin from one end to the other, begging of everybody to come to his exhibition, gathering up the ladies into groups, giving them all something to do, telling one that she must collect subscriptions to buy a certain picture, another one that she must play the piano for him; another would oblige him by playing, or trying to play, it did not matter which, a violin solo, the "Kreutzer Sonata," or anything else she liked. He discovered a young gentleman who sang comic songs very well; for the sake of Art he was asked to sing. Anybody who could write at all was asked to write letters to the papers. Everybody in Dublin was swept into the exhibition, and as soon as the receipts began to decline Lane was again devising some new method. So far I had resisted him, but no one resists Lane to the end. At last he got me. He came one evening to ask me to write an article.

"No, ten thousand times no."

Lane laughed, and suggested a lecture.

"Lane, you tempt me. I am the only one in Dublin who knew Manet, Monet, Sisley, Renoir, Pissaro —I knew them all at the Nouvelle Athènes."

"When will you be able to give the lecture?"

A terror came upon me, and I stuttered, "When? One has to speak for an hour, an hour and ten minutes, an hour and fifteen minutes. That would make two fortnightly articles at the very least. Oh, Lane!"

VALE

"I'll begin to advertise the lecture to-morrow. You'll have four days to prepare it."

"Four days!"

And Lane, who is always in a hurry, bade me good-night abruptly.

VI

It is to Mr. Lane's extraordinary enthusiasm,
energy, and love of Art that we owe the pleasure
of this beautiful collection of pictures, and, that it
may not be but a passing pleasure, it is his proposal
to collect funds for the purchase of these pictures,
and to found a Gallery of Modern Art in Dublin.
A few days before the Exhibition opened he came to
ask for an article about these pictures, but it seemed
to me that all I had to say about pictures in the
form of articles I had already said; and I did not
dare to accept his proposal to deliver a lecture on
French Art until it occurred to me that being probably the only person in Dublin who had known the
painters whose works hang on the wall, I might,
without being thought too presumptuous, come here
and—I will not say discuss French Art—I prefer to
say talk about Manet, Degas, Renoir, Pissaro,
Monet, and Sisley, and in doing so to discuss French
Art indirectly.

Yes, it was my good fortune to know these men
when their talent was beginning, before they were
known to the rest of the world. When my mother
offered me my choice of Oxford or Cambridge, I told
her that I had decided to go to Paris. "My dear
boy, your education—you learned nothing at

school." "That is why, my dear mother, I intend to devote myself entirely to my own education, and I think it can be better conducted in a café than in a university." So I went to Paris with a valet. It is necessary that I should mention him, for a valet means conformity to certain conventions; and the young man who sets out on artistic adventure must try to separate himself from all conventions, whether of politics, society, or creed.

My valet did not remain with me for more than six or eight months, "his continual sighing after beef, beer, and a wife, his incapacity for learning a single word of a foreign language—the beds he couldn't sleep on, and the wines he couldn't drink" —I forget how the sentence runs on, it is Byron's description of his valet (I forget which one), should I say my memory of Byron's description of his valet? Be that as it may, the passage, I may remark, occurs in one of his letters, and no doubt the sentence closes, "obliged me to send him back to England." That is what happened in my case, and my valet's dismissal was led up to by circumstances precisely similar to those described by Byron. But behind these material reasons for getting rid of him, there was a deeper reason—his presence stood between me and myself; I wished above all things to be myself, and to be myself I felt I should have to live the physical as well as the intellectual life of the Quarter. Myself was the goal I was making for, instinctively if you will, but still making for it; I felt that I must think out life for myself, and from end to end, and to do this I felt—I must not be

afraid to repeat the verb, for at times I was guided
more by feeling than by reason—well, I felt that
my first business was the discovery of a café where
I could pass the evening—nothing seemed to me
more essential than that. In the mornings I worked
at L'Ecole des Beaux Arts, but one's evenings
are more important than one's mornings, the soul
evolves in the gaslight; and as soon as my valet left
me I started on the quest of the café of my instinctive predilection round the Odéon and the Luxembourg Gardens.

In the Middle Ages young men went in search of
the Grail; to-day the café is the quest of a young
man in search of artistic education. But the cafés
about the Odéon and the Luxembourg Gardens did
not correspond to my need, I wearied of noisy stu-
dents, the Latin Quarter seemed to me a little out
of fashion; eventually I immigrated to Montmartre,
and continued my search along the Boulevard Extérieur. One evening I discovered the ideal café on
the Place Pigalle. I cannot say now if it were instinct that guided me there, or, if, perchance, I met
someone who told me that Manet spent his evenings
in the café of the Nouvelle Athènes. The name
sounds as if it were invented on purpose, "The New
Athens." You wouldn't have thought it was "a new
Athens" if you had seen it, but it was one for all
that. . . . I can see it now, the white nose of a
block of buildings, stretching up the hillside into the
Place Pigalle opposite the fountain. Men of letters
went there, too—Duranty, one of the original Real-
ists, a contemporary of Flaubert, used to stay with

VALE

us for an hour or so every night; a quiet, elderly
man who knew that he had failed, and whom failure
had saddened. The Nouvelle Athènes was a café of
ratés, literary and pictorial. The literary *ratés*
were Alexis, Céard, and Hennique. At the time I
am speaking of Zola had ceased to go to the café,
he spent his evenings with his wife; but his disciples
—all except Maupassant and Huysmans, I do not
remember ever having seen them there—collected
about the marble tables, lured to the Nouvelle
Athènes by their love of Art. One generation of
littérateurs associates itself with painting, the next
clings to music. The aim and triumph of the Realist
were to force the pen to compete with the painter's
brush and the engraver's needle in the description,
let us say, of a mean street, just as the desire of a
symbolistic writer was to describe the vague but
intense sensations of music so accurately that the
reader would guess the piece he had selected for
description, though it were not named in the text.
We all entertained doubts regarding the validity of
the Art we practiced and envied the Art of the
painter, deeming it superior to literature; and it is
hardly an exaggeration to say that we used to weary
a little of conversation among ourselves, just as
dogs weary of their own society, and I think there
was a feeling of relief among us all when the painters
came in. We raised ourselves up to welcome them—
Manet, Degas, Renoir, Pissaro, Monet, and Sisley;
they were our masters. A partition rising a few
feet or more over the hats of the men sitting at the
usual marble tables separated the glass front from

141

the main body of the café; two tables in the right-hand corner were reserved for Manet and Degas and for their circle of admirers. It is pleasant to remember my longing to be received into that circle, and my longing to speak to Manet, whom I had begun to recognize as the great new force in painting. Evening after evening went by and I did not dare to speak to him, nor did he speak to me, until one evening—thrice happy evening!—as I sat thinking of him, pretending to be busy correcting proofs, he asked me if the conversation of the café did not distract my attention, and I answered: "Not at all; I was thinking of your painting." It seems to me that we became friends at once; he invited me to his studio in the Rue d'Amsterdam, where his greatest works were painted—all the works that are Manet and nothing but Manet, the real Manet, the Parisian Manet. But before speaking of his painting some description of his personality is essential to an understanding of Manet. It is often said that the personality of the artist concerns us not, and in the case of bad Art it is certainly true, for bad Art reveals no personality, bad Art is bad because it is anonymous. The work of the great artist is himself, and, being one of the greatest painters that ever lived, Manet's Art was all Manet; one cannot think of Manet's painting without thinking of the man himself. The last time I saw Monet was at dinner in the Café Royal, and, after talking of many things, suddenly, without any transition, Monet said, speaking out of a dream: "How like Manet was to his painting," and I answered delighted, for it is always exciting to talk about Manet: "Yes, how like. That blonde, amusing face, the clear eyes that saw simply, truly, and quickly"; and having said so much, my thoughts went back to the time when the glass door of the café grated upon the sanded floor, and Manet entered. Though by birth and by education essentially Parisian, there was something in his appearance and manner of speaking that often suggested an Englishman. Perhaps it was his dress— his clean-cut clothes and figure. That figure! Those square shoulders that swaggered as he went across the room, and the thin waist; the face, the beard, and the nose, satyr-like shall I say? No, for I would evoke an idea of beauty of line united to that of intellectual expression—frank words, frank passion in his convictions, loyal and simple phrases, clear as well-water, sometimes a little hard, sometimes as they flowed away bitter, but at the fountain-head sweet and full of light.

I should emphasize Manet's courage, for without courage there cannot be Art. We have all heard the phrase, "I should not like to think like that"; and whosoever feels that he would not like to think out to its end every thought that may happen to come into his mind, I would dissuade from Art if I could. Manet's Art is the most courageous ever seen. One looks in vain for those subterfuges that we find in every other painter. What he saw he stated candidly, almost innocently, and what he did not see he passed over. Never in his life did he stop to worry over a piece of drawing that did not interest him because it was possible that somebody might notice the omission. It was part of his genius to omit what did not interest him. I remember a young man whom Manet thought well of—a frequent visitor to the studio—and one day he brought his sister with him—not an ill-looking girl, no better and no worse than another, a little commonplace, that was all. Manet was affable and charming; he showed his pictures, he talked volubly, but next day when the young man arrived and asked Manet what he thought of his sister, Manet said, extending his arm (the gesture was habitual to him): "The last girl in the world I should have thought was your sister." The young man protested, saying Manet had seen his sister dressed to her disadvantage—she was wearing a thick woolen dress, for there was snow on the ground. Manet shook his head. "I haven't to look twice; I'm in the habit of judging things."

These were his words, or very nearly, and I think this anecdote throws a light upon Manet's painting. He saw quickly and clearly, and he stated what he saw candidly, I repeat almost innocently. It was not well-mannered perhaps to speak to a brother of his sister in those terms, but we have not come here to discuss good manners—what are manners but the conventions that obtain at a certain moment, and among a certain class? Well-mannered people do not think sincerely, their minds are full of evasions and subterfuges. Well-mannered people constantly feel that they would not like to think like this or that they would not like to think like that, and, as I have said, whoever feels that he would not like to think out to the end every thought that may come

VALE

into his mind should turn away from Art. All conventions of politics, society, and creed, yes, and of
Art, too, must be cast into the melting-pot; he who
would be an artist must melt down all things; he
must discover new formulas, new moulds, all the
old values must be swept aside, and he must arrive
at a new estimate. The artist should keep himself
free from all creed, from all dogma, from all opinion.
As he accepts the opinions of others he loses his
talent, all his feelings and his ideas must be his own,
for Art is a personal re-thinking of life from end to
end, and for this reason the artist is always eccentric. He is almost unaware of your moral codes,
he laughs at them when he thinks of them, which is
rarely, and he is unashamed as a little child. The
word "unashamed" perhaps explains Manet's Art
better than any other. It is essentially unashamed,
and in speaking of him one must never be afraid to
repeat the word "unashamed." Manet was born in
what is known as refined society; he was a rich man;
in dress and appearance he was an aristocrat; but
to be aristocratic in Art one must avoid polite society. Manet was obliged for the sake of his genius
to separate himself from his class; he was obliged
to spend his evenings in the café of the Nouvelle
Athènes, and his friends were artists; however poor
and miserable, if they were artists, they were welcome in Manet's studio. We have often heard artists laughed at for wearing long hair, for not speaking as ambassadors speak; but how superficial is
this criticism when the essence of Art is to separate,
to repudiate all conventions, to be ashamed of noth-

ing but to be ashamed! The price one pays for shamelessness, for truth, sincerity, personality, is public neglect. During the years that I knew Manet he never sold a picture. Some years earlier Durand Ruel bought two thousand pounds' worth of his pictures, but as these remained on his hands he bought no more. You will wonder why, in a city like Paris, he did not find support. Support means money, and monied men do not appreciate shamelessness in art. In many ways Paris is more like the rest of the world than we think, and the monied man in Paris, like the monied man in London, admires pictures in proportion as they resemble other pictures; those who like pictures in proportion as they differ from others are rare.

After Manet's death his friends made some little stir; there was a sale, and then the prices sank again, sank almost to nothing, and it seemed as if the world would never appreciate Manet. There was a time, fifteen or sixteen years ago, when Manet's pictures could have been bought for twenty, thirty, forty, or fifty pounds apiece. I remember saying to Albert Wolff, some years after Manet's death— it was at Tortoni's; the celebrated café is now gone:

"How is it," I said, "that Degas and Whistler and Monet have come into their inheritance, but there is no sign of recognition of Manet's Art?"

Wolff was the Art critic of the *Figaro*, and understood painting as well as another. He answered: "Put that hope aside; the time will never come when people will care for Manet's painting."

I can recall the feeling of depression that this

pronouncement caused me, and how I went away asking myself if the most beautiful painting the world had ever seen was destined to remain the most unpopular. That was fifteen years ago. We are impatient for the triumph of the things we love, and it took fifteen years for the light of Manet's genius to reach Ireland.

I have been asked which of the two pictures hanging in this room it would be better to buy for the Gallery of Modern Art, the "Itinerant Musician" or the portrait of Mademoiselle Gonzales. Mr. Lane himself put this question to me, and I answered: "I am afraid whichever you choose you will regret you had not chosen the other." The picture of the "Itinerant Musician" is a Spanish Manet, it was painted after Manet had seen Goya, but it is as obviously a Manet as the portrait of Mademoiselle Gonzales. To anyone who knows Manet's work it possesses all the qualities which we associate with Manet; the eye that sees clearly and quickly is as apparent in one picture as in the other. Manet saw Nature rapidly, and in full contour, and before he began to paint all those people were seated and standing in his mind's eye as they are on the canvas. The painting is as unashamed as Whitman; Manet is a sort of Whitman in paint. Look at that girl's foot—it is stated without either fear of offending or desire of pleasing anybody! And was not that Whitman's attitude of mind? Mademoiselle Gonzales' rounded white arm is even more courageously stated, for it is entirely without sexual appeal, and I am afraid the picture will, to many people, seem vulgar for that very reason. In the Spanish picture Manet is disguised a little, so little that one hesitates to admit it; but one should never hesitate about saying anything—the larger picture is Manet and Goya, whereas the portrait is Manet and nothing but Manet. That portrait is an article of faith. It says: "Be not ashamed of anything but to be ashamed." Never did Manet paint more unashamedly. There are Manets that I like more, but the portrait of Mademoiselle Gonzales is what Dublin needs. In Dublin everyone is afraid to confess himself. Is it not clear that whosoever paints like that confesses himself unashamed? He who admires that picture is already half free—the shackles are broken, and will fall presently. Therefore I hope it will be Mademoiselle Gonzales that will be purchased, for it will perhaps help to bring about the crisis we are longing for—that spiritual crisis when men shall begin once more to think out life for themselves, when men shall return to Nature naked and unashamed.

Some day this question will have to be discussed —whether the buying of odds and ends, chairs, fire-irons and decanters, and building at a great cost places in which to store them, along with stuffed birds and Esquimaux boats and all the paraphernalia of the South Sea Islanders, is not a waste of public money? Every age has its folly, and the folly of the twentieth century is probably the desire to educate. I do not say the desire of education, of that desire there is very little—it is not uncommon to meet men who will admit that they are not edu-

148

cated, and we may meet men who admit that they
are incapable of education, but we never meet anyone who will admit that he cannot educate somebody
else. Hence the great vogue of museums. But man
is full of subterfuge and evasions. He would fain
educate somebody, but he shrinks from doing anything that would disturb the present; that is the
great fear of the ordinary man, to disturb the present ever so slightly; so he would fill museums with
dead things that can never awaken desire or im-
pulse or idea, and gain credit for contributing to the
education of a nation without contributing anything
at all. Or maybe I am unjust to the ordinary rich
man. Perhaps the reason why his gifts to museums
consist principally of old dead things, out of which
the spirit of life has departed—ancient coins, ancient parchments, and ancient pictures—is because
he does not know how to acquire valuable modern
pictures. I admit that the difficulty is a serious one,
and the attempts that have been made to acquire
collections of modern pictures have not been successful. I am alluding now to the Tate Gallery and the
Chantry Bequest. But of the value of the present
collection of modern pictures there can be no question, and what is wanted is a standard, a criterion.
London wants this, and so does every town in England; but no town wants it so much as Dublin.
Though there be no unimpeachable collection of
modern pictures in London, yet there are modern
pictures to be seen in different galleries, but in Dublin there is no criterion. The only beautiful pictures in the National Gallery are ancient pictures,

and for the purpose of instruction in the art of
modern painting ancient pictures are useless. The
student will never look into Ruysdael's brown woods
and gray skies for instruction in the art of painting; nor will he seek Ruysdael's mournful moods
amid the woods of Malahide and Blessington, for
Ruysdael's mind exists in his painting, and is dependent upon it. And as the whole method of painting has changed within the last hundred years—
and changed radically—we moderns no longer feel
and see like the ancient masters. And this will be
apparent to anyone who goes to the Louvre with a
view to examining how the ancient masters painted;
he will find that all pictures painted before the nineteenth century were painted first in black and white,
and were then glazed. To explain a word that will
be very well understood in the studios, I will say
that "glazing" means the use of transparent colors
without any admixture of white. However much
the artists of Italy, Spain, Holland, and France
differed, they all painted alike in this respect; their
pictures were painted in black and white, and then
the natural colors were applied. The roses painted
in Holland in the seventeenth century were painted
black first and then glazed with crimson lake.

Boucher's unfinished pictures are all in *terre verte*
and white; Greuze was perhaps the last painter who
glazed always. We find the two methods in David;
he is sometimes an eighteenth-century, sometimes a
nineteenth-century, painter, and as a great many of
his nineteenth-century pictures are no more than
du carton peint, it has been rumored, and is still

being rumored, in the studios, that to bring about
a revival of painting it is necessary that we should
begin by reviving the handicraft of our forefathers.
But the craft of glazing was merely an outward
sign, as much as Chaucer's syntax was the outward
sign of his mind. There is no returning, in literature any more than in painting; we must write and
paint in the idiom of our time; however bad it may
be, we shall do better in it than in any other idiom.
Our minds are the outcome of our artistic method.
At last I have said it, and if anybody doubts it, let
him paint a landscape in black and white and then
glaze it, as the ancients did, and he will find that he
has painted, if not an archaic picture, at least a
picture wearing a slightly archaic air. The ancient
painters, perhaps owing to their method, saw Nature
in large aspects; we are interested in detail, and
we are eager to note every passing effect of rain or
shine; we desire light above all things, and chiaro-
scuro bores us; we do not omit a stone in the foreground, though its value is the same as the value of
a bit of wall in the middle distance. To explain
myself in a way that will make my meaning clear to
everyone, I will say, "Our pictures are no longer
vignetted." The first thing we note in Claude
Monet is his escape from the vignette of Turner and
Constable—so a vainer suggestion was never put
forward than that the Impressionists derived their
art from England. There is no escaping from the
conclusion that the modern mind is dependent upon
the modern method; some may prefer to think that
it was the modern mind that invented the modern

method—well, it will be always difficult to decide whether the egg preceded the chicken or the chicken preceded the egg. But this at least is certain, that the event of solid painting was bound to lead to Impressionism.

At this time a new faith was abroad, a new manner of thinking, and I find I have already written this description of the naturalistic movement in which I found myself caught: "The idea of a new art based upon science in opposition to the art of the old world that was based upon imagination, an art that should explain all things and embrace life in its entirety, in its endless ramifications, be, as it were, a new creed in a new civilization, filled me with wonder, and I stood dumb before the vastness of the conception and the height of the ambition. In my fevered fancy I saw a new race of writers that would arise, and, with the aid of the novel, continue to a more glorious and legitimate conclusion the work that the Hebrew prophets had begun." A few pages later I find the admission that I was deceived, as was all my generation, by a certain externality, an outer skin, a nearness, *un approchement;* in a word, by the substitution of Paris for the distant and exotic backgrounds so beloved of the romantic school.

The glass door of the café grates upon the sand again. It is Degas, a round-shouldered man in a suit of pepper and salt. There is nothing very trenchantly French about him either, except the large necktie. His eyes are small, his words sharp, ironical, cynical. Manet and Degas are the leaders of the Impressionistic school, but their friendship has been jarred by inevitable rivalry. "Degas was painting 'Semiramis' when I was painting 'Modern Paris,' " says Manet. "Manet is in despair because he cannot paint vulgar pictures like Duran, and be fêted and decorated; he is an artist not by inclination but by force; he is a galley-slave chained to the oar," says Degas. Degas is more inclined to look back than Manet; even his portraits are composed from drawings and notes, and looking at a picture by Degas we think, "Yes, that was how we thought in the seventies and in the eighties." Manet desired modernity as earnestly as Degas, but his genius saved him from the ideas that were of his time. Manet was a pure painter, and it mattered nothing to him whether he painted a religious subject—angels watching by the side of the Dead Christ—or yachting at Argenteuil. Manet was an instinct, Degas is an intellectuality, and believes with Edgar Poe that one becomes original by saying, "I will not do a certain thing because it has been done before."

So the day came when Degas put "Semiramis" aside for a ballet girl. "Semiramis" had been painted again and again; but the ballet girl in pink tights, clumsy shoes, and bunched skirts, looking unnatural as a cockatoo, had not. And it was Degas who introduced the acrobat into art, and the *repasseuse*. His portrait of Manet on the sofa listening to Madame Manet playing the piano is one of the most intellectual pieces of painting ever done in the world; its intellectuality reminds one of Leonardo da Vinci, for, like Degas, Leonardo painted by intellect rather

153

than by instinct. It was in the Louvre a few months ago that it occurred to me to compare Leonardo with Degas. I had gone there on a special errand, and when wearied with examination and debate, I turned into the Salle Carrée for relaxation, and there wandered about, waiting to be attracted. Long ago the "Mona Lisa" was my adventure, but this year Rembrandt's portrait of his wife held me at gaze. It did not delight me as Manet delights; the emotion was deeper, vaguer and more intense, and I seemed to myself like a magnetic patient in the coil of some powerful enchantment. The emotion that this picture awakens is almost physical. It gets at you like music, like a sudden breath of perfume. When one approaches, the eyes fade into brown shadow, and when one withdraws, they begin to tell their story, and the story they tell is of a woman's soul. She seems conscious of her weakness, of her sex, and the burden of her own special lot—she is Rembrandt's wife, a servant, a satellite, a watcher. The mouth is no more than a little shadow, but what wistful tenderness there is in it! and the color of the face is white, faintly tinted with bitumen, and in the cheeks some rose madder comes through the yellow. She wears a fur jacket, but the fur was no trouble to Rembrandt; he did not strive for realism. It is fur, that is sufficient. Gray pearls hang in her ears; there is a brooch upon her breast, and a hand at the bottom of the picture passing out of the frame, and that hand reminds one as the chin does, of the old story that God took a little clay and made man out of it. That chin and that hand and

154

arm are moulded without display of knowledge as
Nature moulds. The picture seems as if it had been
breathed upon the canvas. Did not a great poet
once say that God breathed into Adam? The other
pictures seem dry and insignificant, the "Mona Lisa,"
celebrated in literature, hanging a few feet away,
seems factitious when compared with this portrait;
that smile, so often described as mysterious, that
hesitating smile which held my youth in a little
tether, has come to seem to me but a grimace, and
the pale mountains no more mysterious than a globe
or map seems at a distance.

The "Mona Lisa" is a sort of riddle, an acrostic, a
poetical decoction, a ballade, a rondel, a villanelle,
or ballade with double burden, a sestina—that is
what it is like, a sestina or chant royal. The "Mona
Lisa," being literature in intention rather than painting, has drawn round her many poets. We must
forgive her many mediocre verses for the sake of one
incomparable prose passage. She has now passed
out of that mysterious misuse of oil paint, that arid
glazing of *terre verte*, and has come into her possession of eternal life, into the immortality of Pater's
prose. The "Mona Lisa" and Degas's "Leçon de
Danse," are intellectual pictures; they were painted
with the brains rather than with the temperaments;
and what is any intellect compared to a gift like
Manet's? The intellectual pleasure that we receive
from a mind so curiously critical, inquisitive, and
mordant as Degas' withers, but the joy we get from
the gift of painting like Manet's is a joy that lasts
forever. Of what value are Degas's descriptions of

washerwomen and dancers and race-horses compared with that fallen flower, that Aubusson carpet, above all, the footstool? The pleasure of an early Degas, the "Semiramis," is more lasting than that which we get from the dancers plunging forward in the blaze of the "limes." By the "Semiramis" hangs a tale—Degas painted Semiramis at the head of a group of women admiring the walls of Babylon; there were hanging gardens in the background. But one day he scratched half the picture away, and his explanation was that Semiramis would not surround herself with women; she would walk surrounded by men. His best pictures were painted before he began to think, when he was merely interested in Nature, and if any one of Degas's pictures is bought for this gallery I hope it will be one of these early pictures, the red-headed girl, for instance, an unfinished sketch, exhibited some time ago at Knightsbridge, the property, I believe, of Durand Ruel.

In the days of the Nouvelle Athènes we used to repeat Degas's witticisms, how he once said to Whistler, "Whistler, if you were not a genius you would be the most ridiculous man in Paris." Leonardo made roads, Degas makes witticisms. I remember his answer when I confided to him one day that I did not care for Daumier—the beautiful "Don Quixote and Sancho Panza" that hangs on the wall I had not then seen; that is my excuse—an insufficient one, I admit. Degas answered, "If you were to show Raphael a Daumier he would admire it, he would take off his hat; but if you were to show him a Cabanel he would say with a sigh, 'That is my fault.' " It is not possible to be wittier than this or more appreciative, but, I ask again, what does such intellect amount to when compared to that fallen flower or the beautiful painting of Mademoiselle Gonzales's white arm, or the dress so liquid, so beautiful, more beautiful than silk or ivory, every accent in its place? To omit any one of them would be a loss, to add another would be a redundancy. Manet said to me once, "I tried to write, but I couldn't write," and I thought he spoke apologetically, whereas his words were a boast. "He who paints as I paint could never think of doing anything else" was what was in his mind, and if Manet had lived till he was a hundred, he would have painted to the last. But Degas, being merely a man of intellect, wearied of painting; he turned to modeling for relaxation, and he has collected pictures. His collection is the most interesting in Paris, for it represents the taste of one man. His chief admirations are Delacroix and Ingres and Manet, especially Ingres. There was a time when he knew everyone who owned an Ingres, and it is said that the concierges used to keep him informed as to the health of the owners of certain pictures, and hearing of an appendicitis that might prove fatal, or a bad attack of influenza, Degas at once flapped his wings and went away like a vulture. One day I met him in the Rue Maubeuge. "I've got it," he said, and he was surprised when I asked him what he had got; great egotists always take it for granted that everyone is thinking of what they are doing. "Why, the 'Jupiter,' of course the 'Jupiter,' " and he

took me to see the picture—not a very good Ingres,
I thought—good, of course, but somewhat tedious—
a Jupiter with beetling brows, and a thunderbolt in
his hand. But next to it was a pear, and I knew that
pear, just a speckled pear painted on six inches of
canvas; it used to hang in Manet's studio, six inches
of canvas nailed to the wall, and I said to Degas, "I
think, after all, I like the pear better than 'Jupiter'"; and Degas said, "I put it there, for a pear
painted like that would overthrow any god." There
is a picture by Mr. Sargent in this room—one of his
fashionable women. She is dressed to receive visitors,
and is about to spring from her chair; the usual
words, "How do you do, Mary," are upon her crimson lips, and the usual hysterical lights are in her
eyes, and her arms are like bananas as usual. There
is in this portrait the same factitious surface-life
that informs all his pictures, and, recognizing fashionable gowns and drawing-room vivacities as the
fundamental Sargent, Degas described him as *Le
chef de rayon de la peinture*. *Le chef de rayon* is
the young man behind the counter who says, "I
think, madam, that this piece of mauve silk would
suit your daughter admirably, ten yards at least
will be required. If your daughter will step upstairs,
I will take her measure. *Vous pouvez me confier
votre fille; soyez sûr que je ne voudrais rien faire
qui pût nuire à mon commerce.*"

"Anyone," Degas said once to me, "can have talent
when he is five-and-twenty; the thing is to have
talent when you are fifty." I remember the Salon
in which Bastien Lepage exhibited his "Potato Har-

vest," and we all admired it till Degas said, "A Bouguereau of the modern movement." Then everyone understood that Bastien Lepage's talent was not an original but a derivative talent. When Roll, another painter of the same time, exhibited his enormous picture entitled "Work," containing fifty figures, Degas said, "One doesn't make a crowd with fifty figures, one makes a crowd with five." But what is all this intellect compared with that flower fallen on the carpet, or that plump white arm moulded without a shadow.

Monet, being a landscape painter, only appeared in the Nouvelle Athènes after long absences; he would return suddenly from the country, bringing with him twenty or thirty canvases, all equally perfect. He seemed to be doing always what he set out to do, whether a row of poplars seen in perspective against a gray sky, or a view of the Seine with a bridge cutting the picture in equal halves, or a cottage shrouded in snow with some low hills over yonder and some poplar-trees, and one mutters, "The touch is as beautiful as Sisley's." One of the few things this exhibition lacks is a picture by Sisley, and it is my hope that the Sisley that will come into this collection in due time may be the one that I saw many years ago in the galleries of George Pettit: the bare wall of a cottage, a frozen pond, and on the other side of the pond some poplar-trees —these trees and their shadows are the picture. The delicacy of the vision that saw these trees against the winter sky, and their mauve and transparent shadows floating over the frozen ground to

the pond's edge, enchants us as music does, and we
are unable to put back the thought that a picture
like this makes Constable's vision seem coarse and
his craft very clumsy. Monet or Sisley—which is
the greater? Monet is more external, more decorative than Sisley—that is all one can say. But those
who like to trace all individual qualities back to
race influence may, if they will, trace back the exquisite reverie which distinguishes Sisley's pictures
from Monet's to Sisley's northern blood.

Of the originality of these two painters, and of
the originality of the Impressionist school, one cannot think too often or too long; there arose suddenly an art in France unlike any other art that
had ever been seen in the world before, and no
country, not even France, is prepared for such
surprising innovations as Monet's and Sisley's pictures. Monet especially paid dearly for the gift of
his genius, he very nearly starved; there were times
when he could not get more than one hundred francs
apiece for his pictures, very often no price could
be obtained, and Monet went without his dinner.
He began by imitating Manet, and Manet ended by
imitating Monet. They were great friends. Manet
painted Monet and Madame Monet in their garden,
and Monet painted Manet and Madame Manet in the
same garden; they exchanged pictures, but after a
quarrel each returned the other his picture. Monet's
picture of Manet and his wife I never saw, but
Manet's picture of Monet and Madame Monet belongs to a very wealthy merchant, a Monsieur Pel-
lerin, who has the finest collection of Manet's and

Cézanne's in the world. I do not remember ever to
have seen Cézanne at the Nouvelle Athènes; he was
too rough, too savage a creature, and appeared in
Paris only rarely. We used to hear about him—
he used to be met on the outskirts of Paris wandering about the hillsides in jack-boots. As no one
took the least interest in his pictures he left them in
the fields; when his pictures began to be asked for,
his son and daughter used to inquire them out in the
cottages, and they used to keep watch in the hedges
and collect the sketches he had left behind him. It
would be untrue to say that he had no talent, but
whereas the intention of Manet and of Monet and
of Degas was always to paint, the intention of
Cézanne was, I am afraid, never very clear to himself. His work may be described as anarchical. It
is impossible to deny to this strange being a certain
uncouth individuality; uncouth though it be, there
is life in his pictures, otherwise no one would remember them. I pause to ask myself which I would
prefer—one of Millet's conventional, simpering
peasants or one of Cézanne's crazy cornfields peo-
pled with violet reapers. But why do I linger
talking of Cézanne when the greatest of all this
group of painters has only been mentioned by name
—Renoir. Nor is this the first time I have delayed
to speak of him, and so betrayed a lack of appreciation. Among the Impressionist painters there
was an English, I should say an American, Mary
Casatt. She did not come to the Nouvelle Athènes
it is true, but she lived on the Boulevard Extérieur;
her studio was within a minute's walk of the Place

Pigalle, and we used to see her every day. Her art was derived from Degas as Berthe Morisot's art was derived from Manet. Berthe Morisot was Manet's sister-in-law, and I remember him saying to me once, "My sister-in-law would not have existed without me; she did nothing but carry my art across her fan." Berthe Morisot is dead, and her pictures are very expensive—picture-dealers do not make presents; but Mary Casatt is alive, and she is a rich woman, and I take this opportunity of suggesting that she should be asked to give a picture. But to the anecdote. After an absence of many years I met her in Durand Ruel's, and at breakfast next day we talked of all the people we had known, and at the end of breakfast she said, "There is one we haven't spoken about, perhaps the greatest of all." I said, "You mean Renoir?" And she accused me of having been always a little indifferent to Renoir's art. I don't think that this is true, or if it is true, it is only true in a way. I know of nothing that I would sooner possess—and by our desire of possession we may measure our admiration—than one of Renoir's nudes. He has modeled whole bodies of women in the light, and the light is not only on the surface, apparently; it is under the surface. Some of his portraits of children are the most beautiful I know—they are white and flower-like, and therefore very unlike the stunted, leering little monkeys which Sir Joshua Reynolds persuaded us to accept as representative of tall and beautiful English children. Renoir's life supplies me with an instructive anecdote; but for you to approve of the anecdote

you must know something of his early days. So I
will tell you that he began life as a porcelain painter
—I have seen flowered vases painted by him and
pictures of flowers painted exactly as a porcelain
painter would paint them. It was not till the sixties
that he began to paint portraits. I think that it was
at the end of the sixties that he painted the celebrated picture of the woman looking into the canary
cage—a wonderful picture, but very unlike the
Renoir of the nudes that I hunger to possess. Is it
not strange that an art so strangely personal as
Renoir's should have been developed by degrees?
Manet was Manet as soon as he left Couture's studio
—even before he went there. Degas always was
Degas, but there was no sign of the late Renoir even
in the portrait of the lady looking into the canary
cage. The beautiful nudes would never have been
painted if he had not come to the café of the Nouvelle
Athènes. But do I admire the nudes as much as I
say I do? Renoir as a whole—is he the equal of
Manet? Good heavens, no! And, indeed, at the
bottom of my heart I always suspect Renoir's art of
a certain vulgarity. If this be true, all the more
strange that he, who was influenced by everybody,
should have ended by influencing all the others.
Manet's last pictures were certainly influenced by
Renoir; Manet's last years were spent in thinking of
Renoir. Renoir was always in the café of the
Nouvelle Athènes, and I remember well the hatred
with which he used to denounce the nineteenth century—the century in which he used to say there
was no one who could make a piece of furniture or

a clock that was beautiful and that was not a copy of an old one. It was about that time that Durand Ruel began to buy his pictures, and one day, finding himself in easier circumstances, he thought he would take what the newspapers call a well-deserved—or is it a well-earned?—holiday. For some time he was not sure whether he should lay in a stock of wine or cigars and give dinner-parties, or should furnish a flat and fall in love. These are the outlets that life offers to the successful painter, and it would have been well for Renoir if he had not been so virtuous: for he went instead to Venice to study Tintoretto, and when he returned to Paris he entered a studio with a view to perfecting his drawing, and in two years he had destroyed for ever the beautiful art which had taken twenty years to elaborate. The last time I saw him was on the Butte Montmartre, a decaying quarter, full of crumbling façades, pillars, and abandoned gardens. He was living in a small house at the end of one of these gardens, interested far more in his rheumatism than in painting. I was talking to him of Aungtin, who believes that the whole century has gone astray, that we must return to the painting of our ancestors, to glazes: but Renoir showed little interest—he only said, *"Chacun a sa marrotte,"* which means that everyone has a bee in his bonnet. But why should this old man take an interest in Aungtin's new æstheticism? Renoir has said what he had to say, and when a man has done that, the rest had better be silence.

The evenings that Pissaro did not come to take

his coffee in the Nouvelle Athènes were very rare
indeed. He was there more frequently than Manet
or Degas, and when they were there he sat listening,
approving of their ideas, joining in the conversation
quietly. A wise and appreciative Jew, who looked
like Abraham; his beard was white and his hair
was white and he was bald, though at the time he
could not have been much more than fifty. He was
the oldest of that group, and died two years ago
at an advanced age, I think seventy-five. The last
time I saw him was at Rouen, about six years ago,
and he did not look older then than he had looked
twenty years before, nor was he older in mind. He
was enthusiastic and interested in everything; he
was painting the Cathedral, I suppose because Monet
had been there the year before and had painted the
Cathedral. Pissaro always followed in somebody's
footsteps; he was a sort of will-o'-the-wisp of painting, and his course was zig-zag. But though his
wanderings were many and sudden, he never quite
lost his individuality, not even when he painted
yachts after the manner of Signac, in dots. The
picture in the present exhibition, which I hope Dublin will be able to acquire, is a very good example
of Pissaro's work: it represents Pissaro in his first
period, when he followed Corot. In the "Confessions
of a Young Man" I find an appreciation of Pissaro,
and, as I think to-day as I thought then, I may
quote it. Speaking of a group of girls gathering
apples in a garden, I wrote: "Sad grays and vio-
lets, beautifully harmonized. The figures seem to
move as in a dream; we are on the thither side of

life, in a world of quiet color and happy aspiration. Those apples will never fall from the branches, those baskets that the stooping girls are filling will never be filled, that garden is the garden that life has not for giving, but which the painter has set in an eternal dream of violet and gray." Pissaro has painted many such pictures—pictures of hillsides, where the peasants hoe the little mildew that has collected on the earth's surface. No one has understood the pathos of the peasant's lot better than Pissaro; he has understood it far better than Millet who has never seemed to me much more than an eighteenth-century painter. Millet's subjects differ from Romney or Greuze, but the painting is much the same, and the mind is the same—given over to tedious sentimentalities.

When Pissaro died, the question was asked: Who had invented Impressionism? and attempts were made to trace Monet back to Turner. Monet, it was said, had been to England, and in England he must have seen Turner, and it was impossible to see Turner without being influenced by Turner. Yes! Monet was in England many times, and he painted in England, and one day we went together to an Exhibition of Old Masters in Burlington House; we saw there a picture for which many thousands of pounds had just been paid, and Monet said, "Is that brown thing your great Turner?" It is true, the picture we were looking at was not much more interesting than brown paper, and I told him that Turner had painted other pictures that he would like better, "The Frosty Morning," and he said he had seen it, and that Turner had painted that morning with his eyes open. Whistler liked "Calais Pier" much better than "The Frosty Morning," for it was more like his own painting. We cannot be sincere in our own work and admire the very opposite to ourselves, and no very special discernment is required to understand that Turner and Constable could not have influenced painters whose desire was to dispense altogether with shadow. Whether, by doing so, they failed sometimes to differentiate between a picture and a strip of wallpaper is a question that does not come within the scope of the present inquiry. Mr. Lane is asking us to consider if a collection of Impressionist pictures would be of advantage to Dublin, and it seems to me that the pictures he offers us could not fail to inspire freedom of thought. All are a departure from precedent, and Manet, even more than Monet and Sisley, urges revolt against the old. Adam standing in Eden looking at the sunset was not more naked and unashamed than Manet. I believe that a Gallery of Impressionist pictures would be more likely than any other pictures to send men to France, and in some café in some Nouvelle Athènes, named though it be not in any Baedeker, nor marked on any traveler's chart, their souls will be exalted to praise life. Art is but praise of life, and it is only through the arts that we can praise life. Life is a rose that withers in the iron fist of dogma, and it was France that forced open the deadly fingers of the Ecclesiastic and allowed the rose to bloom again. He started out to crush life about two thousand years ago, and in three centuries humility, resignation, and obedience were accepted as virtues; the shrines of the Gods were abandoned; the beautiful limbs of the lover and the athlete were forbidden to the sculptor, and the meager thighs of dying saints were offered him instead. Literature died, for literature can but praise life. Music died, for music can but praise life, and the lugubrious Dies Irae was heard in the fanes. What use had a world for art when the creed current among men was that life is a mean and miserable thing? So amid lugubrious chant and solemn procession the dusk thickened, until the moment of deepest night was reached in the ninth and the tenth and the eleventh centuries. In the fifteenth century the dawn began in Ialy, and sculptors and painters turned their eyes toward Greece. Donatello and Michael Angelo replaced Praxiteles and Phidias. Day follows night as surely as night follows day, and the light that began in Italy in the fifteenth century has been widening ever since, veil after veil has been scattered, and now there is broad daylight in the land of France. News of the white town far away, news of its gardens, its statues and monumented swards reach us; and we go there like humble rag-pickers with baskets on our backs and hooked sticks in our hands, and we come back rich men. . . . The light is spreading northward; light is on the mountain-tops, while the valleys are still in darkness. The light will rise higher and higher, Northern Europe will again bask in sunlight, the beams will reach this lonely Western valley—not in our time; a hun-

dred years hence the sun will be again overhead,
and life shall be praised again, praise of the incomparable gift shall be sung in joyous procession about
the temples of "the young compassionate gods."

VII

As soon as the applause died away Yeats, who
had lately returned to us from the States with a
paunch, a huge stride, and an immense fur overcoat,
rose to speak. We were surprised at the change in
his appearance, and could hardly believe our ears
when, instead of talking to us as he used to do about
the old stories come down from generation to generation, he began to thunder like Ben Tillett himself against the middle classes, stamping his feet,
working himself into a great passion, and all because
the middle classes did not dip their hands into their
pockets and give Lane the money he wanted for his
exhibition. It is impossible to imagine the hatred
which came into his voice when he spoke the words
"the middle classes"; one would have thought that
he was speaking against a personal foe; but there
are millions in the middle classes! And we looked
round asking each other with our eyes where on
earth our Willie Yeats had picked up such extraordinary ideas. He could hardly have gathered in
the United States the ridiculous idea that none but
titled and carriage-folk can appreciate pictures.
And we asked ourselves why Willie Yeats should
feel himself called upon to denounce the class to
which he himself belonged essentially: on one side

excellent mercantile millers and ship owners, and on the other a portrait painter of rare talent. With so admirable a parentage it did not seem to us necessary that a man should look back for an ancestry, and we had laughed at the story, looking upon it as *ben trovato*, that on one occasion when Yeats was crooning over Æ's fire he had said that if he had his rights he would be Duke of Ormonde, and that Æ had answered, "In any case, Willie, you are overlooking your father,"—a detestable remark to make to a poet in search of an ancestry, and the addition, "Yeats, we both belong to the lower middle classes," was in equally bad taste. Æ, who is usually quick-witted, should have guessed that Yeats's belief in his lineal descent from the great Duke of Ormonde was part of his poetic equipment. . . . It did not occur to us till this last minute; but Æ knew that there were spoons in the Yeats family bearing the Butler crest, just as there are portraits in my family of Sir Thomas More, and he should have remembered that certain passages in "The Countess Cathleen" are clearly derivative from the spoons. He should have remembered that all the romantic poets have sought illustrious ancestry, and rightly, since romantic poetry is concerned only with nobles and castles, gonfalons and oriflammes. Villiers de l'Isle Adam believed firmly in his descent, and appeared on all public occasions with the Order of Malta pinned upon his coat; and Victor Hugo, too, had inquired out his ancestry in all the archives of Spain and France before sitting down to write "Hernani" . . . and with good reason, for with the disappearance of gonfalons and donjons it may be doubted if—— My meditation was interrupted by Yeats's voice.

"We have sacrificed our lives for Art; but you, what have you done? What sacrifices have you made?" he asked, and everybody began to search his memory for the sacrifices that Yeats had made, asking himself in what prison Yeats had languished, what rags he had worn, what broken victuals he had eaten. As far as anybody could remember, he had always lived very comfortably, sitting down invariably to regular meals, and the old green cloak that was in keeping with his profession of romantic poet he had exchanged for the magnificent fur coat which distracted our attention from what he was saying, so opulently did it cover the back of the chair out of which he had risen. But, quite forgetful of the coat behind him, he continued to denounce the middle classes, throwing his arms into the air, shouting at us, and we thinking not at all of what he was saying, but of a story that had been floating about Dublin for some time. A visitor had come back from Coole telling how he had discovered the poet lying on a sofa in a shady corner, a plate of strawberries on his knee, and three or four adoring ladies serving him with cream and sugar, and how the poet, after wiping his hands on a napkin, had consented to recite some verses, and the verses he recited were these:

"I said, 'A line will take us hours maybe,
    Yet if it does not seem a moment's thought

Our stitching and unstitching has been naught.
Better go down upon your marrow-bones
And scrub a kitchen pavement, or break stones
Like an old pauper in all kinds of weather;
For to articulate sweet sounds together
Is to work harder than all these and yet
Be thought an idler by the noisy set
Of bankers, schoolmasters and clergymen,
The martyrs call the world.' "

The poet advanced a step or two nearer to the edge of the platform, and stamping his foot he asked again what the middle classes had done for Art, and in a towering rage (the phrase is no mere figure of speech, for he raised himself up to tremendous height) he called upon the ladies and gentlemen that had come to hear my lecture to put their hands in their pockets and give sovereigns to the stewards who were waiting at the doors to receive them, or, better still, to write large checks. We were led to understand that by virtue of our subscriptions we should cease to belong to the middle classes, and having held out this hope to us he retired to his chair and fell back overcome into the middle of the great fur coat, and remained silent until the end of the debate.

As soon as it was over criticism began, not of my lecture, but of Yeats's speech, and on Saturday night all my friends turned in to discuss his contention that the middle classes had never done anything for Art; the very opposite seemed to Æ to be the truth. He pointed out that the aristocracy had given England no great poet except Byron, whom many people did not look upon as a poet at all, and though Shelley's poetry was unquestionable, he could hardly be considered as belonging to the aristocracy, his father having been merely a Sussex baronet. All the other poets, it was urged, came from the middle classes, not only the poets, but the painters, the musicians, and the sculptors. "Yeats's attack upon the middle classes," somebody cried, "is the most absurd that was ever made; the aristocracy have Byron, and the peasants have Burns, all the others belong to us." Somebody chimed in, "Not even the landowners have produced a poet," and he was answered that Landor was a considerable landed proprietor. But he was the only one. Not a single painter came out of the aristocracy. Lord Carlyle's name was mentioned; everybody laughed, and I said that the distinction of classes was purely an arbitrary one. It was agreed that if riches can poison inspiration, poverty is a stimulant, and then leaning out of his corner Æ remarked that Willie Yeats' best poems were written when he was a poor boy in Sligo, a remark that fanned the flame of discussion, and the difficult question was broached why Yeats had ceased to write poetry. All his best poems, Æ said, were written before he went to London. Apart from the genius which he brought into the world, it was Sligo that had given his poetry a character. Everybody knew some of his verses by heart, and I took pleasure in listening to them again. The calves basking on the hillside were mentioned, the colleen going to church. "But," somebody cried

174

out suddenly, "he took his colleen to London and put paint upon her cheeks and dye upon her hair, and sent her up Piccadilly." Another critic added that the last time he saw her she was wearing a fine hat and feathers. "Supplied by Arthur Symons," cried another. "As sterile a little wanton as ever I set eyes upon," exclaimed still another critic, "who lives in remembrance of her beauty, saying nothing." And the silences that Yeats's colleen had observed these many years were regretted, somewhat hypocritically I think, for, as Æ says, a literary movement consists of five or six people who live in the same town and hate each other cordially. But, if we were not really sorry that Yeats's inspiration was declining, we were quite genuinely interested to discover the cause of it. Æ was certain that he would have written volume after volume if he had never sought a style, if he had been content to write simply; and all his utterances on the subject of style were repeated.

"He came this afternoon into the National Library," John Eglinton said, breaking silence, "and he told me he was collecting his writings for a complete edition, a library edition in ten or twelve volumes."

"But he is only thirty-seven."

"He said his day was over," John Eglinton answered . . . "and in speaking of the style of his last essay, he said: 'Ah, that style! I made it myself.'"

"But," Longworth argued, "I fail to understand how anybody can speak of a style apart from some definite work already written by him in that style. A style does not exist in one's head, it exists upon paper, and Yeats has no style, neither bad nor good, for he writes no more."

Æ thought that Yeats had discovered a style, and a very fine style indeed, and compared it to a suit of livery which a man buys before he engages a servant; the livery is made of the finest cloth, the gold lace is the very finest, the cockade can be seen from one side of the street to the other, but when the footman comes he is always too tall or too thin or too fat, so the livery is never worn.

"Excellent!" cried Gogarty, "and the livery hangs in a press upstairs, becoming gradually moth-eaten."

Æ regretted the variants; he knew them all and preferred the earlier text in every case, and when literary criticism was over we turned to the poet's own life to discover why it was that he sang no more songs for us. We had often heard him say that his poems had arisen out of one great passion, and this interesting avowal raised the no less interesting question—which produces the finer fruit, the gratified or the ungratified passion. It was clearly my turn to speak, and I told how Wesendonck had built for Wagner a pavilion at the end of his garden so that Wagner might compose the "Valkyrie," and how at the end of every day when Wagner had finished his work, Mathilde used to come down the lawn to visit him, inspiring by degrees a great passion in him, but which, out of loyalty to Wesendonck, they resisted until the fatal day when he read

176

her the poem of "Tristan and Isolde." After the
reading they had stood looking at each other; the
poem was a magic draught. "I am Tristan, thou art
Isolde." But it was not many days before Minna,
Wagner's wife, intercepted a letter which she took
to Madame Wesendonck, and the interview between
the two women was so violent that Wagner had to
send his wife to Dresden, and himself retired to
Venice to meditate on suicide and his setting of
some verses of the well-beloved.

"Regret nothing," he writes from Venice, "I beseech you, regret nothing. Your kisses were the
crown of my life, my recompense for many years of
suffering. Regret nothing, I beseech you, regret
nothing."

Minna had no doubt as to Richard's guilt, nor
have we, but the translator of the letters, Mr. Ash-
ton Ellis, and others, have preferred to regard
this passion as ungratified, and it is evident that
they think that the truth is not worth seeking since
the drama and the music and the letters cannot now
be affected thereby. "For better or worse you have
the music, you have the drama, you have the correspondence," they declare. "What can it matter to
you whether an act purely physical happened, or
failed to happen?" "Everything," I answer, "for
thereof I learn whether Wagner wrote out of a realized or an unrealized desire."

As we sat round the fire I broke silence again:

"Love that has *not* been born again in the flesh
crumbles like peat ash."

And then John Eglinton's voice broke in:

"Every man is different," and he reproached me with arguing for myself.

"The love we are considering has lasted for many years and will continue, and I know for certain that it has always been a pure love."

"A detestable phrase, Æ, for it implies that every gratified love must be impure. None except the lovers themselves know the truth."

And from that day onward I continued to meditate the main secret of Yeats's life, until one day we happened to meet at Broadstone Station. We were going to the West; we breakfasted together in the train, and after breakfast the conversaticn took many turns, and we talked of her whom he had loved always, the passionate ideal of his life, and why this ideal had never become a reality to him as Mathilde had become to Richard. Was it really so? was my pressing question, and he answered me:

"I was very young at the time and was satisfied with. . . ." My memory fails me, or perhaps the phrase was never finished. The words I supply "the spirit of sense" are merely conjectural.

"Yes, I understand, the common mistake of a boy"; and I was sorry for Yeats and for his inspiration which did not seem to have survived his youth, because it had arisen out of an ungratified desire. Hyacinths grown in a vase only bloom for a season. But if it had been otherwise? On such questions one may meditate a long while, and it was not until the train ran into Westport that I remembered my prediction when Symons had shown me "Rosa Alchemica."

"His inspiration," I had said, "is at an end, for he talks about how he is going to write." I had told Symons that I had noticed all through my life that a man may tell the subject of his poem and write it, but if he tells how he is going to write his poem he will never write it. Mallarmé projected hundreds of poems, and, like Yeats, Mallarmé was always talking about style. The word never came into Mallarmé's conversation, but, like Yeats, his belief was that the poet should have a language of his own. "Every other art," I remember him saying, "has a special language—sculpture, music, painting; why shouldn't the poet have his?" He set himself to the task of inventing a language, but it was such a difficult one that it left him very little time for writing; we have but twenty sonnets and "L'Après-midi d'un Faune" written in it. *Son œuvre* calls to mind a *bibelot*, a carven nick-nack, wrought ivory, or jade, or bronze, and like bronze it will acquire a patina. His phrases will never grow old, for they tell us nothing; the secret meaning is so deeply embedded that generations will try to puzzle through them; and in the volume entitled "The Wind among the Reeds" Yeats has written poems so difficult that even the adepts could not disentangle the sense; and since "The Wind among the Reeds" he has written a sonnet that clearly referred to a house. But to what house? Æ inclined to the opinion that it referred to the House of Lords, but the poet, being written to from Ely Place, replied that the subject of his sonnet was Coole Park. Mallarmé could not be darker than this. But whereas to write a lan-

guage apart was Mallarmé's sole æstheticism and one
which he never abandoned after the publication of
"L'après-midi d'un Faune," Yeats advocated two languages, one which he employs himself, another which
he would use if he could, but being unable to use it he
counsels its use to others, and has put up a sign-
post "This way to Parnassus." It is amusing to
think of Mallarmé and Yeats together; they would
have got on famously until Yeats began to tell Mallarmé that the poet would learn the language he
required in Le Berry. Mallarmé was a subtle mind,
and he would have thought the idea ingenious that
a language is like a spring which rises in the highlands, trickles into a rivulet and flows into a river,
and needs no filter until the river has passed through
a town; he would have listened to these theories with
interest, but Yeats would not have been able to
persuade him to set out for Le Berry, and the
journey would have been useless if he had, for
Mallarmé had no ear for folk, less than Yeats himself, who has only half an ear; an exquisite ear for
the beauty of folk imagination, and very little for
folk idiom. Are not the ways of Nature strange?
for he loves folk idiom as none has ever loved it,
and few have had better opportunities of learning
it than he along his uncle's wharves in Sligo Town
and among the slopes of Ben Bulben, whither he
went daily, interested in birds and beasts and the
stories that the folk tell. As pretty a nosegay as
ever was gathered he tied on those slopes; there is
no prettier book of literature than "Celtic Twilight," and one of the tales, "The Last Gleeman,"

must have put into Yeats's mind the idea that he has followed ever since, that the Irish people write very well when they are not trying to write that worn-out and defaced idiom which educated people speak and write, and which is known as English. And it is Yeats's belief that those among us who refuse to write it are forced back upon artificial speech which they create, and which is often very beautiful; the beauty of Meredith's speech, or Pater's, or Morris's, cannot be denied, but their speech, Yeats would say, lacks naturalness; it is not living speech, that is how he would phrase it, and his thoughts would go back to Michael Moran, the last of the Gleemen, who, he thinks, was more fortunate than the three great writers mentioned, for Michael wrote (it would be more correct to say he composed, for it is doubtful if he knew how to write) living speech— *i. e.*, a speech that has never been printed. Yeats's whole æstheticism is expressed in these words, "A speech that has never been printed." It is printing that makes speech ugly, that is Yeats's belief, and the peasant is the only one who can give us unblunted speech. But is it not true that peasant speech limits the range of our ideas? The dropping of ideas out of literature would be a pure benefit, Yeats would say. Modern literature is dying of ideas. The literature that has come down to us is free from ideas. Ideas are the portion of vestrymen. But peasant speech is only adapted to dialogue. He might answer with Landor that Shakespeare and the best parts of Homer were written in dialogue, and it would be heartless to reply, "But

181

not the best part of your own works, Yeats. Your
mind is as subtle as a Brahmin's, woven along and
across with ideas, and you cannot catch the idiom as
it flows off the lips. You are like Moses, who may
not enter the Promised Land." He would not care
to answer, "Even if what you say be true, you must
admit that I have led some others there"; he would
fold himself up like a pelican and dream of his
disciples. He was dreaming of them before he had
collected any, when I met him in the Cheshire
Cheese; he was ever looking for disciples, and sought
them in vain till he met Lady Gregory. It was a
great day for Ireland the day that she came over
to Tillyra. Here I must break off my narrative
to give a more explicit account of Lady Gregory
than the reader will find in "Ave."

Lady Gregory is a Persse, and the Persses are an
ancient Galway family; the best-known branch is
Moyaude, for it was at Moyaude that Burton Persse
bred and hunted the Galway Blazers for over thirty
years . . . till his death. Moyaude has passed
away, but Roxborough continues, never having indulged in either horses or hounds, a worthy but
undistinguished family in love, in war, or in politics,
never having indulged in anything except a taste for
Bible reading in the cottages. A staunch Protestant
family, if nothing else, the Roxborough Persses certainly are. Mrs. Persse and her two elder daughters were ardent soul-gatherers in the days gone by
but Lady Gregory did not join them in their mis-
sionary work, holding always to the belief that
there was great danger in persuading anyone to

leave the religion learnt in childhood, for we could never be sure that another would find a place in the heart. In saying as much she wins our hearts, but our intelligence warns us against the seduction, and we remember that we may not acquiesce in what we believe to be error. The ignorant and numbed mind cannot be acceptable to God, so do we think, and take our stand with Mrs. Persse and the elder sisters. We are glad, however, though we are not sure that our gladness on such a point is not a sign of weakness, still we are glad that Sir William chose Augusta rather than one of her elder sisters, either of which would certainly have fired up in the carriage when Sir William, on his way to Coole, suggested to his bride that she should refrain from pointing out to his tenants what she believed to be the different teaching of the Bible to that of the Catholic Church. He would probably say, "You have made no converts—(we have forgotten Mrs. Shaw Taylor's Christian name, but Agnes will serve our purpose as well as another)—you have made no converts, Agnes, but you have shaken the faith of thousands. The ground at Roxborough has been cleared for the sowing, but Kiltartan can wait." "Which Path Should Agnes Have Followed?" is clearly the title of a six-shilling novel which I pass on to my contemporaries; meanwhile I have pleasure in stating here, for my statement is implicated in an artistic movement, the Abbey Theater, that the Gospels were never read by Lady Gregory round Kiltartan. I should like to fill in a page or two about her married life, but though we know our neighbors very well in one direction, in another there is nothing that we know less than our neighbors, and Lady Gregory has never been for me a very real person. I imagine her without a mother, or father, or sisters, or brothers, *sans attache*. It is difficult to believe, but it is nevertheless true, that fearing a too flagrant mistake, I had to ask a friend the other day if I were right in supposing that Mrs. Shaw Taylor was Lady Gregory's sister, an absurd question truly, for Mrs. Shaw Taylor's house (I have forgotten its name) is within a mile of Tillyra, and I must have been there many times. We may cultivate our memories in one direction, but by so doing we curtail them in another, and documentary evidence is not of my style. I like to write of Lady Gregory from the evening that Edward drove me over to Coole, the night of the dinner-party. There is in "Ave" a portrait of her as I saw her that night, a slim young woman of medium height and slight figure; her hair, parted in the middle, was brushed in wide bands about a brow which even at that time was intellectual. The phrase used in "Ave," if my memory does not deceive me, was "high and cultured"; I think I said that she wore a high-school air, and the phrase expresses the idea she conveyed to me—an air of mixed timidity and restrained anxiety to say or do nothing that would jar. On the whole it was pleasant to pass from her to Sir William, who was more at his ease, more natural. He spoke to me affably about a Velasquez in the National Gallery, which was not a Velasquez; it is now set down as a Zurbaran, but the last attribution does not convince me any more than the first. He wore the Lord Palmerston air, it was the air of that generation, but he did not wear it nearly so well as my father.

These two men were of the same generation and their interests were the same; both were traveled men; Sir William's travels were not so original as my father's, and the race horses that he kept were not so fast, and his politics were not so definite; he was more of an opportunist than my father, more careful and cautious, and therefore less interesting. Galway has not produced so many interesting men as Mayo; its pastures are richer, but its men are thinner in intellect. But if we are considering Lady Gregory's rise in the world, we must admit that she owes a great deal to her husband. He took her to London, and she enjoyed at least one season in a tall house in the little enclosure known as St. George's Place; and there met a number of eminent men whose books and conversation were in harmony with her conception of life, still somewhat formal. One afternoon Lecky the historian left her drawing-room as I entered it, and I remember the look of pleasure on her face when she mentioned the name of her visitor, and her pleasure did not end with Lecky, for a few minutes after Edwin Arnold, the poet of "The Light of Asia," was announced. She would have liked to have had him all to herself, and I think that she thought my conversation a little ill-advised when I spoke to Sir Edwin of a book lately published on the subject of Buddhism, and asked him what book was the best to read on this subject. He did not answer my question directly, but very soon he was telling Lady Gregory that he had just received a letter from India from a distinguished Buddhist who had read "The Light of Asia" and could find no fault in it; the Buddhist doctrine as related by him had been related faultlessly. And with this little anecdote Sir Edwin thought my question sufficiently answered. The conversation turned on the colored races, and I remember Sir Edwin's words, "The world will not be perfect," he said, "until we get the black notes into the gamut." A pretty bit of telegraphese which pleased Lady Gregory; and when Sir Edwin rose to go she produced a fan and asked him to write his name upon one of the sticks. But she did not ask me to write my name, though at that time I had written not only "A Modern Lover," but also "A Mummer's Wife," and I left the house feeling for the first time that the world I lived in was not so profound as I had imagined it to be. If I remember the circumstances quite rightly, Sir William came into the room just as I was leaving it, and she showed him the fan; he looked a little distressed at her want of tact, and it was some years afterward that I heard, and not without surprise, that she had shown some literary ability in the editing of his "Memoirs." The publication of these "Memoirs" was a great day for Roxborough, and a great day for Ireland it was when she drove over to Tillyra.

I was not present at the time, but from Edward's account of the meeting she seems to have recognized her need in Yeats at once, foreseeing dimly, of course, but foreseeing that he would help her out

of conventions and prejudices, and give her wings
to soar in the free air of ideas and instincts. She
was manifestly captured by his genius, and seemed
to dread that the inspiration the hills of Sligo
had nourished might wither in the Temple where
he used to spend long months with his friend Arthur
Symons. He had finished all his best work at the
time, the work whereby he will live; "The Countess
Cathleen" had not long been written, and he was
dreaming the poem of "The Shadowy Waters," and
where could he dream it more fortunately than by
the lake at Coole? The wild swans gather there,
and every summer he returned to Coole to write
"The Shadowy Waters," writing under her tutelage
and she serving him as amanuensis, collecting the
different versions, etc.

So much of the literary history of this time was
written in "Ave," but what has not been written, or
only hinted at, is the interdependence of these two
minds. It was he, no doubt, who suggested to her
the writing of the Cuchulain legends. It must have
been so, for he had long been dreaming an epic
poem to be called "Cuchulain"; but feeling himself
unable for so long a task he entrusted it to Lady
Gregory, and led her from cabin to cabin in search
of a style, and they returned to Coole ruminating
the beautiful language of the peasants and the
masterpiece quickening in it, Yeats a little sad, but
by no means envious toward Lady Gregory, and
sad, if at all, that his own stories in the volume
entitled "The Secret Rose" were not written in living
speech. It is pleasant to think that, as he opened

the park gates for her to pass through, the thought
glided into his mind that perhaps in some subsequent
edition she might help him with the translation.
But the moment was for the consideration of a
difficulty that had arisen suddenly. The legends of
Cuchulain are written in a very remote language,
bearing little likeness to the modern Irish which
Lady Gregory had learnt in common with everybody
connected with the Irish Literary Movement, Yeats
and myself excepted. A dictionary of the ancient
language exists, and it is easy to look out a word;
but a knowledge of early or middle Irish is only
obtained gradually after years of study; Lady
Gregory confesses herself in her preface to be no
scholar, and that she pieced together her text from
various French and German translations. This
method recommends itself to Yeats, who says in
his preface that by collating the various versions of
the same tale and taking the best bits out of each
the stories are now told perfectly for the first time,
a singular view for a critic of Yeats's understanding
to hold, a strange theory to advocate, the strangest,
we do not hesitate to say, that has ever been put
forward by so distinguished a poet and critic as
Yeats. He was a severer critic the day that he
threw out Edward's play with so much indignity in
Tillyra. He was then a monk of literature, an in-
quisitor, a Torquemada, but in this preface he bows
to Lady Gregory's taste as if she were the tale-
teller that the world had been waiting for, one whose
art exceeded that of Balzac or Turgenev, for neither
would have claimed the right to refashion the old

legends in accordance with his own taste or the
taste of his neighborhood. "I left out a good deal,"
Lady Gregory writes in her preface, "I thought you
would not care about." The "you" refers to the
people of Kiltartan, to whom Lady Gregory dedi-
cates her book. It seems to me that Balzac and
Turgenev would have taken a different view as to the
duty of a modern writer to the old legends; both
would have said, "It is never justifiable to alter a
legend; it has come down to us because it contains
some precious message, and the message the legend
carries will be lost or worsened if the story be altered or mutilated or deformed." "And who am I,"
Balzac would have said, "that I should alter a message that has come down from a far-off time, a message often enfolded in the tale so secretly that it is
all things to all men. My province," he would have
said, "is not to alter the story, but to interpret it,"
and we have not to listen very intently to hear him
say, "Not only I may, I must interpret." There
can be little doubt that Yeats is often injudicious
in his noble preface, and he exposes Lady Gregory
to criticism when he depreciates the translation from
which Lady Gregory said she worked. She might
have written "which I quote," for she follows Kuno
Meyer's translation of the "Wooing of Emer" sentence by sentence, and it is our puzzle to discover
how Kuno Meyer's English is worthless when he signs
it and beautiful when Lady Gregory quotes it. "A
clear case of literary transubstantiation," I said,
speaking of the miracle to a friend who happened
to be a Roman Catholic, and she gave me the defini-

tion of the catechism; the substance is the same, but the incident is different. Or it may have been that the incident is the same and the substance is different; one cannot ever be sure that one remembers theology correctly. A little examination, however, of Lady Gregory's text enabled us to dismiss the theological aspect as untenable. Here and there we find she has altered the words; Kuno Meyer's title is "The Wooing of Emer"; Lady Gregory has changed it to "The Courting of Emer" (she is writing living speech); and if Kuno Meyer wrote that Emer received Cuchulain in her bower, Lady Gregory, for the same reason, would certainly change it to "she asked him into her parlor." The word "lawn" in the sentence "and as the young girls were sitting together on their bench on the lawn they heard coming toward them a clattering of hooves, the creaking of a chariot, the grating of wheels," belongs to Lady Gregory; of that I am so sure that it would be needless for me to refer to Kuno Meyer's version of the legend.

It is no light diadem of praise that Yeats sets on Lady Gregory's brow; she has discovered a speech, he says, "as beautiful as that of Morris, and a living speech into the bargain; as she moved among her people she learnt to love the beautiful speech of those who think in Irish, and to understand that it is as true a dialect of English as the dialect that Burns wrote in." But when we look into the beautiful speech that Lady Gregory learnt "as she moved among her people," we find that it consists of no more than a dozen turns of speech, dropped into pages of English so ordinary, that redeemed from these phrases it might appear in any newspaper without attracting attention. And she does not seem to have inquired if the phrases she uses are merely local or part of the English language; she writes again and again a phrase which we find in "The Burial of Sir John Moore," evidently under the impression that she is writing something extremely Irish:

> "That the foe and the stranger should tread o'er his head,
> And we far away on the billow."

I remember having heard an Irish writer say that the line, "And we far away on the billow," marked that poem as having been written by an Irishman, a careless criticism, for it is certain that the turn of speech referred to is to be found in Shakespeare, in Milton, in Morris, even in Dickens. It is heard in England in everyday speech, though not so often as it is heard in Ireland, but it is heard, and it was a mistake on Lady Gregory's part to accept it as characteristically Irish. And her mistake shows how very little thought she gave to the question of idiomatic speech. She writes "he, himself," instead of omitting the parasitical "he" as she might very well have done. The omission would have suggested Ireland without any violation to the English language; and her attitude toward the verb "to be" is quite unconsidered and commonplace. She does not seem to have realized that in Ireland the verb "to be" is used to imply continuous action; and it

seems to me very important to have noticed that
Irish English and Provincial English preserve a distinction that has disappeared from English as
spoken in polite society and taught at Oxford and
Cambridge. Everybody in Ireland and a great many
among the English middle classes still say, "I shall
be seeing So-and-so to-night and will tell him," etc.,
and everybody in Ireland and a great number among
the English middle classes still say, "Will you be
having your letters sent on," which is surely richer
English than, "Will you have your letters sent on?"
My parlormaid always says, "Will you be dressing
for dinner to-night?" and "Will you be wearing your
silk hat to-night?" thereby distinguishing between
a simple and a continuous future action. It is our
parlormaids and their likes that carry on these
subtleties of tense, a much more important point
than the aspiration of the letter "h." I have heard
of something called Extension Lectures at Oxford
and Cambridge, but, without having the least notion
of what is meant by extension lectures, I would
suggest that some of the yeomen of Oxfordshire
should be sent for to teach the professors, learned,
no doubt, in the Latin and Greek languages, but
who have no English.

But the efforts of the uneducated to teach the
educated would be made in vain; the English language is perishing and it is natural that it should
perish with the race; race and grammatical sense
go together. The English have striven and done
a great deal in the world; the English are a tired
race, and their weariness betrays itself in the lan-

guage, and the most decadent of all are the educated
classes. We say in Ireland, "I am just after feeding
the birds," and this is a richer phrase, faintly different from "I have just fed the birds." All these
delicate shades have dropped out of modern English;
they still exist in the language, but they are no
longer used, they are slightly archaic to-day, or
provincial; and the source wherefrom the language
is refreshed—rural English—is being destroyed by
Board-schools. God help the writer who puts pen
to paper in fifty years' time, for all that will be
left of the language will be a dry shank-bone that
has been lying a long while on the dust-heap of
empire.

The difference between rural and urban speech
should have been studied by Lady Gregory, but
we fear she has not given a thought to it; she was
just content to pepper her page with a few idiomatic turns of speech which she very often does not
use correctly. "It is what I think," said Ferogain,
"that it is the fire of Conaire, the High King, and
I would be glad he not to be there to-night, for it
would be a pity if harm would come on him or his
life be shortened, for he is a branch in its blossom."
To my ear—and I come from the same country as
Lady Gregory—this is not living speech. What
the Galway, and I may add the Mayo, peasant
would say is, "And it's glad I'd be if he wasn't there
to-night." We read on and at the end of about
ten lines we come upon, "What use will it be I to
speak to him?" And then her pen fills up another
page before she thinks it necessary to drop in, "A

welcome before you," a pretty phrase which may be idiom, though I have never heard it in either Mayo or Galway. We turn the leaves and catch sight of, "And it's you have what all the men of Ulster are wanting in." If we continued a little further it is quite possible we should come upon, "And they do be saying," and "It is what I think," but we should not meet anywhere in the book an attempt to make, to mold, or to fashion a language out of the idiom of the Galway peasant, and it is astonished I am altogether that Yeats could have brought himself to compare this patchwork to the beautiful speech of Morris or of Burns, and to speak of the manuscripts that were consulted, for Lady Gregory says herself in her preface that she cannot read the manuscripts, but has translated from the French and German versions of the stories. And it is mighty hard to know how he could have reconciled himself to the adaptation of barbaric tales to the drawing-room. He must have often said to himself, "She wouldn't bowdlerize the Bible in the interests of the drawing-room." And the constant repetition of a phrase like, "And it wasn't a chair they gave him but a stool, and it not in the corner," must have ended by boring him, for no one is so easily bored by the repetition of a phrase as Yeats; it must have been that phrase that drove him out of Coole and sent him off again in pursuit of the golden-haired Isolde, whom, perhaps, the poet missed or found in Brittany or in Passy.

And it was on one of those journeys that he discovered Synge, a man of such rough and unculti-

vated aspect that he looked as if he had come out
of Derrinrush. He was not a peasant as Yeats first
supposed, but came, like all great writers, from the
middle classes; his mother had a house in Kingstown which he avoided as much as possible, and it
was in the Rue d'Arras that Yeats found him, *dans
une chambre meublée* on the fifth floor. He was on
his way back to Ireland, and might stay at Kingstown for a while, till his next quarter's allowance
came in (he had but sixty pounds a year), but as
soon as he got it he would be away to the West, to
the Arran Islands. Yeats gasped; and it was the
romance of living half one's life in the Latin Quarter and the other half in the Arran Islands that
captured Yeats's imagination. He must have lent a
willing ear to Synge's tale of an unpublished manuscript, a book which he had written about the Arran
Islands; but his interest in it doubtless flagged when
Synge told him that it was not written in peasant
speech. Synge must have answered, "But peasant
speech in Arran is Irish." Yeats remembered with
regret that this was so, for he would have preferred
Anglo-Irish; and he listened to Synge telling him
that he had some colloquial knowledge of the Irish
language. He had had to pick up a little Irish; life
in Arran would be impossible without Irish, and
Yeats awoke from his meditation.

This strange Irishman was a solitary, who only
cared to talk with peasants, and was interested in
things rather than ideas. In the Rue d'Arras it
must have been Yeats that did all the admiration,
and Synge must have been a little bored, but quite

willing that Yeats should discover in him a man of genius, a strange experience for Synge, who, however convinced he was inly of his own genius, must have wondered how Yeats had divined it, for Yeats had not pretended to feel any interest in the articles on French writers that Synge had sent round to the English Press, adding thereby sometimes a few pounds to his income, but only sometimes, for these articles were so trite that they were seldom accepted; John Eglinton confesses once a year that he could not stomach the article that Synge sent to him for publication in *Dana*; and they were so incorrectly written that Best, who knew Synge in the Rue d'Arras, tells that he used to go over them, for Synge could not write correctly at that time. Only one out of three was accepted, and the one that came to *Dana* no doubt came with all the edges worn by continual transmission through the post. It is Best that should write about Synge, for he helped him to furnish his room in the Rue d'Arras; Synge was very helpless in the actual affairs of life; he could not go out and buy furniture; Best had to go with him, and they brought home a mattress and some chairs and a bed on a barrow, and then returned to fetch the rest. There was a fiddle hanging on the wall of the garret in the Rue d'Arras, but as Synge never played it, Best began to wonder if Synge could play, and as if suspecting Best of disbelief in his music, Synge took it down one evening and drew the bow across the strings in a way that convinced Best, who played the fiddle himself; and, as if satisfied, he returned the fiddle to its nail, saying that he

only played it in the Arran Islands in the evenings
when the peasants wanted to dance. "They have
no ear for music," he said, "and do not recognize
a melody." "What!" exclaimed Best. "Well, only
as they recognize the cry of a bird or animal, not
as a musician." "Only the beat of the jig enters
their ears," Best replied in a voice tinged with melancholy.

In Yeats's imagination playing the fiddle to the
Arran Islanders, or reciting poems to them, is one
and the same thing, and he recognized instantly in
Synge the Gleeman that was in himself, but had
remained, and would remain for ever, unrealized;
and his imagination caught fire at the conjunction
of the Rue d'Arras and the Arran Islands. "Music
coming to them in the springtime," he may have
murmured. It was easy to imagine that Synge could
draw sweet music from the fiddle on the wall; for
Yeats was at that time avid of music; he had lost
his flute irreparably. . . . Synge would play new
music for him, and he would beat the time, and it
would be just the music that he wanted; his ears
were weary of the three-holed Kiltartan whistle, and
he forgot to ask himself if Lady Gregory would care
for the richer music he was bringing back with him.

"Leave off writing articles on Anatole France,
François Coppée, and Baudelaire, and come back to
Ireland and write plays for me."

Whosoever has followed this narrative so far can
see Yeats leaning forward in Synge's chair, getting
more and more interested in him at every moment,
his literary passions rising till they carried him to

his feet and set him walking about the dusty carpet from the window to the table at which Synge worked, crying:

"You must make use of your Arran experiences."

"But they are written; only no one will publish my book."

"Your book is not written in the language of the peasant; I don't mean Irish, but Anglo-Irish, peasant idiom. You'll be able to translate from the Irish, and so thicken the idiom. Come to Ireland and write folk-plays for me. A play about Arran."

"But the play I've shown you——"

"Is of no account. The language will help you to know your own people."

And, better than any description, this dialogue represents the meeting of Yeats and Synge in the Rue d'Arras, Synge's large impassive face into which hardly any light of expression ever came, listening to Yeats with a look of perplexity moving over its immobility, and Yeats's passion, purely literary, steadily mounting.

"You must come back and perfect yourself in the language. You must live among the people again," he reports himself to have said. "You must come to Ireland. A theater is building in Dublin for the production of folk-plays."

"Building!"

"Well, it will soon be building"; and he told Synge how Miss Horniman, a lady of literary tastes and ample income, had decided to give to Dublin what no other city in an English-speaking country possessed—a subventioned theater. "Write me an

Arran play. We will open the theater with it"; and he began to speak of Synge's immediate return.

"As soon as the summer comes again."

But that promise would not satisfy Yeats. Synge must return to Arran at once.

"I should die," Synge is reported to have answered.

"Not before you have written the masterpiece." Yeats's answer as related by himself, and Yeats continued day after day to subjugate Synge's mind, till one Saturday evening, after a talk lasting till long past midnight, Synge declared his adherence to the new creed.

"When a man's mind is made up, his feet must set out on the way." Yeats's own words as reported by himself. He allowed, however, Synge to wait for two little cheques which were due to him for articles, and as soon as he received them he folded his luggage according to promise, and a few days after presented himself at the Nassau Hotel, and was introduced to Lady Gregory, who, of course, perceived there was something on his mind. She encouraged him to confide in her, and he confided to her the story of his health, and she very kindly took his part against Yeats, who was all for Arran, not for the middle island, for there only Irish is spoken. "And the dialect is what we want."

"That may be, Mr. Yeats, but Mr. Synge may not be able to stand the climate in the autumn." And she turned to Synge, who told her that the best time would be a little later, when the people would be out digging in their potato fields. Lady Gregory agreed that this was so, and after some demur Yeats yielded, as he always does to Lady Gregory, and the three were of one mind that the mild climate of Wicklow was most suitable for "listening."

"The tinkers meet there in the autumn."

"You mustn't miss the gathering."

He went away next morning, and his admirers were overjoyed when he wrote to them a few days afterward saying that he had been fortunate enough to fall in with a band of tinkers driving their shaggy ponies, bony horses, and reliable asses up a hillside, making for their annual assemblage. They were exchanging their wives and arranging the roads they were to take, the signs to be left at the cross-roads, the fairs they were to attend, and the meeting-places for the following year. He had been very lucky, for he had fallen in with the tinkers at the moment when a tall, lean man turned to run after a screaming girl. "Black Hell to your sowl! you've followed me so far, you'll follow me to the end!" he roared, seizing her by the wrist, a girl no doubt that had yielded to the call of the vagrant and had begun to regret her comfortable stead.

Without a trull, it is true, or the desire to win or to capture one, Synge, by his harmless appearance and his fiddle, gained the good-will of the tinker and his wife, and he followed the fortune of this family, listening to their talk as they strolled along the lanes, cadging and stealing as they went, squatting at eventide on the side of a dry ditch. Like a hare in a gap he listened, and when he had mastered every turn of their speech he left the tinker and turned into the hills, spending some weeks with a cottager, joining a little later another group of tinkers, accompanied by a servant-girl who had suddenly wearied of scrubbing and mangling, boiling for pigs, cooking, and working dough, and making beds in the evening. It would be better, she had thought, to lie under the hedgerow; and in telling me of this girl, Synge seemed to be telling me his own story. He, too, disliked the regular life of his mother's house, and preferred to wander with the tinkers, and when tired of them to lie abed smoking with a peasant, and awake amid the smells of shag and potato-skins in the sieve in the corner of the room. He told me how after breakfast he scrambled over a low wall out of which grew a single hawthorn, and looked round for a place where he might loosen his strap, and when that job was done he kept on walking ahead thinking out the dialogue of his plays, modifying it at every stile after a gossip with some herdsman or pig-jobber, whomever he might meet, returning through the cold spring evening, when the stars shine brightly through the naked trees, licking his lips, appreciating the fine flavor of some drunkard's oath or blasphemy.

He extended his tour through Connaught, spending a long time in my own native town, Castlebar, where it is said he picked up no less than three or four turns of speech, and on his return to Dublin he had collected some hundreds in the different counties, and from different classes, and these he was able to work up together, creating what amounted practically to a small language understandable by everybody who knows English, but sufficiently far removed from ordinary speech to give his plays an air that none others have—that air of aloofness, of art, which Yeats deems necessary, which we all deem necessary, though we differ as to how it may be obtained. Synge had done what none had done before—he had discovered that it was possible to write beautifully in peasant idiom. Everybody could write it, Lady Gregory as well as another, but no one but Synge could write beautifully in it.

Yeats was at this time in the hands of the Fays and a Committee, and the performances of the National Theater were given in different halls; and when Synge came up from the country to read "Riders to the Sea" to the company, Yeats, who did not wish to have any misunderstanding on the subject, cried "Sophocles" across the table, and, fearing that he was not impressive enough, he said: "No, Æschylus." And that same afternoon he said to me in Grafton Street: "I would I were as sure of your future and of my own as I am of Synge's." One of those exaggerated appreciations that annoy and estrange, and, when I heard this one-act play, it seemed very little more than the contents of Synge's notebook, an experiment in language rather than a work of art, a preparatory essay; he seemed to me to have contented himself with relating a painful rather than a dramatic story, his preoccupation being to discover a style, a vehicle of expression, and it was not until Synge wrote "The Well of the Saints" that I began to feel that a man of genius had been born unto Ireland.

Irishmen had written well before Synge, but they had written well by casting off Ireland; but here was a man inspired by Ireland, a country that had not inspired any art since the tenth or twelfth century, a country to which it was fatal to return. Was Synge the exception, and was he going to find his fortune in Ireland? His literary fortune, for "The Well of the Saints" had very nearly emptied the Abbey Theater. The audiences had always been scanty—fifty or sixty spectators—but after the performance of "The Well of the Saints" we were but twenty, the patrons of the stalls being the Yeats family, Sarah Purser, William Bailey, John Eglinton, Æ, Longworth, and dear Edward, who supported the Abbey Theater, believing himself in duty bound to do so. He was averse from peasant plays, and "The Well of the Saints" annoyed him very much, but he held on till the "Playboy" was produced. "All this sneering at Catholic practices is utterly distasteful to me. Don't think I don't see it. I understand it very well, and I can hear it all, and the whining voice of the proselytizer. I never will go against my opinions. When I hear the Sacred Name I assure you——"

"You mean the name of God, Edward, don't you?"

"I never like to mention it. The Sacred Name is sufficient."

"But if you are speaking French you say 'mon Dieu' at every sentence. If it isn't wrong in one language, how can it be wrong in another?"

A smile trickled across Edward's face, round and large and russet as a ripe pumpkin, and he muttered:

"*Mon ami Moore, mon ami Moore.*" He was in the Abbey the first night of the "Playboy," and on my return from Paris he told me that though the noise was great, he had heard enough blasphemy to keep him out of the theater from thenceforth, and next morning he had read in the papers that Ireland had been exhibited in a shameful light as an immoral country.

"And oddly enough, the scene of the immorality is your own native town, George."

He told me that the hooting had begun about the middle of the third act at the words: "If all the women of Mayo were standing before me, and they in their——" He shrank from completing the sentence, and muttered something about the evocation of a disgusting spectacle.

"I agree with you, Edward, that shift evokes a picture of blay calico; but the delightful underwear of Madame——"

"Now, George."

And then, amused at his own folly, which he can no more overcome than anybody else, he began to laugh, shaking like a jelly, puffing solemnly all the while at his churchwarden.

"The indignation was so great that I thought sometimes the pit was going to break in. 'Lower the bloody curtain, and give us something we bloody well want,' a well-filled pit kept on shouting." And looking at Edward I imagined I could see him in the stalls near the stage, turning round in terror, his face growing purpler and purpler. "All the same," he said, "though the pain that Synge's irreverent remarks caused me is very great, I disapprove altogether of interrupting a performance. But Yeats shouldn't have called in the police. A Nationalist should never call for the police."

"But, Edward, supposing a housebreaker forces his way in here or into Tillyra?"

He said that that was different, and after wasting some time in discussion regarding the liberty of speech and the rights of property, he asked me if I had read the play, and I told him that on reading about the tumult in the Abbey Theater I had telegraphed from Paris for a copy, and that the first lines convinced me that Ireland had at last begotten a masterpiece—the first lines of Pegeen Mike's letter to Mr. Michael O'Flaherty, general dealer, in Castlebar, for six yards of stuff for to make a yellow gown, a pair of boots with lengthy heels on them and brassy eyes, a hat is suited for a wedding day, a fine tooth-comb. "Never was there such a picture of peasant life in a few lines"; and at every sentence my admiration increased. At the end of the act I cried out: "A masterpiece! a masterpiece! Of course, they were insulted." The girls coming in with presents for the young stranger pleased me, but a cold wind of doubt seemed to blow over the pages when the father came on the stage, a bloody bandage about his head, and—"Edward—you're asleep!"

"No, I'm listening."

"So clearly did I see disaster in that bloody bandage that I could hardly read through the third act. But you see nothing in the play."

"Yes, I do, only it's a little thing. Shawn Keogh

205

is a very good character, and the Widow Quinn is not bad either."

"But the language, Edward."

"You have made up your mind that this play is a masterpiece, but I am not going to give in to you."

"But the style, Edward?"

"It isn't English. I like the Irish language and the English language, but I don't like the mixture"; and then puffing at his pipe for a few seconds he said, "I like the intellectual drama."

The conversation turned upon Ibsen, and we talked pleasantly until one in the morning, and then bidding him good-night I returned to Ely Place, delighted at my own perspicacity, for there could be no doubt that it was the bloody bandage that caused the row in the Abbey Theater.

"The author and Yeats expect too much from the audience; the language is beautiful, but——" I had admitted to Edward that I had only glanced through the third act, and Edward had answered, "If you had read the whole of it you might be of my opinion." It wasn't likely that Edward and I should agree about the "Playboy," but it might well be that I was judging it hurriedly, and it would have been wiser, I reflected, to have read the play through before attempting to explain why the humor of the audience had changed suddenly, and I resolved to read the play next morning. But my dislike of reading is so great that I overlooked it, and when Yeats came to see me, instead of the praise which he had come to hear, and which he was craving for, he heard some rather vain dissertations and only half-hearted praise. Again my impulsiveness was my ruin. The play would have been understood if it had been read carefully, and the evening would have been one of exaltation, whereas it went by mournfully, Yeats in the chimney-corner listening to suggestions that would preserve the comedy note. He went away depressed, saying, however, that it would be as well that I should write to Synge about his play, since I liked the greater part. But he did not think that Synge would make any alterations. And the letter I sent to Synge was superficial. I hope he destroyed it. He was glad that his play had pleased me, but he could not alter the third act. It had been written again and again—thirteen times. That is all I remember of his letter, interesting on account of the circumstances in which it was written and the rarity of Synge's correspondence. It is a pity his letter was destroyed and no copy kept; our letters would illuminate the page that I am now writing, exhibiting us both in our weakness and our strength— Synge in his strength, for if the play had been altered we should have all been disgraced, and it was Yeats' courage that saved us in Dublin. He did not argue, he piled affirmation upon affirmation, and he succeeded in the end . . . but we will not anticipate.

But if Dublin would not listen to the "Playboy," Dublin read the text; edition after edition was published, and we talked the "Playboy" round our firesides. How we talked! Week after week, month after month, the Abbey Theater declining all the while, till at last the brothers Fay rose in revolt against Yeats' management, accusing him of hindering the dramatic movement by producing no plays except those written by his intimate friends. Yeats repelled the accusation by offering to submit those that he had rejected to the judgment of Professor Tyrrell, a quite unnecessary concession on the part of Yeats, for Willie Fay is but an amusing Irish comedian, and it was presumptuous for him and his brother to set themselves against a poet. They resigned, and one night Yeats came to me with the grave news that the Fays had seceded.

"I feel I must talk to somebody," he said, flinging himself into a chair.

Æ is the only man who can distribute courage, but Yeats and Æ were no longer friends, and I was but a poor purveyor. It is true that I told him, and without hesitation, that the secession of the Fays was a blessing in disguise, and that now he was master in his own house the Abbey Theater would begin to flourish, and it would have been well if I had confined myself to pleasant prophesying; but very few can resist the temptation to give good advice.

"One thing, Yeats, I have always had in mind, but never liked to tell you; it is that the way you come down the steps from the stage and stride up the stalls and alight by Lady Gregory irritates the audience, and if you will allow me to be perfectly frank, I will tell you that she is a little too imposing, too suggestive of Corinne or Madame de Staël. Corinne and Madame de Staël were one and the same person, weren't they? But you don't know, Yeats, do you?"

And so I went on pulling the cord, letting down volumes of water upon poor Yeats, who crouched and shivered. The water, always cold, was at times very icy, for instance when I said that his dreams of reviving Jonson's "Volpone" must be abandoned.

"If you aren't very careful, Yeats, the Academic idea will overgrow the folk." And Yeats went away overwhelmed, and I saw no more of him for many months, not until it became known that Synge's persistent ill health had at last brought him to a private hospital, where he lay waiting an operation. "He lives by the surgeon's knife," Yeats said to me, and I welcomed his advice to save myself from the anguish of going to see a man dying of cancer. And while Synge perished slowly, Gogarty recovered in the same hospital after an operation for appendicitis. One man's scale drops while another goes up. As I write this line I can see Synge, whom I shall never see again with my physical eyes, sitting thick and straight in my arm-chair, his large, uncouth head, and flat, ashen-colored face with two brown eyes looking at me, not unsympathetically. A thick, stubbly growth of hair starts out of a strip of forehead like black twigs out of the head of a broom. I see a ragged mustache, and he sits bolt upright in my chair, his legs crossed, his great country shoe spreading over the carpet. The conversation about us is of literature, but he looks as bored as Jack Yeats does in the National Gallery. . . . Synge and Jack Yeats are like each other in this, neither take the slightest interest in anything except life, and in their own deductions from life; educated men, both

of them, but without æsthetics, and Yeats' stories
that Synge read the classics and was a close student
of Racine is a piece of Yeats' own academic mind.
Synge did not read Racine oftener than Jack Yeats
looks at Titian, and no conclusion should be drawn
from the fact that among his scraps of verse are to
be found translations from Villon and Marot; they
are merely exercises in versification; he was curious
to see if Anglo-Irish idiom could be used in poetry;
Villon wrote largely in the slang of his time, therefore Villon was selected; and whosoever reads Villon
dips into Marot and reads "Une Ballade à Double
Refrain." And that is all, for, despite his beautiful
name, Marot is an insipid poet. I am sorry that
Yeats fell into the mistake of attributing much reading to Synge; he has little love of character and
could not keep himself from putting rouge on
Synge's face and touching up his eyebrows. He
showed greater discrimination when he said, "You
will never know as much about French poetry as
Arthur Symons. Come to Ireland and write plays
for me." And for his great instinct we must forgive
him his little sins of reason. He very rightly speaks
of Synge as a solitary, and it is interesting to specu-
late what made him a solitary. Was it the sense that
death was lurking round the corner always, and
the sense that he possessed no social gifts that helped
to drive him out into the Arran Islands where he
knew nobody, and to the Latin Quarter behind the
Luxembourg Gardens where nobody knew him? A
man soon perceives if he be interested in others and
if others be interested in him, and if he contribute

nothing and get nothing, he will slink away as
Synge did.

Yeats had called him out of obscurity for a little
while, and now he was to pass from us into the
night that never melts into dawn, unless glory be
the dead man's dawn. It seemed a cruel fate that
decreed that Synge must die before his play could
be revived in Dublin, but his fate was cruel from
the beginning. Yeats tells me that these lines were
found among his papers: "I am five-and-twenty
to-day; I wonder will the five-and-twenty years
before me be as unhappy as those I have passed
through." And well might he have doubted that
his middle life would be less unpleasant. He received Yeats's belief in his genius, and that was all.
He wrote but little, but that little was his own: *Mon
verre n'est pas grand, mais je bois dans mon verre.*
His last strength he reserved for "Deirdre," working
at the play whenever he could, determined to finish
it before he died. But he wrote slowly, and the disease moved quickly from cell to cell, and before
the last writing was accomplished Synge laid aside
the pen and resigned himself to death. It is curious
that he should have met his old friend Best on his
way to the hospital. Best tells these things signifi-
cantly. He asked Synge if he were going in for an
operation. Synge answered no; and when Best
called to see him in the hospital, he found Synge
clinging to a little hope, though he knew there was
none, saying that people often got better when
nobody expected them to get better; and he
seemed to experience some disappointment when

Best did not answer promptly that that was so.

He used to speak of "Deirdre" as his last disappointment; but another awaited him. An hour before he died he asked the nurse to wheel his bed into a room whence he could see the Wicklow mountains, the hills where he used to go for long solitary walks, and he was wheeled into the room, but the mountains could not be seen from the windows; to see them it was necessary to stand up, and Synge could not stand or sit up in his bed, so his last wish remained ungratified, and he died with tears in his eyes.

VIII

From a publishing point of view Synge's death seems to have done him a great deal of good. Almost at once quarto after quarto of each play was issued, and three or four hundred copies of each were sold straight away; a complete edition was contemplated, comprising the plays and his Wicklow Sketches and the Blaskit Islands; the newspaper articles that he had written upon the French poets—the poets that in Yeats's words he would never understand as well as Arthur Symons, were all sought for and discovered, and, what was still more important, Yeats decided upon a revival of the "Playboy."

We were all agog and prayed that the play would be allowed to pass without protest; it seemed very likely that this would be permitted, for Synge's success had sobered Dublin, especially its journalists. A sad thing it is for a journalist to find the play that he has described as contemptible, as an insult to Ireland, accepted by all the world as a masterpiece, and the newspaper that smells like a musty sacristy held its peace, or only sent one poor little voice to utter a faint squeak in the gallery from time to time. The play was the same, the text was the same, the caste was the same with one exception. The part of the "Playboy" was entrusted to Fred

O'Donovan, and thereby hangs a tale that I should like to tell.

Synge had written the play knowing that the part of Christy Mahon was going to be played by Willie Fay, a little man five feet three or four; allusions to his size had crept into the text, and Willie Fay, who is a true artist, had exhibited Christy Mahon in the condition of a wayfarer who had been wandering for at least a fortnight, sleeping in a barn when he could find an open door, and a dry ditch when he could not find a barn. A weary and forlorn Christy would appeal not only to the pity but to the imagination of women, and if Willie Fay had been a broad-shouldered, stalwart, fine young fellow, he might have exaggerated the disreputable appearance of Christy Mahon with impunity. But as has been said, he is not more than five feet four or five, and the very qualities which made him so admirable an exponent of the part of Michael O'Dowd in "The Well of the Saints" were against him in the "Playboy." An actor's stock-in-trade is his personality, and Fay's personality is of the crab-apple kind, and it was necessary that the story that Christy had to tell should be told with an engaging simplicity; the audience must sympathize with the son whom the father persecuted because he would not marry an old woman; the audience must see the father raise the scythe, and poor Christy, the loy, to defend himself. The father is cloven by the loy, but that is an accident. I did not see Willie Fay in the part, but it is easy to imagine how his reading would alienate the sympathy of the audience. He might point to certain passages which would support his reading; no doubt he could; but these are not the passages that should be brought into light. It just comes to this, that no man living can play the two parts, the "Playboy" and the blind man in "The Well of the Saints," any more than any man can play "Hamlet" and "Othello" satisfactorily. A different personality is required, and Fred O'Donovan is a well-favored young man whom any girl would like for his appearance, and he told the story of how he had killed his father, simply, almost innocently, as an unfortunate accident that had happened to him, and Pegeen Mike pitied him. He was no doubt occasionally against the words, but that was unavoidable; the part cannot be played any other way. A few phrases were dropped out here and there; in the second act the bandage was no longer blood-stained, and in the third, when Christy went out to kill his father for the second time, the father came in on all fours; this kept the comedy note, which was in danger of being lost, for Pegeen Mike is very angry with Christy in the third act, believing him to be a mere braggart—the weak spot in the play, but it passes rapidly; and it was interesting to speak about it to Miss Maire O'Neill, who played to Pegeen Mike out of a very clear vision of the character and with all the finish of a true artist.

"However we look at it," I said, "we seem up against a contradiction. It is difficult to see how Pegeen Mike could have brought the peat from the fire to burn her lover's feet, and three minutes after rush to the door to watch him leaving her for ever;

going away with his father back to their own country-side. I wonder if you could speak your words so that the audience would understand that your anger against Christy was simulated?" She said she didn't think she could. "Well, imperfection is often a zest," I answered, and left the theater thinking that Fate had allowed Synge to accomplish very little; two one-act plays, purely tentative, a three-act play upon an old theme, "The Tinker's Wedding," and a dramatic version of the legend of "Deirdre," which it would have been well for me to have read before writing this page, for the printed page alone is veracious; our ears, however quick, cannot take in the whole of a play. But the book is not on the table, nor in the house, nor at the bookseller's round the corner, and it is well that it isn't, for it is pleasant sometimes to believe that one's ears are trustworthy, and, amid my oral experiences, I have none more agreeable than the music of the dialogue about Naisi's grave, though memory recalls but one tiny phrase: "Death is a poor untidy thing." The writing of "Deirdre" in peasant speech was Yeats's idea; and the text bears witness that when Synge had written an act he began to feel that peasant speech is unsuited to tragedy. Only the second and third acts are of much account, only these are finished, and to finish the first act Synge would have had to redeem it from peasant speech, ridiculous and out of place at the court of Kings, though the Kings be but shepherd Kings. There is less idiom in the second act than in the first, and none at all in the third; and when I mentioned these things to Yeats he told me that Synge had begun to weary of the limitations of peasant speech. . . . It is difficult to imagine Synge writing about the middle classes and their tea-parties, or the upper classes and their motor cars. Would Synge's talent have been applied to legend or to history? Or would he have been suborned by Tree and have written for a London audience? One may indulge in many curious conjectures, but it would be more interesting to tell how Lady Gregory came to the rescue of the Abbey Theater and saved it after the secession of the Fays. She could write easily and well, and had shown aptitude for writing rural anecdotes in dialogue. It is an open secret that she was Yeats's collaborator in the "Pot of Broth" and in "Cathleen ni Houlihan," and feeling that the fate of the movement depended upon her, she undertook the great responsibility of keeping the theater open with her pen, writing play after play, three or four a year, writing in the space of ten years something like thirty plays. Is there one among us who would undertake such a job of work and accomplish it as well as Lady Gregory? The plays that flowed from her pen so rapidly are not of equal merit, nor is there anyone that compares with the "Playboy," but all are meritorious, all are conceived and written in the same style. She is herself in her little plays, a Galway woman telling rural anecdotes that amuse her woman's mind, and telling them gracefully, never trying to philosophize, to explain, but just content to pick her little flower, to place it in a vase for our amusement, and to go on to another flower. "The Rising of the Moon" is a very pretty bit of artless dramatic writing, with a fine folk flavor, hardly written, told as the people would tell it by their firesides. "Hyacinth Halvey" has been played all over the world with success; and one must not look too scornfully at success; a certain measure is necessary in a theater. "Spreading the News" is even more natural than "The Rising of the Moon"; it is just the gossip of a village thrown easily into dramatic form. Nobody could have done Lady Gregory's plays as well as she did them herself, and "The Workhouse Ward" must not be forgotten, a trifle somewhat sentimental, but just what was wanted to carry on the Abbey Theater, which, for a moment, could do very well without the grim humors of Synge. We must get it into our heads that the Abbey Theater would have come to naught but for Lady Gregory's talent for rolling up little anecdotes into one-act plays. She has written three-act plays, but her art and her humor and her strength rarely carry her beyond a one-act. The best of her three-act plays is probably "The Image," in which she sets a whole village prattling, the characters go on talking about very little, yet always talking pleasantly, and we go away pleasantly amused and pleasantly weary. The telling of "The Jackdaw" is a little confused, but whosoever writes thirty plays in ten years will sometimes be sprightly, sometimes confused, sometimes languid, and will sometimes choose subjects that cannot very well be written. She has told that she wrote plays in the first instance because she believed it to be her duty to write for the Abbey Theater, and afterwards, no doubt, took

an interest in the writing for its own sake, and in
this her story nowise differs from many another's,
chance playing in our lives a greater part than we
would care to admit. She never would have written
a play if she had not met Yeats, nor would Synge,
who is now looked upon as an artist as great as
Donatello or Benvenuto Cellini, and perhaps I
should not have gone to Ireland if I had not met
Yeats, and if I had not gone to Ireland I should not
have written "The Lake" or "The Untilled Field,"
or the book I am now writing.

So all the Irish movement rose out of Yeats and
returns to Yeats. He wrote beautiful lyrics and
narrative poems from twenty till five-and-thirty, and
then he began to feel that his mission was to give a
literature to Ireland that should be neither Hebrew,
nor Greek, nor French, nor German, nor English—a
literature that should be like herself, that should
wear her own face and speak with her own voice, and
this he could only do in a theater. We have all
wanted repertory theaters and art theaters and
literary theaters, but these words are vain words
and mean nothing. Yeats knew exactly what he
wanted; he wanted a folk theater, for if Ireland were
ever to produce any literature he knew that it would
have to begin in folk, and he has his reward. Ireland
speaks for the first time in literature in the Abbey
Theater.

IX

But my thoughts have begun to wander from Synge and Lady Gregory and Yeats to all the critics of "Ave" who have complained that instead of creating types of character like Esther Waters or Dick Lennox, I have wasted my time describing my friends, mere portrait-painting. But was not Dick Lennox Dick Maitland? And in writing "Esther Waters" did I not think of one heroic woman? We all have models, and if we copy the model intelligently, a type emerges. In writing "Patience," Gilbert thought he was copying Oscar Wilde, whereas he was drawing Willie Yeats out of the womb of Time; and when Flaubert wrote "Bouvard and Pecuchet" he thought he was creating, but he was really performing the same kind offices for Plunkett and Gill, giving them names much more significant than the names they are known by in Ireland, but doing no more.

A letter from Plunkett regretting that a broken leg prevented him from being present at the great dinner at the Shelbourne Hotel was alluded to in "Ave," and in "Salve" he was whirled rapidly before the reader's eyes as he repaired on an outside car to an agricultural meeting with Yeats, but no portrait of him has appeared, and the reader has not heard how we became acquainted. It was dear Edward who brought the meeting about, overriding Plunkett, who is a timid man, and fears to meet anyone with a sense of humor; he dreads laughter as a cat dreads cold water. But Edward insisted.

"You are both public men and you cannot avoid knowing each other sooner or later, and now is the moment for you both to take the plunge."

And one evening at the end of a long summer's day a lean man of medium height, courteous and dignified, clearly of the Protestant ascendancy, came forward through the dusk of a drawing-room—the lamps had just been lighted—to thank me for having accepted his invitation to dinner. I liked his well-designed oval face, his scanty beard, and his eyes pleasantly gray and perplexed. A long, straight, well-formed nose divided the face, and a broad strip of forehead lay underneath the brown stubbly crop of hair that covered a small round skull. The arrival of a guest obliged him to turn away, but before doing so he shook hands with me a second time, and in this supplementary handshake it seemed to me that that something which is genuine in him had passed into his hand. What is in the mind transpires in the hand; and this is quite natural, and it is still more natural that what is not in the mind should not transpire in the hand. There is no grip in Gill's hand; one remembers its color and its dangle, that is all; and his manner, though pleasing, is flimsy; not that Plunkett's manners are hard and disagreeable; on the contrary, they are rather soft and affable. But there is something pathetic in him which strikes one at first in the brow, in the gray eyes under it, and all over the flat face marked with a prominent nose, and in the hesitancy of his speech, which straggles with his beard, and his exclamation, "Er—er—er," without which he cannot speak half a dozen words.

So much did I see of Plunkett in the red twilight, with glimpses through it of silken gowns, of shoulders and arms, all effaced, a dim background. One felt on entering his room that his dinner was not a sexual one. Everybody seemed anxious to speak on what is known as serious subjects, but restrained himself out of deference to the gowns. But as soon as sex had cleared out cigars were lighted and important matters were on the verge of discussion. Plunkett was visibly relieved, and with brightening face he began to talk. He talked rapidly, he broke down, now he lost the thread and sought for it, er—er—er; the uneconomic man in his economic holding, er—er—er, is a danger to the state, and the economic man in his uneconomic holding, er—er —er, is probably a greater danger, and to relieve the producer of the cost of distribution is the object of the Coöperative movement. It seemed to me that we could have discovered what he was saying in any sixpenny text-book, but Plunkett was so interested that it is not likely he perceived he was boring the company and me.

"Plunkett," I said to myself, "is one of those men whose genius is in practical work, and who, in order to obtain foundation for his work, seeks blindly for first principles; as soon as we get to practical work he will talk quite differently." And I looked forward to questioning him on matters about which I had definite information. But as I was about to speak, a pallid parliamentarian, whose name I have forgotten, weary like myself of the economic man and the uneconomic holding, turned to me to get news of O'Brien, whose headquarters were in the County of Mayo, thinking that, as I came from that part of the country, I should be able to tell him something regarding the chances of an anti-grazing movement. It so happened that I had had that morning a long talk with my agent about Mayo, and forgetful for the moment of my intention to question Plunkett about the egg industry, overborne by a desire to escape from platitudes, I began to repeat all I had heard, saying I could vouch for the facts, my agent being an old friend on whose veracity and accuracy of observation I could depend.

The parliamentarian leaned forward anxious to get the truth from me, and whatever information might be picked up on the way to pad his speeches for the next session; and perhaps what I was saying, by force of contrast with Plunkett's generalities, attracted the attention of those present, and as they leaned forward interested to hear some facts the humor of the situation began to tickle me. The absent O'Brien had become the center of interest, and a cloud of melancholy appeared in Plunkett's face, his mechanical smile broke down, he seemed troubled and irritated. "Then," I said, "it is really true that he delights in his talk of the economic man and the uneconomic holding—er—er—er, and *vice versa*," and I began to doubt if Nature in her endless discrepancies had really created such a discrepancy as I had imagined: a practical man unable to get to practical work before drinking platitudes from a sixpenny text-book.

By this time my knowledge of O'Brien's movement was exhausted, and I should have been pleased to change the subject, but the parliamentarian was insistent, and had it not been for the intervention of Plunkett I should not have been able to rid myself of him. But Plunkett, unable to endure rivalry with O'Brien for another moment, turned to the pallid parliamentarian, saying that in two or three years his coöperative followers would be masters of all local assemblies, and he spoke in such a way as to lead the gentleman to understand that enough had been said about O'Brien.

At last my chance seemed to have come to get a word with Plunkett regarding the details of his scheme for the regeneration of Ireland. I was at that time interested in a Coöperative Egg Society, which had been started at Plunkett's instigation by my brother; he had discovered, after a little experience, that more extended business arrangements were necessary if the profits were to cover the expenses; and knowing more of this matter than I did about O'Brien's anti-grazing movement I moved up toward Plunkett, anxious to hear his opinion and to try to induce him to modify the measures he was taking for spreading these societies all over the country. At the mention of the blessed word "cooperation" Plunkett's face brightened, and he began to discuss the subject, but in general terms, more, it seemed to me, for the edification of the parliamentarian than for any practical purpose. As I knew from my brother all about the general theory and only wanted to study its application, I returned to the details again and again, going into figures, showing how the system could not be carried out exactly as Plunkett had dreamed it, and having some experience about the conveying of eggs from Pulborough to London (they arrived nearly always broken; true that the South Coast Railway paid for the breakage without murmuring; all the same it was annoying to have one's eggs broken), I tried to learn from him if more reliance could be placed upon Irish railways.

"One cannot discuss," I remember him saying, "the fate of the individual egg."

"But, Plunkett, your whole system rests on the individual egg," a fact which he could not contravene and so he became melancholy. "Nothing," I said to myself, "bores him so much as detail. He loves dreaming like every other Irishman," and we did not see each other for many a month until we met in Gill's rooms in Clare Street, or in the offices of the *Daily Express*, after the Boer War had driven me out of England. The *Daily Express* had been bought by Plunkett, or it had come into Plunkett's control, and Gill had been appointed editor, and feeling, I suppose, that it was necessary to redeem the *Express* from its sectarian tone, Gill dared one day to write of Dr. Walsh as the Archbishop of Dublin, causing a great uproar among the subscribers. An attack on the Great Southern Railway caused the withdrawal of a great advertisement; but nothing mattered so long as Plunkett and Gill succeeded in convincing Gerald Balfour that what Ireland needed was a new State Department of Agriculture and Art. Like all dreamers, Plunkett is an inveigling fellow, and he inveigled Gerald Balfour, and Gerald Balfour inveigled his brother, and his brother inveigled the ministry, and the end of all this inveigling was a grant of one hundred and seventy thousand a year to found a Department of Agriculture and Art in Ireland. But the inveigler had been inveigled; Gill's ambition stretched beyond mere agriculture; how Art was gathered into the scheme I do not know, probably as a mere makeweight; the mission of the Department was the reformation of Ireland, and, from end to end, the very task that Flaubert's heroes . . . but it would be well to tell my readers who were the heroes of this not very well-known book.

Bouvard and Pecuchet were two little city clerks, who became acquainted in a way that seemed marvelous to both of them. It was their wont to seek a certain bench after dinner, and to spend what remained of their dinner-hour watching the passersby. One day they took off their hats to mop their brows: Bouvard looked into Pecuchet's, Pecuchet looked into Bouvard's, both were amazed by the coincidence; they had gotten their hats from the same hatter! A great friendship arose out of this circumstance, the twain meeting every day, delighting more and more in each other's company; and when Bouvard inherits considerable wealth he renounces his clerkship and invites Pecuchet to come to live

with him. The first thing to do is to get a fine
appartement, but life in a flat becomes monotonous;
they must perforce do something to relieve the
tedium of an unmeasured idleness; market garden-
ing strikes their imagination, for a reason which I
have forgotten, and having read the best books on
the subject of vegetable growing they buy some
land, but only to discover after considerable loss of
money that the vegetables grown by their neighbors,
ignorant peasants, are far better than theirs and
cheaper. It is thirty years since I read "Bouvard
and Pecuchet," but nobody forgets the story of the
melon. Bouvard and Pecuchet had learnt all the
material facts about the growing of melons from
books, and one would have thought that that was
enough, but no; the melon is one of the most immoral of vegetables, and if great care be not taken
it will contract incestuous alliances, uncles and
aunts, sisters and brothers; and Bouvard and
Pecuchet were not sufficiently concerned with the
morals of their pet. They were content to watch
it growing day after day, bigger and bigger, exceeding the size of all melons; prodigious, gigantic,
brobdingnagian, were the adjectives they murmured.
At last the day came to cut the wonderful fruit. It
was splendid on the table; it had all the qualities
that a melon should have, all but one—it was uneat-
able. Bouvard spat his mouthful into the grate;
Pecuchet spat his, I think, out of the window.

Bouvard and Pecuchet turn from agriculture to
Druidic remains, and Pecuchet feels that his life
would be incomplete without a love adventure. The

serving-maid seems to him suitable to his enterprise; and having assurances of her purity from her, emboldened, he follows her into the wood-shed. A painful disease is the strange ending of this romance, and as soon as Pecuchet is restored to health the twain are inspired to write a tragedy. But having no knowledge of dramatic construction they send to Paris for books on the subject, and in these books they read of the faults that the critics have discovered in Shakespeare and Molière and Racine and other famous writers, and they resolve to avoid these faults. Pecuchet wanders from tragedy to Biblical criticism, and no one forgets the scene between him and Monsieur le Curé under a dripping umbrella. Biblical criticism is succeeded by another folly, and then by another; I do not remember the book in detail, but the best established theories are always being overturned by the simplest fact.

This great book was described as an extravaganza by the critics of the time, and it was said that Flaubert's admiration of human stupidity was so great that he piled absurdity upon absurdity, exceeding the modesty of Nature; but nothing is so immodest as Nature, and when she picked up the theme suggested by Flaubert and developed it human stupidity gave forth flowers that would have delighted and saddened him, saddened him, for it is difficult to imagine him writing his book if he had lived to watch the Department at work in Ireland. He would have turned away regretfully saying, "I have been anticipated; Plunkett and Gill have transferred my dreams into real life," and he would have

admitted that some of their experiments equaled
those that he had in mind—for instance, the calf
that the Department sent to the Cork Exhibition
as an example of the new method of rearing calves.

Bouvard and Pecuchet (we will drop the Plunkett
and Gill) invited all the Munster farmers to view
the animal, and they had been impressed by its appearance, a fine happy beast it seemed to be, but
very soon it began to droop, causing a good deal of
anxiety, and the news of its death was brought one
evening to the Imperial Hotel where Bouvard and
Pecuchet were lodging. After a hurried consulta-
tion Pecuchet looked at his watch. "We have several hours before us to find a similar calf." "But,
Pecuchet, do you think that we are justified, er—er
—er, in replacing a dead calf by a healthy one?"
At this question Pecuchet flamed a little. "The
honor of the Department is at stake," he said; "we
must think of the Department." "The Department,
er—er—er, is judged by its results." Again a light
flamed into Pecuchet's eyes, and though he did not
say it, it was clear that he looked upon the Department as something existing of and through itself
which could not be judged by its mere works. "There
has been some foul play. Our enemies," he muttered, and sent a telegram to the expert of the Department to come down at once. A post-mortem was
ordered, but no new fact transpired, and the advice
of the vet. was that the new method should be
abandoned and the second calf be fed upon milk and
linseed meal, and upon this natural diet it prospered
exceedingly.

Bouvard and Pecuchet's experiments were not limited to teaching the finest herdsmen in the world how to raise cattle; it was necessary that they should spread themselves over the entire range of human activities in order to get rid of the one hundred and seventy thousand a year that the Department was receiving from the State. A good many hundred pounds were lost in a shoe factory in Ballina, but what are a few hundred pounds when one is dealing with one hundred and seventy thousand a year? And there were moments of sad perplexity in the lives of our reformers. A gleam came into Pecuchet's eyes. "Have you thought of anything?" said Bouvard, and Pecuchet answered that it had just occurred to him it would be a great advantage to Ireland and to the Department if a method could be discovered of turning peat into coal. "These experiments will be costly, Pecuchet. How much do you think we can spend?" Pecuchet was full of hope, but the factory turned out so complete and sudden a failure that it had to be closed at once. Oyster beds were laid in Galway and given in charge of a young man who had read all that had ever been written on the subject of oyster culture. The Colonel told me that he met him at a tennis party, and the charming young man, who was a great social advantage to the neighborhood, explained to the Colonel that Portuguese oysters could only live three or four days in the creek, Whitstables could endure our waters a little longer.

"The French oyster," he said, "is the shortest lived of all."

VALE

"I thought," said the Colonel, "that the object of the Department was rather to cultivate than to destroy oysters."

"We are only experimenting; we must have facts," he answered, and next day on their way to the creek the Colonel said:

"There must be a drain hereabouts," and pointing to one flowing over the oyster beds, he added: "I think this accounts for a great deal of the mortality in which you are experimenting."

A gloom came into the young man's face and he promised to write up a report for the Department.

I think it was the fishing interests of Galway that next attracted the attention of Bouvard and Pecuchet. The fishermen were in sad need of piers, and the Department undertook the construction of some two or three, but a very few spring tides cast them hither and thither; some of them can still be reached at low tide, some show a few rocks out in the bay, and these are much appreciated by gannets in the breeding season.

Bouvard felt the disappearance of the piers deeply, and so did Pecuchet, but they found consolation in the thought that experimentation is the source of all knowledge, and one day Bouvard said to Pecuchet:

"Our staff is miserably underpaid."

"You are quite right, Bouvard, you are a rich man and can do without a salary, but for the honor of the Department it seems to me that I should be placed on a level with the Under-Secretary; we must never forget that ours is a great State Department."

And the twain fell to thinking how some more
money might be expended for the good of Ireland.
The establishment of a bacon factory was considered, and the advantage lectures on the minding of
pigs would be to the inhabitants of the west of
Ireland. The egg and poultry industry might be
greatly benefited by a little knowledge. Lecturers
were sought and found, and they departed to in-
struct, and capons were imported from Surrey to
improve the strains, and there was great lamentation
at the end of the hatching season. Some wonderful
letters reached the Department, strangely worded
letters from which I have room for only one sentence,
"Sorra cock was among the cocks you sent us."
Pecuchet rang the bell, but the poultry expert was
out at the time, and a deputation was waiting in the
ante-room. After listening to all the evidence on
the subject of cooking he agreed that the culinary
utensils at the disposal of the peasant were anti-
quated, and it was arranged that ladies should be
sent out; one arrived at Ballinrobe, and the peasants learnt from her how to make meringues. But
meringues were a little beyond the reach of the
peasant's bill-of-fare, and after a long correspondence with the Department the lecturers were
ordered to substitute *maccaroni au gratin*, and
I remember a girl coming back from Ballinrobe bringing the dish with her, and her enthusiasm about it was the same as Bouvard's and
Pecuchet's over the melon, and its success was the
same as the melon; one of the family spat it into
the grate, another spat it out of the window. The

VALE

Department had forgotten that Catholics do not like cheese.

Undeterred by such incidents as these, the wheels of the Department grind on and on, reproducing all the events of Flaubert's book in every detail, but sooner or later Nature outstrips the human imagination, and Flaubert would have thrown up his arms in significant gesture if he were alive to hear the story of how Bouvard and Pecuchet decided one day to improve the breed of asses in Ireland.

"The ass is an animal much used in Ireland by the peasant," Bouvard began, Pecuchet acquiesced, and during the course of the evening it was agreed that it would be a great advantage to the country if the Irish ass were improved. Books on the subject of the ass were sent for to London, and it was discovered that the Spanish asses were the finest of all, and Bouvard said to Pecuchet, "We must import sires." Pecuchet hesitated, and with his usual instinct for compromise suggested Shetland ponies. Bouvard was of opinion that the Shetland pony was too small for the friendly ass, but Pecuchet said that there were in Kerry asses of a sufficient size, and a breed of small mules would be of great use in the mountainy districts. Bouvard pointed out that mules were sterile; Pecuchet referred Bouvard to "The Reminiscences of a Veterinary Surgeon"; and he read in this book that mules had been seen with foals. There was no case, however, of these foals having bred in their turn, so the mule must be said to be sterile in the second generation for certain. The mule is, moreover, a vicious animal, and Bouvard passed the book back to Pecuchet, and for one reason or another it was decided that the Department would be well advised to leave the mule alone and direct all its attention to the improvement of the ass.

"What do you think, Pecuchet, of the Scotch ass?"

"Our importations from Scotland have been considerable lately."

"You would like something Continental, Pecuchet. The Spanish ass, you will see, is highly recommended; but the sires are expensive; two hundred pounds are paid for the tall ass standing over fourteen hands high, and able to cover a sixteen-hands mare; and we should have to import at least fifty sires to visibly affect the Irish strain. You see that would be ten thousand pounds, and we could hardly risk so large an outlay. You will notice that the Egyptian ass is described as being smaller than the Spanish, altogether a lighter animal, and we could buy Egyptian sires for a hundred apiece; they run from seventy-five to a hundred pounds. We might get them cheaper still by taking a large number."

Pecuchet was in favor of a small commission that would take evidence regarding not only the Egyptian, but the Barbary and the Arabian ass, but this commission Bouvard pointed out would be a delay and an expense, and an order was sent to Alexandria to purchase asses. The Department of Agriculture in Ireland was anxious to buy sire asses, sure foal-getters, and the selection was confided to— whom? The archives of the Department would have to be searched for the name of the agent, a useless labor, for no blame attaches to him; his selection was approved by everybody, and the herd was much admired as it trotted and cantered through the morning sunlight on the way to the docks, beautiful little animals, alert as flies, shaking their ears and whisking their long, well-furnished tails, a sight to behold, as docile as they were beautiful, until they reached the gangway. But as soon as they were asked to step on board every one was equally determined to stay in his own country, and much pressure had to be used, and some accidents happened; but human energy prevailed; the asses were all shipped in the end, and it was thought that no untoward incident could happen, so admirable were the arrangements for their reception. Every ass had a stall to himself, and to make sure that there could be no mutual biting and kicking each one was barred in his stall. And it was this very bar that proved the undoing of Bouvard and Pecuchet's great experiment. The temper of the asses had already been tried, and they were now roused to such a stubbornness by the bar that they preferred to die rather than to stale without stretching themselves, and when the steamer put into Malta only seven were able to proceed down the gangway. The telegram that brought the news of the loss of ten asses set Bouvard and Pecuchet pondering.

"Sea-sickness, I suppose," said Pecuchet.

"It may have been home-sickness," Bouvard replied. "Be that as it may, the seven must be landed at Marseilles," and a telegram with these instructions was sent to Malta. It reached there in time but the boat was delayed by the breaking of a screw, and the grooms, unsuspicious of the reluctance of the asses to stale, again, dropped the bars on their hind-quarters, with the result that one after another, those grand asses burst their bladders, only one arriving at Marseilles, a forlorn and decrepit scarecrow ass that would not as much as look at the pretty white and black and brown asses that had come up from Kerry. He chased them with bared teeth out of his field. Pecuchet thought that a chestnut ass might tempt him, but the color is rare among asses, and after a long search the task of finding one was given up as hopeless, the expert declaring that it was doubtful if even a chestnut ass would revive any of the fervor of old Nile in him: a gaunt, taciturn, solitary animal, that moved away from human and ass kind, a vicious unkempt brute that had once turned on Pecuchet; but he had sat on the fence in time; a silent animal by day, and noisy at midnight, when Bouvard sat considering his book for Ireland. On the table by his side lay the "Different Methods of Famous Authors," and learning from it that Byron wrote late at night and drank soda-water, Bouvard determined that he, too, would sit up late and drink soda-water, but strange to relate, though his health declined his book did not progress. His mind was teeming with ideas, but he found it very difficult to disentangle them, and adopted a new method of work. Balzac used to go to sleep early in the evening, and wake up at twelve and write all night and all day, drinking

black coffee, but a very few days proved to Bouvard
that his health was not equal to the strain, and he
resolved to adopt another method. It was also
stated in the "Different Methods of Great Authors"
that Dumas was often glad to call in a collaborator,
and this seemed an excellent idea, for what concerned
Bouvard were not his rhythms, but his ideas. Others
could put his ideas into rhythms, and the help of all
kinds of people was evoked. We used to hear a
great deal about Bond, a German economist, and
Coyne, a gentleman engaged in the Department,
was entrusted with the task of gathering statistics.
Memoranda of all kinds were piled up; a commission sent to Denmark to report on the working of
Danish dairies came back with the information that
the dairies in Denmark were kept remarkably clean.
The Commission was accompanied by a priest, and
he returned much shocked, as well he might be, for
he had found no organized religion whatever in Denmark. One day a chapter was sent round and everybody was asked to mark what he thought should be
omitted and to add what he thought should be included. Dear Edward did not think that Bouvard
had gone far enough in his praise of the Gaelic, and
Pecuchet, whom we met going out to luncheon, declined to give any opinion on the subject of
Bouvard's book.

"I will not speak on the subject." ("Then," I
said to myself, "there is a subject on which Pecuchet
is not willing to advise," and with interest heighten-
ing I listened to Pecuchet.) "I have told Bouvard,"
he said, "that he cannot be at once the savior and

the critic of Irish society, 'If you must write a book, Bouvard,' I have said, 'write what your own eyes have seen and your ears have heard.' It would be better if he didn't write the book at all," he added, "but if he must write one let him write a book out of himself. But if he persists in his philosophy he will harm the Department." Pecuchet threw up his arms, and I said to Edward:

"There is a certain good fellowship in Pecuchet; he would save his old pal from his vanity, the vanity of a book which he hopes will prove him to be far-seeing—*i. e.*, the deep thinker and the brooding sage of Foxrock."

So long as breath remains in my body I will avouch that Pecuchet was firm in his determination not to have anything to do with Bouvard's book. He threw up his hands when I came to him with the news that Bouvard had tired of coffee and unseemly hours, and had sent his manuscript to Rolleston, who had turned up his shirt-sleeves and thrown it into a tub, and had sent it home carefully starched and ironed. The book got a good many reviews— the Fool's Hour it was, for the Catholic Celt let a great screech out of him and demanded that the redeemer should be put in the pillory.

"My friend, John Redmond, will set up a Nationalist candidate against him for South Dublin; he will be beaten at the polls," wailed Pecuchet. And very soon after the defeat predicted by Pecuchet the Nationalist members began to remind the Government that Bouvard remained at the head of the Department, though it had always been understood that the Vice-President of the Department should be a member of the House of Commons. The Nationalists yelped singly and in concert, and so loud grew the pack that Pecuchet could restrain Bouvard no longer, and he went down to Galway to try his luck. "A nice kind of luck he'll meet there," Pecuchet said, and when Bouvard returned from Galway crestfallen, Pecuchet determined to speak out. He was not unmindful of past favors, but the kindest thing he could do would be to remind Bouvard that his clinging to office was undignified.

"Not only undignified," he said to me one day, "but a very selfish course which I never should have suspected. Our mutual child is the Department," he muttered savagely in his beard as we leaned over Baggot Street Bridge, and as the boat rose up in the lock he added, "And he has no thought for it, only for himself."

The words, "an unworthy parent," rose up in my mind, but I repressed them, and applied myself to encouraging Pecuchet to unfold his soul to me.

"So long as the Department," he said, "is represented in Parliament it takes its place with the Admiralty, the Foreign Office, and the other Departments of State, but unrepresented in Parliament it sinks at once——"

"I understand. It sinks to the level of the Board of Charitable Bequests, to the Intermediate Board, or to any of the other Irish boards on which you, Pecuchet, used to pour forth your wrath when you were a Nationalist and a Plan of Campaigner."

"Our joint efforts created the Department, and if

239

he were to retire now like a man instead of clinging on and embarrassing the Government——"

"So he is embarrassing the Government," I interjected. But without noticing my interruption Pecuchet continued:

"If he were to retire, I say, now, like a man, the Liberal Government, the Conservative Government, any Government worthy of its name, would seize the first opportunity to pick Bouvard out as a distinguished Irishman, who, irrespective of party or of creed, should be allowed to serve his country."

It seemed rather shabby of Pecuchet to round like this on his old pal, but not feeling sure that I should act any better in like circumstances, I poked him up with an observation which I have forgotten and listened with interest.

"He loves the Department," I said to myself, "its emptiness responds to his own, and its baffling routes to the flexures of his mind. He goes down to the office every day, signs a few letters, and imagines he is running the country."

"But, you see, Pecuchet, the Government asked Bouvard to stay on, and it was to oblige the Government——"

"But the Government did not promise to keep him on indefinitely; if it did, the Department, as you have yourself admitted, would sink to the level of the Board of Charitable Bequests. He should resign, and not wait to be kicked out."

"But he is engaged on a pamphlet on the economic man and the uneconomic holding, and the uneconomic man and the economic holding, and is convinced that his work should be published during his Presidency. He sits up till four in the morning. He has reverted to the Balzac method."

"Why doesn't he send for Rolleston? If not for Rolleston, why not Hanson? If not Hanson, why not Father Finlay? If not Father Finlay, why not Bond?"

"Bond is in Munich," I answered. And the weeks and the months went by, and we were never sure that the morrow would not see Bouvard flung out of Merrion Street. He did not behave with much dignity during these months, complaining on every occasion and to everybody he met that the Government was treating him very badly, and darkly hinting that Roosevelt had asked him to go to America, and apply his system to the United States; and that if the Government were to go much further he might be induced to accept Roosevelt's offer. But the Roosevelt intrigue, though it found much support in *The Homestead,* failed to impress anybody, and suddenly it began to be rumored that Bouvard was locking himself in, and we were disappointed when about two o'clock the newsboys were shouting, "Resignation of Misther Bouvard," and we all began to wonder who would take his place in Merrion Street, a beautiful street that had been bought up by the Department, and was about to be pulled down to make way for public offices.

It would have suited Flaubert's ironical style to say that the destruction of Merrion Street was Bouvard's real claim to immortality.

In Flaubert's book Bouvard and Pecuchet become

copying clerks again, but Nature was not satisfied with this end. She divided our Bouvard from our Pecuchet. Bouvard returned to *The Homestead* dejected, overwhelmed, downcast, believing his spirit to be irreparably broken, but he found consolation in Æ's hope-inspiring eyes and in Anderson's manliness and courage, fortitude and perseverance. The prodigal was led to a chair, and his faithful lieutenants sat on either side and told him that no happier head in Ireland would lie on a pillow that night.

"Far happier," said Anderson, "than the miserable Pecuchet, who never will get free from the toothed wheel of the great State machine that has caught him up; round and round he will go like a rabbit in the wheel of a bicycle."

Æ looked at Anderson, who had never used an image before, and he took up the strain.

"You have come back," he said, "to a particular and a definite purpose, to individual effort, to economics." Bouvard raised his eyes.

"We have not been idle," Anderson said, "progress has been made"; and he picked up a map from the table and pointed to five-and-twenty more creameries.

"The coöperative movement," Æ said, "has continued; the farmers are with us."

"That is good," said Bouvard.

"Whereas with all its thousands the Department is effecting nothing." A cloud came into Bouvard's face, for he hoped one day to return to the Department, and reading that cloud Æ said: "No, Bouvard, no, never hope to return again to that dreadful place where all is vain tumult and salary."

"I hear," said Anderson, "that Pecuchet is making arrangements to bring the School of Art under the management of the Department; he believes that by coördination——"

"I have heard nothing else but coördination since I left you; it has been dinned into my ears night, noon, and morning, how one must delegate all detail to subordinates, and then, how by the powers of coördination——"

"Yes," Anderson added, "the man who is to take your place comes with a system of the re-afforestation of Ireland, and Pecuchet agrees with him that by compromise——"

"The last we heard of Pecuchet," Æ said, "was from George Moore who met him at the Continental Hotel in Paris one bright May morning, and Pecuchet took him for a drive, telling him that he had an appointment with the Minister of Agriculture. The appointment, however, was missed that morning, or perhaps it was delegated to the following morning; be that as it may, George Moore describes how they went for a drive together, stopping at all the book-shops, Pecuchet springing out and coming back with parcels of books all relating to horse-breeding."

"He has spoken to me about the Normandy sires," said Bouvard.

"George Moore said he was after Normandy sires, and went to Chantilly to view them next day."

And it seemed from Bouvard's face that he could hear the braying of the vicious scarecrow ass that awaited him on his return to Foxrock.

X

I cannot think that any two men ever bore names
more appropriate to their characters than Bouvard
and Pecuchet, not even Don Quixote and Sancho
Panza. Are not the vanity and kindliness and stupidity of Bouvard set forth in the two heavy syllables? And do not the three little snappy syllables
represent with equal clearness Pecuchet's narrow
intellect . . . and cunning on occasions? Again,
the dissyllable "Bouvard" evokes indistinct outlines,
pale, perplexed eyes, and a vague and somewhat
neglected appearance, whereas we naturally associate Pecuchet with a neat necktie, a pointed beard,
and catchwords rather than ideas. Bouvard has
tried to think out one or two questions, but Pecuchet
was content from his early youth with words. He
began with "Nationalism," and when he met Bouvard
he picked up "Coöperation"—the word; and when
he got into the Department he discovered "Delega-
tion"; and Heaven only knows how the word "Co-
ordination" got into his head; but it stuck there,
and he could not get it out of his talk, bothering
us all with it. But nothing lasts for ever, and when
he wearied of "Coördination" he happened to meet
the word "Compromise"; and this word must have
been a great event in his life, for it revealed to him

the Pecuchet of his dreams, the statesman which he always believed to be latent in him, and which more fortunate circumstances would have realized. It was a great treat to hear him on the subject of statesmanship the day that Sir Anthony MacDonnell found himself forced to resign. I led him round Merrion Square and Fitzwilliam Square, over many bridges, through Herbert Street, round again, and on again; and on leading him I should have rushed to the scrivener's, but could not resist the temptation to run up the steps of Plunkett House to tell Æ all about it, regretting all the while that my weakness would cost me many admirable pages.

"I shall never be able to improvise it all again. My memory is wonderful, I admit, but Pecuchet's slumberous phrases, tall, bent weeds, and matted grasses, with the snapping of an occasional aphorism, a dead branch, should be dictated at once and to the nearest scrivener. I am paying dearly for the pleasure of your company."

"I can see you," Æ answered, his imagination enabling him to see us in our walk, and his wit putting just the right words into his mouth—"I can see you stopping at the pavement's edge asking Pecuchet to repeat one of the dead branch aphorisms; I can see you hanging on his words with a sort of literary affection; and I could listen to you for a good deal longer, but I am due to-night at the Hermetic Society, and must get home. Won't you walk a little way with me?"

The proposal that we should walk a little way together reminded me that the old bicycle that had carried Bouvard's ideas all over Ireland so valiantly was now enjoying a well-earned rest in some out-house or garden shed. Æ would not like to sell it for scrap-iron or to buy another; or it may be that he thinks bicycle riding unsuited to a fat man. He has fattened. A great roll of flesh rises to his ears, and his interests have gone so much into practical things that we think the Æ of other days is dead. We are mistaken, the Æ of our deepest affection is not dead, but sleeping; an unexpected word tells us that he has not changed at all. "Relieve him," we say to ourselves, "of his work at *The Homestead*, loose him among the mountains, and in a few weeks he will be hearing the fairy bells again." And happy at heart, though sorry to part with him, I returned home to a lonely meal, hoping to find courage about eight to do some reading.

A lecture was stirring in me at that time—a lecture showing that it is impossible to form any idea of the author of "the plays." "We can see Virgil," I said to myself, "Dante, and Balzac, but Shakespeare is an abstraction, and as unthinkable as Jehovah. We know that somebody must have written the plays; but only of one thing are we sure—that Sidney Lee is always wrong. But I will think no more, I will read." I took down the dreaded volume, and a smile began to trickle round my lips as a picture of the dusty room at the end of many dusty corridors rose up before me, with Æ sitting at a small table teaching that there is an essential oneness in all the different revelations that Eternity has vouchsafed to mankind. It amused me to imagine a discourse for him. . . . The Celtic Gods of our ancestors were only those of the Roman calendar under another name. The week is composed of them. Moon-tag (Monday) is the day of the Moon; Tues-tag (Tuesday) is the day of Mars; Wednes-tag (Wednesday) is the day of Mercury; Theuus-tag (Thursday) is the day of Jupiter; Frey-tag (Friday) is . . . "the day of Venus!" I cried, rising from my chair. Freia, the Goddess of Love in Wagner's trilogy. The beautiful *motif* of the Golden Apples rose up in my mind; and it seemed to me for a moment that there was more in Æ's comparative mythology than seemed at first sight. "And when these gods are translated back again," I cried, "into the language of the primitive Celtic tribes that migrated from the tablelands of Asia, we get Tinguel, Ghervai, Budda, Viagam, Velli, Sani, Nair." A little intoxicated by the ideas that were mounting to my head, I threw my arm across the chimney-piece, and, looking into the dark corner of the room, I could see Æ fidgeting in his chair waiting to confound some speaker, and when his chance came crying: "If the barbarians had only known that the new God which they imposed by the sword was no other than Chris-na, the Indian Bacchus—that is to say, the third Bacchus of the mysteries of Eleusis, called Iacchus, to distinguish him from Dionysius and Zagreus, his brother." "Splendid!" I cried; "and he would add that, without regard for the symbol, they had merely kept the consecrative rite of bread and wine."

I returned to my chair, and, falling into it, listened, hearing his voice getting calmer every minute, solemn and awe-inspiring when he commended toleration to the Hermetics. "You need not be," he said, "too disdainful of the essential worshipers of Iacchus-Iesus, better known in Dublin under the name of Christ. . . . He, too, was a God." There were moments when it seemed to me that I could hear his voice refuting Colum, who had ventured to remind him of Diocletian. "It was not for its Christianity that the ancient creed had persecuted the new, but for its intolerance and profanity."

"There never was anybody like him," I said, and my thoughts melted into a long meditation, from which I awoke, saying: "His conversion, or whatever it was, gave him such an iron grip on himself that, when Indian mysticism flourished in No. 3, Upper Ely Place, he submitted his genius to the directors of the movement, asking them if they would prefer his contributions to the *Theosophical Review* in verse or in prose. The directors answered "In verse," and Æ wrote "Homeward Songs." But even these would not have strayed beyond the pages of the review if Æ's friend, Weekes, had not insisted that the further publication of these poems would bring comfort and peace to many. The last days of the beautiful Duchess of Leinster were spent reading his poems, and they consoled her in her passing as no other poems could have done. He could have been a painter if he had wished it, and possibly a great painter; but a man's whole life is seldom long enough for him to acquire the craft of the painter; and, setting life above craftsmanship,

VALE

Æ denied himself the beautiful touch that separates
the artist from the amateur, and he did well. Ac-
complishment estranges from the comprehension of
the many, and for the first time in the world's history we get a man stopped midway by a scruple of
conscience or love of his kindred—which? If he
had devoted all his days to art, his Thursday evenings at the Hermetic Society would have had to be
abandoned, and the editing of *The Homestead*. He
could not be a painter and write eight or nine columns of notes and a couple of articles on Monday
and Tuesday and Wednesday. A man must have
a terrible hold on himself to pursue the routine of
The Homestead week after week without hope of
reward, and it is this uncanny hold that Æ has on
himself that makes him seem different from other
men, for though in many ways more human than
any of us, he wears the air of one that has lived
before and will live again. How shall I word it?
A demoniac air, using the word in the Goethian
sense, a Lohengrin come to fight the battle of others.
One day he announced to us that he was going to
publish the verses of his disciples, with a preface
by himself, and we muttered among ourselves: "Our
beloved Æ is going to stumble." But the volume
was received by the English press as a complete
vindication of Celtic genius. "Contrairy John"
answered all the effusive articles that appeared with
one sentence: "The English have so completely lost
all standard of poetic excellence that anyone can
impose upon them." A very materialistic explanation which we were loath to accept, preferring to

attribute the success of the volume to the demoniac
power that Æ inherits from the great theosophical
days when he used to sit up in bed, his legs tucked
under his nightshirt.

He was offered some hundreds of pounds by Lord
Dunsany to found a review, but he had not time to
edit it, and proposed John Eglinton. "Contrairy
John" wanted to see life steadily, and to see it whole;
and Yeats came along with a sneer, and said: "I
hear, Lord Dunsany, that you are going to supply
groundsel for Æ's canaries." The sneer brought
the project to naught, and Yeats went away laughing, putting the south of Ireland above the north
and the east and the west, saying that Munster was
always Ireland's literary portion. The first harpers
of Ireland and the first story-tellers were Munster-
men, and his own writers came to him from Munster.
He got nothing out of Dublin. Murray and Ray
and Robinson had all begun by writing for the *Cork
Examiner* and the *Constitutional;* Æ might search
the columns of *Sinn Fein* for ever and ever.

"And never find," I said, "a blackbird, or thrush,
or skylark, or nightingale."

The portentous critic giggled a little in his stride
down the incline of Rathmines Avenue, and was
moved to change the conversation from *Sinn Fein,*
that journal having spoken of him disrespectfully
since he had accepted a pension from the English
Government. Griffith, the editor of *Sinn Fein,* or
"Ourselves Alone," had butted him severely in several paragraphs—butted him is the word, for in
appearance and mentality Griffith may be compared

to a ram. He butts against England every week with admirable perseverance, and while he butts, he allows all the poets of Rathmines to carol.

"A pretty banner," I said as we crossed the bridge, "for *Sinn Fein* would be a tree full of small singing birds caroling sonnets and rondeaux, ballades and villanelles, with a butting-ram underneath, and this for device: 'Believe that England doesn't exist, and it won't.'"

"Yes, there is an element of Christian Science in our friend Griffith," Yeats answered, and we crossed the bridge.

"You don't think that Æ will ever discover anyone in *Sinn Fein* comparable to Synge?"

Yeats threw up his hands.

"It would be better," he said, "if all his little folk went back to their desks."

When this remark was repeated to Æ, he said: "Column was earning seventy-eight pounds a year when he was at his desk at the Railway Clearing House, and now he is earning four or five pounds a week. So Willie says that I shall never find anything that will compare with Synge. Well, we shall see."

And every Thursday evening the columns of *Sinn Fein* were searched, and every lilt considered, and every accent noted; but the days and the weeks went by without a new "peep-o-peep, sweet, sweet," until the day that James Stephens began to trill; and recognizing at once a strange songster, Æ put on his hat and went away with his cage, discovering him in a lawyer's office. A great head and two soft brown eyes looked at him over a typewriter, and an alert and intelligent voice asked him whom he wanted to see. Æ said that he was looking for James Stephens, a poet, and the typist answered: "I am he."

And next Sunday evening he was admitted to the circle, and we were impressed by his wit and whimsicality of mind, but we thought Æ exaggerated the talents of the young man. True that all his discoveries had come to something, but it was clear to us that he was anxious to put this new man alongside of Synge, and that we could not consent to do. He was a little distressed at our apathy, our unwillingness, our short-sightedness, for he was certain that James Stephens was a new note in Irish poetry. Our visions were not as clear as his. I was conscious of little more than harsh versification, and crude courage in the choice of subjects. Contrairy John was confused and roundabout, and at the end of many an argument found himself defending the very principles that he had started out to controvert. It was clear, however, that he did not think more of James Stephens than we ourselves. Yeats was the blindest of us all, and it was with ill-grace that he consented to hear Æ read the poems, giving his opinion casually; and when Æ spoke of the advantage the publication of a volume would be to Stephens, he answered: "For me, the æsthetical question; for you, my dear friend, the philanthropic." Æ was hurt, but not discouraged; and to interest us he told us stories from the life of the new poet, who was a truer vagrant than ever Synge had been. Synge had fifty pounds a year; but Stephens, a poor boy without education or a penny, had wandered all over Ireland, and would have lost his life in Belfast from hunger had it not been for a charitable apple-woman. Æ was delighted at the thought of the material that his pet would have to draw upon later on when he turned from verse to prose, for Æ divined that this would be so.

"James Stephens has enough poetry in him," he said to me, "to be a great prose-writer."

"But when he left the apple-woman?" I answered, always curious.

Æ could not tell me how Stephens had picked up his education, or had learnt typewriting and shorthand and got employment in a lawyer's office at five-and-twenty shillings a week—well enough for a girl who has a home, but a bare sufficiency for a man whose head is full of dreams and who has a wife and child to support. His life must have been very hard to bear, without the solitude of a room in which to write his poems or intellectual comradeship until he met Æ, a friend always ready to listen to him, to be enthusiastic about his literary projects. What a door was opened to him when he met Æ! Of what help Æ was to him in his first prose composition (no one can help another with poetry) none knows but Stephens himself; Æ forgets what he gives, but it is difficult for me to believe that Stephens did not benefit enormously,. as much as I did myself. How much that was I cannot tell, for Æ was always helping me directly and indirectly. Shall I ever forget the day when, after three weeks' torture trying to write· the second chapter of "Ave," I went down to Plunkett House to see if Æ could help me out of my difficulty.

"I am waiting for proofs, and am free for an hour. If you like we will walk round Merrion Square, and you can tell me all about it."

We turned to the east and walked along the north side, and it was opposite the National Gallery that he told me my second chapter must be in Victoria Street; and after a little argument, to which he listened very gently, he led me as a mother leads a child. I saw the error of my ways, and said: "Good-bye, Æ; I see it all. Good-bye."

As well as anything I can think of, this anecdote shows how we run to Æ in time of need, and never run in vain; but now I find myself in a difficulty out of which he will not be able to help me. He is not satisfied with his portrait, and complains that I have represented him in "Ave" and "Salve" as the blameless hero of a young girl's novel.

"Why have you found no fault with me? If you wish to create human beings you must discover their faults."

Of course, and he is faultless in my narrative up to the present. I am reduced to discovering a stain upon his character. I cannot accuse him of theft, and he never speaks of his love affairs; he may be a pure man; be that as it may, it is not for me to cast the first stone at him; lying and blackmail—of what use to make charges that no one will believe? If he will not sin, why should he object to my white flower in his buttonhole? And feeling that humanity was on the whole very difficult and tiresome, I fell to thinking. . . . But of what I cannot tell; I only know I was awakened suddenly by a memory of a young painter in London, one who brought imagination and wit and epigram and laughter into our midst, and when he left us we used to ponder on the unmerited good fortune of his wife, for to live with him always seemed to us an unreasonable share of human happiness. But one day I made the acquaintance of this woman whom I had only known faintly during her married life, and heard from her that her husband did not speak to her at dinner, but propped a book up against a glass and read; and after dinner sat in his chair composing, and often went up to bed forgetting to bid her good-night. If she reproached him, he assured her there was no other woman in the world he loved as much as her; but being a man of genius his mind was away among his works. "But what proof have I," she said, "that he is a man of genius? Of course, if I were certain, it would be different. . . . All the same, it is a little trying," she added. And her case is the case of every woman who marries a man of genius. A trying tribe, especially at meal-times; ideas and food being apparently irreconcilable. I have often regretted that Æ did not leave some of his ideas on the landing with his hat and coat, for it is distressing to hear a man say that he could not tell the difference between halibut and turbot when you have just apologized to him for an unaccountable mistake on the part of your cook. This painful incident once happened in Ely Place; and I reflected, duly, that if he were indifferent to my food he might show scant courtesy to the food that his wife provided—excellent I am sure it is—but a man of ideas cannot be catered for by friend or wife. I followed him in imagination all the way up the long Rathmines Road, and saw him picking a little from his plate, and then, becoming forgetful, his eyes would rove into dark corners. (His definition of ideas are formless spiritual essences, and the room in 17, Rathgar Avenue is full of them, economic, pictorial, and poetic.) "I have it at last! A blemish, and one is sufficient for my portrait; a little irregularity of feature will satisfy my sitter; in the eyes of the world absent-mindedness is a blemish. But if it be none in his wife's eyes then there is no blemish," and I remembered that he chose her for her intelligence, and it is no mean one. She had abandoned papistry before he met her, and had written some beautiful phrases in her pages of the *Theosophical Review;* and these won his heart. A very gracious presence and personality, too distinct to seem invidious to her husband's genius, or to deem it an injustice to herself that he should be beloved by all. But in his indifference to money we may seek and find cause for complaint. It is possible that in the eyes of women who have not succeeded in marrying men of genius he should apply his talents to increasing his income, for the common belief is that a man's life is not his exclusive possession to dispose of as pleases his good-will, but a sort of family banking account on which his wife and children may draw checks. This is not Æ's view. He has often said to me, "I come into the world without money or

possessions, and have done very well without either.
Why shouldn't my children do the same?" Æ's life
is in his ideas as much as Christ's, and I will avouch
that his wife has never tried to come between him
and his ideas. As much cannot be said for Mary,
whom Christ had to reprove for trying to dissuade
him from his mission, which he did on many occasions. . . . But again I am hoeing and raking,
shoveling up merits instead of picking out the small
but necessary fault. If I dig deeper perhaps my
search will be rewarded. He gives his wife all the
money she asks for, but she does not know what
money he has in the bank. Æ does not know himself, and feeling that Æ was about to be born into
my text, a real man rather than an ideal one, my
heart rose, and I said: "It is not long ago since
he told me that he had given a man who had asked
him for a contribution a long screed for which he
could have had thirty pounds from a certain maga-
zine. In giving his screed for nothing he acted as
all the great dispensers of ideas have done, and the
many will find fault with him, for though they would
like to have prophets and poets they would like
them domesticated, each one bringing home to a
little house in the suburbs a reel of office chit-chat
to unwind for his wife's pleasure, the poet on one
side of the hearth, the wife on the other, the cat
between them. Jane and Minna would listen at-
tentively, but Violet's thoughts would stray and she
would find herself very soon with Cuchulain Caoelte
and Finn. Her thoughts have always been set on
heroes, and picking up from the table her beautiful

book of fairy tales, I read them until I was awakened by a knocking at my front-door. The servants had gone to bed. Who could this be? Æ perhaps. It was John Eglinton.

"Are you sure you aren't busy? If you are, don't hesitate——"

"I was sitting by the fire thinking."

"I am loath to disturb a thinking man"; and he stopped half-way between the arm-chair and the door.

"I assure you I had come to the end of my thinking."

"On what subject?"

"One that you know very well——Æ. Among my portraits he is the least living, and that is a pity. He does not silhouette as Yeats does or as dear Edward. Edward's round head and bluff shoulders and big thighs and long feet correspond with his blunt mind. And Yeats's great height and hierarchic appearance authorize the literary dogmas that he pronounces every season. He is the type of the literary fop, and the most complete that has ever appeared in literature. But Æ! I wonder if we could get him into a phrase, John." After a while I said: "He has the kindly mind of a shepherd, and ten years ago he was thin, lithe, active, shaggy, and I can see him leaning on his crook meditating."

"That is just what I don't think he does. He talks about meditation, but his mind is much too alert. There is this resemblance, however: the shepherd knows little but the needs of his flock, and the other day, at Horace Plunkett's, I heard that Æ exhibited a surprising ignorance in an argument with some English economist. He did not know that the Athenian Society was founded on slavery."

"I am glad to hear it, for if he knew all the things that one learns out of books I should never get him into a literary silhouette."

"You admit," John said, "inspiration in his painting, but you think it lacks quality; and in your study of him you will explain——"

"Of course, a most important point. Æ has come out of many previous existences and is going toward many others, and looks upon this life as an episode of no importance."

"An interesting explanation, but the real one is——"

"Is what?" I asked eagerly.

"He is too impatient. I told him so once, but he answered indignantly that there was no more patient man than he."

"I prefer my explanation," I answered.

"It is the more poetic, but temperament goes deeper than belief," John replied.

"Not deeper than Æ's belief in his own eternity," I said; and my answer had the effect of rolling John for a moment out of his ideas. "He'll soon be back in them again," I said to myself. At the end of another long silence John told me that somebody had said that Æ was an unhappy man.

"It never struck me that he was unhappy. He always seems among the happiest." And I began to wonder if John Eglinton looked upon me as a happy man.

"You're happy in your work, but I don't know if you are happy in your life."

"And you, John," I said, "are happy in your thoughts."

"Yes," he answered, "and my unhappiness is caused by the fact that I get so little time for enjoying them."

It was pleasant for two old cronies to sit by the fire, wondering what they had gotten out of life; and when John bade me good-bye at the door he admonished me to be very careful what I said about Æ's home life.

"But he has asked me to tack him on to life, and now you think, since he has been tacked on, he won't like it."

"Damn these models!" I said, returning to my room. "Models are calamitous, and it would perhaps be calamitous to be without them. Shakespeare, too, is a calamity." And, dismayed by the number of plays I should have to read, my thoughts turned to dear little John Eglinton, to the little shriveled face and the round head with a great deal of back to it, to the reddish hair into which gray is coming, to the gaunt figure, and I fell to thinking how his trousers had wound round his legs as he had walked down the street. It seemed to me that I should never find anything more suitable to my talent as a narrator and as a psychologist than this dear little man that had just left me, dry, determined, and all of a piece, valiant in his ideas and in his life, come straight down from the hard North into the soft Catholic Dublin atmosphere, which was not, however, able to rob him of any of his individuality. The Catholic atmosphere has intensified John Eglinton—boiled him down, as it were—made him a sort of Liebig extract of himself, and I seemed to realize more than ever I had done before how like he was to himself: the little round head and the square shoulders, and the hesitating, puzzled look that comes into his face. I had often sought a reason for that look. Now I know it is because he gets so little time for his ideas. He does not wish to write them out any more than Steer wishes to exhibit his Chelsea figures; he rearranges them and dusts them, and sits among them conscious of familiar presences, and as the years go by he seems to us to sink deeper into his arm-chair, and his contempt of our literary activities strengthens; he is careful to hide the fact from us lest he should wound our feelings, but it transpired the evening I ran over to the Library to tell him of Goethe's craving for information on all subjects, including even a little midwifery. "So that he might continue a little dribble of ink in the morning," he said. John never lacks a picturesque phrase, but that is neither here nor there; the sentiment it expresses is John Eglinton—a lack of faith in all things. Of late years he seems to have been drawn toward Buddhism, and goes out to a lonely cottage among the Dublin mountains in the hope that the esoteric lore of the East may allow him to look a little over the border. I shall never find a better model than John Eglinton. It seems to me that I understand him thoroughly; and what a fine foil he would make

to the soft and peaty Hyde, the softest of all our
natural products, a Protestant that Protestantism
has not been able to harden! And I pondered on
his yellow skull floating back from the temples, collecting hugely on the crown; his black eyebrows and
a drooping black mustache; his laugh, shallow and
a little vacant, a little mechanical; and his words
and thoughts, casual as the stage Irishman's. We
would pick him out for a Catholic in a tram, and if
there were a priest in the tram Hyde would be interested in him at once, and he would like nothing
better than to visit Clare Island with a batch of
ecclesiastics, a dozen or fifteen parish priests, not
one of them weighing less than fifteen stone, and
the bishop eighteen. It would be a pleasure to Hyde
to drop the words "Your Grace" into as many
sentences as possible; whether he would kiss the
bishop's ring may be doubted—being a Protestant,
he could hardly do so—but he would fly for a pillow
to put under His Grace's throbbing head.

On Clare Island the parish priest would have prepared legs of mutton and sirloins of beef, chickens
and geese, and Hyde's comment to His Grace would
be: "The hospitality of the Irish priest is un-
equaled. He will crack a bottle of champagne with
any visitor."

A gathering of this kind is very agreeable to the
Catholic Protestant, and the Catholic bishop likes to
do business with the Catholic Protestant better than
with anybody else. The Catholic might stand up
to him; there are one or two, perhaps, who would
venture to disagree with His Grace, but the Cath-

olic Protestant melts like peat into fine ash before His Grace's ring.

But Hyde was not always Catholic Protestant. In the old Roscommon glebe there was sufficient Protestantism in him to set him learning Irish, to speak it fluently, and to write some very beautiful poems in the language. It is to Hyde that we owe the jargon since become so famous, for the great discovery was his that to write beautiful English one has only to translate literally from the Irish; his prose translations of the "Love Songs of Connaught" are as beautiful as Synge's, and it is a pity he was stopped by Father Tom Finlay, who said: "Write in Irish or in English, but our review does not like mixed languages." And these words and his election to the Presidency of the Gaelic League made an end to Hyde as a man of letters. I took his measure at the banquet at the Shelbourne Hotel, his noisy demonstration in Irish and English convincing me that the potential scholar would be swallowed up in the demagogue. And this is what happened. His Presidency leaving him no time to study Irish in the libraries and in the Irish-speaking districts, he has mouthed the vilest English ever moulded by the lips of man all over Ireland. The Gaelic League must make no enemies; the way to success was to stand well with everybody—members of Parliament, priests, farmers, shopkeepers—and by standing well with all these people, especially with the priests, Hyde has become the arch-type of the Catholic Protestant, cunning, subtle, cajoling, superficial, and affable, and these qualities have enabled him to paddle the old dug-out of the Gaelic League up from the marshes through many an old bog, lake, and river, reaching at last Portobello Bridge, where he took on board two passengers, Agnes O'Farrelly and Mary Hayden, and, having placed them in the stern, he resumed the paddle, and a grand figure he cut in the bow paddling the dug-out right up to the steps of the National University. He gallantly handed them up the steps, and so amazed were the three at the salaries that were offered to them that they forgot the old dug-out; it drifted back whence it came. Worn and broken and water-logged, it drifted back to the original Connemara bog-hole, to sink under the brown water out of sight of the quiet evening sky, unwatched, unmourned save by dear Edward, who will weep a few tears, I am sure, when the last bubbles arise and break.

XI

The sinking of the old dug-out will rob Edward
of an evening's occupation, and the question arises
to what great national or civic end he will devote
his Thursdays. On Monday evening he presides at
the Pipers' Club, on Tuesday he goes to the theater,
on Wednesday he attends a meeting of Sinn Fein,
on Thursday he dozes through the proceedings of
the Coisde Gnotha, on Friday there is choir practice
in the cathedral, on Saturday he speaks severely to
his disobedient choristers, tries new voices in his
rooms in Lincoln Place, and plans new programs
with Vincent O'Brien, his choirmaster, chosen by him
because he believes in his talent and in his desire to
give the music in accordance with tradition and
Edward's own taste. On Sunday he is ever watch-
ful in the cathedral, sitting with his hand to his ear,
noting the time and the efficiency of the singers.

"I had to give way on one point," he said to me,
"but I think I told you already that the Archbishop
stipulated that if a great composer of Church music
should arise, the cathedral should not be debarred
from giving his music. I don't think it will happen
very often, so there was no use in opposing his Grace
on this particular point. We have now eight hundred a year——"

"Eight hundred a year out of ten thousand!"

"You see," he said, "the Archbishop has added ten thousand to mine, and that invested at four per cent. will bring in eight hundred."

"So you succeeded in persuading the Archbishop to give you ten thousand as well as to grant you the Headship!" My admiration for Edward as a business man swelled.

"It was a hard fight," he said, "and very often the negotiations were nearly broken off; but I stuck to my guns, for of course it wasn't likely that I was going to give ten thousand without getting what I was bargaining for."

The sum of money seemed to strike a chord in my memory, and I was moved to ask him what had led him to fix on this sum, but refrained lest I should appear too inquisitive. "Something must have happened," I said, "to fix this sum in his mind. It has never been less, it has never been more, and in the beginning he didn't know how much money was necessary to found the choir. Would he have given the twenty thousand if——"

It suddenly dropped upon me that he had told me in Bayreuth, in the great yawning street between the little bridge and the railway-station, that he had come out of a great conscientious crisis, and had had to go to Bishop Healy and lay the whole matter before him. "What sin can he have committed?" I said to myself, and, quelling my curiosity as best I could, I tried to induce him to confide in me, and after some persuasion he confessed that his mother, fearing the Land Acts, had prevailed upon him to redistribute his grass-farms. He had told the tenants that he would reinstate them; whereas he had given them other farms equally good, but they had found fault with the lands he had put them into, and his bailiff had been fired at on the highroad to Gort. He had received coffins and cross-bones; it was not, however, fear of his life or his money that had brought about the great mental breakdown, but his conscience. If he had acted wrongly, he must make reparation before his sin would be forgiven him . . . And while I pictured him as a prey to remorse, of pallid and rueful countenance, he told me that the one thing that stood to him was his appetite. After a night of agony he would descend his Gothic stairs forgetful of everything but the sirloin on the side-table. "He is always original," I said, "and has discovered an unexpected connection between conscience and appetite." But notwithstanding his appetite, he had had to leave Tillyra for Cork. He had always liked the sea and its influences, and in six weeks he had returned much improved in health, but still unable to smoke his churchwarden, only an occasional cigar, and that a mild one.

"It may have been from too much smoking," I said; "but I can't think why you wanted to send for Bishop Healy. I could have advised you better."

"Nothing would have satisfied me but a bishop," he answered, with a terrified look in his eyes.

"To tell you that you must keep your promise?"

"All these business matters are very intricate, and it is difficult to say who is right and who is wrong.

One doesn't know oneself, and when one's interests
are concerned one doesn't see straight."

My heart went out to him, for it is seldom that
one meets anybody altogether honorable about
money matters, and rarer still is he who accepts the
advice that he asks for: Edward had reinstated his
tenants, and I began to wonder if the ten thousand
that he had spent upon his choir was connected in
some remote way with his management of the property, or with his mother's management, or with his
father's. A conscience like Edward's might lead
him back one hundred years, to his grandfather.

But if he had had any suspicion about this money,
I should have heard of it. He has been confessing
himself to me for the last thirty years. . . . Now I
come to think of it, he never told me how he first
came to hear of Palestrina. It was when we lived
in the Temple together that he began to speak to
me about the Mass of Pope Marcellus; and one
Christmas Eve he persuaded me to go over to Paris
with him to hear it. And shall I ever forget how
he sidled up to me when we came out of the church?

"Now what do you think of Palestrina?"

"About the beauty of the music there can be no
question, and as far advanced in his art as—shall
we say—Botticelli?"

"And what about the plain-chant? You will
never say again that you don't like plain-chant."

"But there was no plain-chant. None was sung
to-day."

"Yes, the hymn. And the boy's voice—how much
purer than a woman's!"

"He sang very beautifully, Edward. . . . You don't mean the 'Adeste Fideles'?"

"Of course I do."

"But Edward——" And we began to argue, myself convinced, in spite of the fact that he showed me the "Adeste Fideles" in his Prayer-Book among plain-chant tunes, that it could not be else than modern music. "A Raphael doesn't become a Rubens because it happens to have been hung among Rubens."

We argued about plain-chant endings till I was on the point of reminding him of the thirteenth-century window in Aix-la-Chapelle, but restrained myself for once.

He always needs a three-mile walk after a heavy meal, and admitted he had eaten too much steak, drunken too much wine, and was taking me to the other end of Paris to buy the masses and motets of the great Italian contrapuntalists. He always knows the way, and we walked and we walked—Edward is so engaging a companion that one does not feel the walk or the time passing—at last arriving at the shop. His negotiations with the music-seller began to astonish me. I had fancied he was going to buy music to the value of a pound or thirty shillings—two pounds, perhaps—but I heard: "And if I add three motets by Clemens non Papa and two masses by Orlando di Lasso, that will come to how much?" "Five hundred francs." "And if I take six more motets and six more masses by Vittoria?" "That will bring up the total to twelve hundred francs." I may be wrong in my figures, but he certainly bought that morning from thirty to forty pounds' worth of music; and while the bundle was being tied, Borde, the conductor, came in, and I told him that my friend Edward Martyn was about to give ten thousand pounds to found a choir in Dublin, and was buying music. Borde was, of course, very much interested in the Dublin choir, and he led me into conversation graciously, in the course of which I said:

"I congratulate you, M. Borde, on your wonderful boy treble."

A cloud came into his face, and after some pressing he admitted that there was no boy in his choir.

"No boy! and Mr. Martyn thinks a boy's voice much more beautiful than a woman's. It wasn't a boy, then, who sang the 'Adeste Fideles'?"

"No . . . a woman." He added that she was fifty. I thanked him inwardly, and, feeling sorry for Edward, persuaded Borde to admit that he had taught her to sing like a boy. But if Edward had mistaken a woman's voice for a boy's he may be mistaken about plain-chant.

"Mr. Martyn tells me that the 'Adeste' is a plain-chant tune. Surely not."

"No," he answered; "it is a Portuguese tune, and it was written about one hundred years ago."

"But," Edward spluttered, "it is in my Prayer-Book among the plain-chant. How did it get there?"

Borde could not enlighten him on that point, and I suggested that he should make application to the publisher of his Prayer-Book and get his money back.

"There is nobody," I said, "like him. He is more wonderful than anything in literature. I prefer him to Sancho who was untroubled with a conscience and never thought of running to the Bishop of Toledo. Edward is not without the shrewdness of his ancestors, and got the better of Archbishop Walsh, and for the last five years Vincent O'Brien has been beating time, and will beat it till the end of his life; and he will be succeeded by others, for Edward has, by deed, saved the Italian contrapuntalists till time everlasting from competition with modern composers. He certainly has gotten the better of Walsh." And I thought of a picture-gallery in Dublin with nothing in it but Botticelli and his school, and myself declaring that all painting that had been done since had no interest for me. . . . A smile began to spread over my face, for the story that was coming into my mind seemed oh! so humorous, so like Ireland, so like Edward, that I began to tell myself again the delightful story of the unrefined ears that, weary of erudite music, had left the cathedral and sought instinctively modern tunes and women's voices, and as these were to be found in Westland Row the church was soon overflowing with a happy congregation. But in a little while the collections grew scantier. This time it couldn't be Palestrina, and all kinds of reasons were adduced. At last the truth could no longer be denied—the professional Catholics of Merrion Square had been driven out of Westland Row by the searching smells of dirty clothes, and had gone away to the University Church in Stephen's Green. So if it weren't Palestrina directly it was Palestrina indi-

271

rectly, and the brows of the priests began to knit when Edward Martyn's name was mentioned. "Them fal-de-dals is well enough on the Continent, in Paris, where there is no faith," was the opinion of an important ecclesiastic. "But we don't want them here," murmured a second ecclesiastic. "All this counterpoint may make a very pretty background for Mr. Martyn's prayers, but what about the poor people's?" "Good composer or bad composer, there is no congregation in him," said a third. "There's too much congregation," put in the first, "but not the kind we want!" The second ecclesiastic took snuff, and the group were of opinion that steps should be taken to persuade dear Edward to make good their losses. The priests in Marlborough Street sympathized with the priests of Westland Row, and told them that they were so heavily out of pocket that Mr. Martyn had agreed to do something for them. It seemed to the Westland Row priests that if Mr. Martyn were making good the losses of the priests of the pro-Cathedral, he should make good their losses. It was natural that they should think so, and to acquit himself of all responsibility Edward no doubt consulted the best theologians on the subject, and I think that they assured him that he is not responsible for indirect losses. If he were, his whole fortune would not suffice. He was, of course, very sorry if a sudden influx of poor people had caused a falling off in the collections of Westland Row, for he knew that the priests needed the money very much to pay for the new decorations, and to help them he wrote an article in the *Independent* praising the new blue ceiling, which seemed, so he wrote, a worthy canopy for the soaring strains of Palestrina.

"Unfortunately, rubbing salt into the wound," I said. "A story that will amuse Dujardin, and it will be great fun telling him in the shady garden at Fontainebleau how Edward, anxious to do something for his church, had succeeded in emptying two. All the way down the alleys he will wonder how Edward could have ever looked upon Palestrina's masses as religious music. "The only music," he will say, "in which religious emotion transpires is plain-chant. Husymans says that the 'Tantum Ergo' or the 'Dies Iræ,' one or the other, reminds him of a soul being dragged out of purgatory, and it is possible that it does; but a plain-chant tune arranged in eight-part counterpoint cannot remind one of anything very terrible." Dujardin knows that Palestrina was a priest, and he will say: "That fact deceived your friend, just as the fact of finding the 'Adeste Fideles' among the plain-chant tunes deceived him." For of course I shall tell Dujardin that story too. It is too good to be missed. "He is wonderful, Dujardin!" I shall cry out in one of the sinuous alleys. "There never was anybody like him!" And I will tell him more soul-revealing anecdotes. I will say: "Dujardin, listen. One evening he contended that the great duet at the end of 'Siegfried' reminded him of a mass by Palestrina." Dujardin will laugh, and, excited by his laughter, I will try to explain to him that what Edward sees is that Palestrina took a plain-chant tune and gave fragments of it to the different voices, and in his mind these become confused with the motives of "The Ring." "You see, Dujardin, the essential always escapes him—the intention of the writer is hidden from him." "I am beginning to understand your friend. He has, let us suppose, a musical ear that allows him to take pleasure in the music; but a musical ear will not help him to follow Wagner's idea—how, in a transport of sexual emotion, a young man and a young woman on a mountain-side awaken to the beauty of the life of the world." Dujardin's appreciations will provoke me, and I will say: "Dujardin, you shouldn't be so appreciative. If I were telling you of a play I had written, it would be delightful to watch my idea dawning upon your consciousness; but I am telling you of a real man, and one that I shall never be able to get into literature." He will answer: "We invent nothing; we can but perceive." And then, exhilarated, carried beyond myself, I will say: "Dujardin, I will tell you something still more wonderful than the last *gaffe*. *Il gaffe dans les Quat'z Arts.* He admires Ibsen, but you'd never guess the reason why—because he is very like Racine; both of them, he says, are classical writers. And do you know how he arrived at that point? Because nobody is killed on the stage in Racine or in Ibsen. He does not see that the intention of Racine is to represent men and women out of time and out of space, unconditioned by environment, and that the very first principle of Ibsen's art is the relation of his characters to their environment. In many passages he merely dramatizes Darwin. There never was anybody so interesting as dear Edward, and there never will be anybody like him in literature. . . . I will explain why presently, but I must first tell you another anecdote. I went to see him one night, and he told me that the theme of the play he was writing was a man who had married a woman because he had lost faith in himself; the man did not know, however, that the woman had married him for the same reason, and the two of them were thinking—I have forgotten what they were thinking, but I remember Edward saying: 'I should like to suggest hopelessness.' I urged many phrases, but he said: 'It isn't a phrase I want, but an actual thing. I was thinking of a broken anchor —that surely is a symbol of hopelessness.' 'Yes,' I said, 'no doubt, but how are you going to get a broken anchor into a drawing-room?' 'I don't write about drawing-rooms.' 'Well, living-rooms. It isn't likely that they would buy a broken anchor and put it up by the coal-scuttle.'

" 'There's that against it,' he answered. 'If you could suggest anything better——' 'What do you think of a library in which there is nothing but unacted plays? The characters could say, when there was nothing for them to do on the stage, that they were going to the library to read, and the library would have the advantage of reminding everybody of the garret in the "Wild Duck." ' "

"A very cruel answer, my friend," Dujardin will say, and I will tell him that I can't help seeing in Edward something beyond Shakespeare or Balzac. "Now, tell me, which of these anecdotes I have told you is the most humorous?" He will not answer my question, but a certain thoughtfulness will begin to settle in his face, and he will say: "Everything with him is accidental, and when his memory fails him he falls into another mistake, and he amuses you because it is impossible for you to anticipate his next mistake. You know there is going to be one; there must be one, for he sees things separately rather than relatively. I am beginning to understand your friend."

"You are, you are; you are doing splendidly. But you haven't told me, Dujardin, which anecdote you prefer. Stay, there is another one. Perhaps this one will help you to a still better understanding. When he brought 'The Heather Field' and Yeats's play 'The Countess Cathleen' to Dublin for performance, a great trouble of conscience awakened suddenly in him, and a few days before the performance he went to a theologian to ask him if 'The Countess Cathleen' were a heretical work, and, if it were, would Almighty God hold him responsible for the performance? But he couldn't withdraw Yeats's play without withdrawing his own, and it appears that he breathed a sigh of relief when a common friend referred the whole matter to two other theologians, and as these gave their consent Edward allowed the plays to go on; but Cardinal Logue intervened, and wrote a letter to the papers to say that the plays seemed to him unfit for Catholic ears, and Edward would have withdrawn the plays if the Cardinal hadn't admitted in his letter that he had judged the play by certain extracts only."

"He wishes to act rightly, but has little faith in himself; and what makes him so amusing is that he needs advice in æsthetics as well as in morals." "We are," I said, "Dujardin, at the roots of conscience." And I began to ponder the question what would happen to Edward if we lived in a world in which æsthetes ruled: I should be where Bishop Healy is, and he would be a thin, small voice crying in the wilderness—an amusing subject of meditation, from which I awoke suddenly.

"I wonder how Dujardin is getting on with his Biblical studies? Last year he was calling into question the authorship of the Romans—a most eccentric view"; and, remembering how weakly I had answered him, I took the Bible from the table and began to read the Epistle with a view to furnishing myself with arguments wherewith to confute him. My Bible opened at the ninth chapter, and I said: "Why, here is the authority for the Countess Cathleen's sacrifice which Edward's theologian deemed untheological. It will be great fun to poke Edward up with St. Paul," and on my way to Lincoln Place I thought how I might lead the conversation to "The Countess Cathleen."

A few minutes afterwards a light appeared on the staircase and the door slowly opened.

"Come in, Siegfried, though you were off the key."

"Well, my dear friend, it is a difficult matter to whistle above two trams passing simultaneously and six people jabbering round a public-house, to say nothing of a jarvey or two, and you perhaps dozing in your arm-chair, as your habit often is. You won't open to anything else except a motive from 'The Ring' "; and I stumbled up the stairs in front of Edward, who followed with a candle.

"Wait a moment; let me go first and I'll turn up the gas."

"You aren't sitting in the dark, are you?"

"No, but I read better by candle-light," and he blew out the candles in the tin candelabra that he had made for himself. He is original even in his candelabra; no one before him had ever thought of a candelabra in tin, and I fell to admiring his appearance more carefully than perhaps I had ever done before, so monumental did he seem lying on the little sofa sheltered from drafts by a screen, a shawl about his shoulders. His churchwarden was drawing famously, and I noticed his great square hands with strong fingers and square nails pared closely away, and as heretofore I admired the curve of the great belly, the thickness of the thighs, the length and breadth and the width of his foot hanging over the edge of the sofa, the apoplectic neck falling into great rolls of flesh, the humid eyes, the skull covered with short stubbly hair. I looked round the rooms and they seemed part of himself. The

old green wallpaper on which he pins reproductions
of the Italian masters, and I longed to peep once
more into the bare bedroom into which he goes to
fetch bottles of Apollinaris. Always original! Is
there another man in this world whose income is two
thousand a year, and who sleeps in a bare bedroom,
without dressing-room, or bath-room, or servant in
the house to brush his clothes? Only a maid of all
work, so he has to go to the baker's for his breakfast. He has always said that he does not care for
private life, only public life. One never knows exactly what he means. He seems to suspect private
life, to be afraid of it.

We had been talking for some time of the Gaelic
League, and from Hyde it was easy to pass to Yeats
and his plays.

"His best play is 'The Countess Cathleen.'"

"'The Countess Cathleen' is only a sketch."

"But what I never could understand, Edward,
was why you and the Cardinal could have had any
doubts as to the orthodoxy of 'The Countess Cathleen.'"

"What, a woman that sells her own soul in order
to save the souls of others!"

"I suppose your theologian objected——"

"Of course he objected."

"He cannot have read St. Paul."

"What do you mean?"

"He can't have read St. Paul, or else he is prepared to throw over St. Paul."

"*Mon ami Moore, mon ami Moore.*"

"The supernatural idealism of a man who would

sell his soul to save the souls of others fills me with awe."

"But it wasn't a man; it was the Countess Cathleen, and women are never idealists."

"Not the saints?"

His face grew solemn at once.

"If you give me the Epistles I will read the passage to you." And it was great fun to go to the book-shelves and read: " 'I say the truth in Christ, I lie not, my conscience also bearing me witness in the Holy Ghost, that I have great heaviness and continual sorrow in my heart. For I could wish that myself were accursed from Christ for my brethren, my kinsmen according to the flesh.' "

Edward's face grew more and more solemn, and I wondered of what he was thinking.

"I think the Church is quite right not to encourage the reading of the Epistles, especially without comments. Paul is a very difficult and a very obscure writer."

"Then you do think there is something in the passage I have read?"

After looking down his dignified nose for a long time, he said:

"Of course, the Church has an explanation. All the same, it's very odd that St. Paul should have said such a thing—very odd."

There is no doubt that I owe a great deal of my happiness to Edward; all my life long he has been exquisite entertainment. And I fell to thinking that Nature was very cruel to have led me, like Moses, within sight of the Promised Land. A story would be necessary to bring Edward into literature, and it would be impossible to devise an action to which he should be a part. The sex of a woman is odious to him, and a man with two thousand a year does not rob nor steal, and he is so uninterested in his fellow-men that he has never an ill word to say about anybody. John Eglinton is a little thing; Æ is a soul that few will understand; but Edward is universal— more universal than Yeats, than myself, than any of us, but for lack of a story I shall not be able to give him the immortality in literature which he seeks in sacraments. Shakespeare always took his stories from some other people. Turgenev's portrait of him would be thin, poor, and evasive, and Balzac would give us the portrait of a mere fool. And Edward is not a fool. As I understand him he is a temperament without a rudder; all he has to rely upon is his memory, which isn't a very good one, and so he tumbles from one mistake into another. My God! it is a terrible thing to happen to one, to understand a man better than he understands himself, and to be powerless to help him. If I had been able to undo his faith I should have raised him to the level of Sir Horace Plunkett, but he resisted me; and perhaps he did well, for he came into the world seeing things separately rather than relatively, and had to be a Catholic. He is a born Catholic, and I remembered one of his confessions— a partial confession, but a confession: "If you had been brought up as strictly as I have been——" I don't think he ever finished the sentence; he often leaves sentences unfinished, as if he fears to think things out. The end of the sentence should run: "You would not dare to think independently." He thinks that his severe bringing-up has robbed him of something. But the prisoner ends by liking his prison-house, and on another occasion he said: "If it hadn't been for the Church, I don't know what would have happened to me."

My thoughts stopped, and when I awoke I was thinking of Hughes. Perhaps the link between Hughes and Edward was Loughrea Cathedral. He had shown me a photograph of some saints modeled by Hughes. "Hughes is away in Paris," I said, "modeling saints for Loughrea Cathedral. The last time I saw him was at Walter Osborne's funeral," and Walter's death set me thinking of the woman I had lost, and little by little all she had told me about herself floated up in my mind like something that I had read. I had never seen her father nor the Putney villa in which she had been brought up, but she had made me familiar with both through her pleasant mode of conversation, which was never to describe anything, but just to talk about things, dropping phrases here and there, and the phrases she dropped were so well chosen that the comfort of the villa, its pompous meals and numerous servants, its gardens and greenhouses "with stables and coach-house just behind" are as well known to me as the house that I am living in, better known in a way, for I see it through the eyes of the imagination . . . clearer eyes than the physical eyes.

It does not seem to me that anyone was ever more conscious of whence she had come and of what she

had been; she seemed to be able to see herself as a
child again, and to describe her childhood with her
brother (they were nearly the same age) in the villa
and in the villa's garden. I seemed to see them always as two rather staid children who were being
constantly dressed by diligent nurses and taken out
for long drives in the family carriage. They did
not like these drives and used to hide in the garden;
but their governess was sent to fetch them, and they
were brought back. Her father did not like to have
the horses kept waiting, and one day as Stella stood
with him in the passage, he rather impatient, calling
to his wife, she saw her mother come out of her
bedroom beautifully dressed. Her father whispered
something in his wife's ear and her mother said, "Oh,
Hubert!" He followed her into her bedroom and
Stella remembered how the door closed behind them.
In my telling, the incident seems to lose some of
its point, but in Stella's relation it seemed to put
her father and his wife before me and so clearly that
I could not help asking her what answer her father
would make were she to tell him that she had a lover.
A smile hovered in her grave face. "He would look
embarrassed," she said, "and wonder why I should
have told him such a thing, and then I think he
would go to the greenhouse, and when he returned
he would talk to me about something quite different."

I don't think that Stella ever told me about the
people that came to their house, but people must
have come to it, and as an example of how a few
words can convey an environment I will quote her:
"I always wanted to talk about Rossetti," she said,

and these seven words seem to me to tell better than any description the life of a girl living with a formal father in a Putney villa, longing for something, not knowing exactly what, and anxious to get away from home. . . . I think she told me she was eighteen or nineteen and had started painting before she met Florence at the house of one of her father's friends; a somewhat sore point this meeting was, for Florence was looked upon by Stella's father as something of a Bohemian. She was a painter, and knew all the Art classes and the fees that had to be paid, and led Stella into the world of studios and models and girl friends. She knew how to find studios and could plan out a journey abroad. Stella's imagination was captured, and even if her father had tried to offer opposition to her leaving home he could not have prevented her, for she was an heiress (her mother was dead and had left her a considerable income); but he did not try, and the two girls set up house together in Chelsea; they traveled in Italy and Spain; they had a cottage in the country; they painted pictures and exhibited their pictures in the same exhibitions; they gave dances in their studios and were attracted by this young man and the other; but Stella did not give herself to anyone, because, as she admitted to me, she was afraid that a lover would interrupt the devotion which she intended to give to Art. But life is for ever casting itself into new shapes and forms, and no sooner had she begun to express herself in Art than she met me. I was about to go to Ireland to preach a new gospel, and must have seemed a very impulsive and fantastic person to her, but were not impulsiveness and fantasy just the qualities that would appeal to her? And were not gravity and good sense the qualities that would appeal to me, determined as I was then to indulge myself in a little madness?

I could not have chosen a saner companion than Stella; my instinct had led me to her; but because one man's instinct is a little more clear than another's, it does not follow that he has called reason to his aid. It must be remembered always that the art of painting is as inveterate in me as the art of writing, and that I am never altogether myself when far away from the smell of oil paint. Stella could talk to one about painting, and all through that wonderful summer described in "Salve" our talk flowed on as delightfully as a breeze in Maytime, and as irresponsible, flashing thoughts going by and avowals perfumed with memories. Only in her garden did conversation fail us, for in her garden Stella could only think of her flowers, and it seemed an indiscretion to follow her as she went through the twilight gathering dead blooms or freeing plants from noxious insects. But she would have had me follow her, and I think was always a little grieved that I wasn't as interested in her garden as I was in her painting; and my absent-mindedness when I followed her often vexed her and my mistakes distressed her.

"You are interested," she said, "only in what I say about flowers and not in the flowers themselves. You like to hear me tell about Miss —— whose business in life is to grow carnations, because you already see her, dimly, perhaps, but still you see her in a story. Forget her and look at this Miss Shifner!"

"Yes, it is beautiful, but we can only admire the flowers that we notice when we are children," I answered. "Dahlias, china roses, red and yellow tulips, tawny wallflowers, purple pansies, are never long out of my thoughts, and all the wonderful varieties of the iris, the beautiful blue satin and the cream, some shining like porcelain, even the common iris that grows about the moat."

"But there were carnations in your mother's garden?"

"Yes, and I remember seeing them being tied with bass. But what did you say yesterday about carnations? That they were the——"

She laughed and would not tell me, and when the twilight stooped over the high trees and the bats flitted and the garden was silent except when a fish leaped, I begged her to come away to the wild growths that I loved better than the flowers.

"But the mallow and willow-weed are the only two that you recognize. How many times have I told you the difference between self-heal and tufted vetch?"

"I like cow-parsley and wild hyacinths and——"

"You have forgotten the name. As well speak of a woman that you loved but whose name you had forgotten."

"Well, if I have, I love trees better than you do, Stella. You pass under a fir unstirred by the mystery of its branches, and I wonder at you, for I am a tree worshiper, even as my ancestors, and am moved as they were by the dizzy height of a great silver fir. You like to paint trees, and I should like to paint flowers if I could paint; there we are set forth, you and I."

I have told in "Salve" that in Rathfarnham she found many motives for painting; the shape of the land and the spire above the straggling village appealed to me, but she was not altogether herself in these pictures. She would have liked the village away, for man and his dwellings did not form part of her conception of a landscape; large trees and a flight of clouds above the trees were her selection, and the almost unconscious life of kine wandering or sheep seeking the sheltering shade of a tree.

Stella was a good walker, and the name Mount Venus and my assurance that it was as beautiful as any spot in Ireland enticed her, and we followed the long road leading from Rathfarnham up the hills, stopping to admire the long plain which we could see through the comely trees shooting out of the shelving hillside.

"If I have beguiled you into a country where there are no artists and few men of letters, you can't say that I have not shown you comely trees. And now if you can walk two miles farther up this steep road I will show you a lovely prospect."

And I enjoyed her grave admiration of the old Queen Anne dwelling-house, its rough masonry, the yew hedges, and the path along the hillside leading to the Druid altar. The coast-line swept in beautiful curves, but she did not like to hear me say that the drawing of the shore reminded her of Corot.

"It is a sad affectation," she said, "to speak of Nature reminding one of pictures."

"Well, the outlines of Howth are beautiful," I answered, "and the haze is incomparable. I should like to have spoken about a piece of sculpture, but for your sake, Stella, I refrain."

She was interested in things rather than ideas, and I remember her saying to me that things interest us only because we know that they are always slipping from us. A strange thing for a woman to say to her lover. She noticed all the changes of the seasons and loved them, and taught me to love them. She brought a lamb back from Rathfarnham, a poor forlorn thing that had run bleating so pitifully across the windy field that she had asked the shepherd where the ewe was, and he had answered that she had been killed overnight by a golf ball. "The lamb will be dead before morning," he added. And it was that March that the donkey produced a foal, a poor ragged thing that did not look as if it ever could be larger than a goat, but the donkey loved her foal.

"Do you know the names of those two birds flying up and down the river?"

"They look to me like two large wrens with white waistcoats."

"They are water-ouzels," she said.

The birds flew with rapid strokes of the wings, like kingfishers, alighting constantly on the river, on large mossy stones, and though we saw them plunge into the water, it was not to swim, but to run along the bottom in search of worms.

"But do worms live under water?"

The rooks were building, and a little while after a great scuffling was heard in one of the chimneys and a young jackdaw came down and soon became tamer than any bird I had ever seen, tamer than a parrot, and at the end of May the corncrake called from the meadow that summer had come again, and the kine wandered in deeper and deeper and deeper herbage. The days seemed never to end, and looking through the branches of the chestnut in which the fruit had not begun to show, we caught sight of a strange spectacle. Stella said, "A lunar rainbow," and I wondered, never having heard of or seen such a thing before.

"I shall never forget that rainbow, Stella, and am glad that we saw it together."

In every love story lovers reprove each other for lack of affection, and Stella had often sent me angry letters which caused me many heart-burnings and brought me out to her; in the garden there were reconciliations, we picked up the thread again, and the summer had passed before the reason of these quarrels became clear to me. One September evening Stella said she would accompany me to the gate, and we had not gone very far before I began to notice that she was quarreling with me. She spoke of the loneliness of the Moat House, and I had answered that she had not been alone two evenings that week. She admitted my devotion. "And if you admit that there has been no neglect——"

She would not tell me, but there was something she was not satisfied with, and before we reached the end of the avenue she said, "I don't think I can tell you." But on being pressed she said:

"Well, you don't make love to me often enough."

And full of apologies I answered, "Let me go back."

"No, I can't have you back now, not after having spoken like that."

But she yielded to my invitation, and we returned to the house, and next morning I went back to Dublin a little dazed, a little shaken.

A few days after she went away to Italy to spend the winter and wrote me long letters, interesting me in herself, in the villagers, in the walks and the things that she saw in her walks, setting me sighing that she was away from me, or that I was not with her. And going to the window I would stand for a long time watching the hawthorns in their bleak wintry discontent, thinking how the sunlight fell into the Italian gardens, and caught the corner of the ruin she was sketching; and I let my fancy stray for a time unchecked. "It would be wonderful to be in Italy with her, but——"

I turned from the window suspicious, for there was a feeling at the back of my mind that with her return an anxiety would come into my life that I would willingly be without. She had told me she had refrained from a lover because she wished to keep all herself for her painting, and now she had taken to herself a lover. She was twenty years younger than I was, and at forty-six or thereabouts one begins to feel that one's time for love is over; one is consultant rather than practitioner. But it was impossible to dismiss the subject with a jest, and I found myself face to face with the question—If these twenty years were removed, would things be different? It seemed to me that the difficulty that had arisen would have been the same earlier in my life as it was now, and returning to the window I watched the hawthorns blowing under the cold gray Dublin sky.

"The problem is set," I said, "for the married, and every couple has to solve it in one way or another, but they have to solve it; they have to come to terms with love, especially the man, for whom it is a question of life and death. But how do they come to terms?" And I thought of the different married people I knew. Which would be most likely to advise me—the man or the woman? "It would be no use to seek advice; every case is different," I said. If anybody were to advise me it would be the man, for the problem is not so difficult for a woman. She can escape from love easier than her lover or her husband; she can plead, and her many pleadings were considered, one by one, and how in married life the solution that seems to lovers so difficult is solved by marriage itself, by propinquity. But not always, not always. The question is one of extraordinary interest and importance; more marriages come to shipwreck, I am convinced, on this very question than upon any other. In the divorce cases published we read of incompatibility of temper and lack of mutual tastes, mere euphemisms that deceive nobody. The image of a shipwreck rose up in me naturally.

"She will return, and like a ship our love for each other will be beaten on these rocks and broken. We shall not be able to get out to sea. She will return, and when she returns her temperament will have to be adjusted to mine, else she will lose me altogether, for men have died of love, though Shakespeare says they haven't. Manet and Daudet—both died of love"; and the somewhat absurd spectacle of a lover waiting for his mistress to return, and yet dreading her returning, was constantly before me.

It often seemed to me that it was my own weakness that created our embarrassment. A stronger man would have been able to find a way out, but I am not one that can shape and mold another according to my desire; and when she returned from Italy I found myself more helpless than ever, and I remember, and with shame, how, to avoid being alone with her, I would run down the entire length of a train, avoiding the empty carriages, crying "Not here, not here!" at last opening the door of one occupied by three or four people, who all looked as if they were bound for a long journey. I remember, too, how about this time I came with friends to see Stella, whether by accident or design, frankly I know not; I only know that I brought many friends to see her, thinking they would interest her.

"If you don't care to come to see me without a chaperon, I would rather you didn't come at all," she said, humiliating me very deeply.

"It seemed to me," I answered, blushing, "that you would like to see ——" and I mentioned the name of the man who had accompanied me.

"If I am cross sometimes it is because I don't see enough of you."

It seems to me that it was then that the resolve hardened in my heart to become her friend . . . if she would allow me to become her friend. But in what words should I frame my request and my apology? All the time our life was becoming less amiable, until one evening I nipped the quarrel that was beginning, stopping suddenly at the end of the avenue.

"It is better that we should understand each other. The plain truth is that I must cease to be your lover unless my life is to be sacrificed."

"Cease to be my lover!"

"That is impossible, but a change comes into every love story."

The explanation stuttered on. I remember her saying: "I don't wish you to sacrifice your life." I have forgotten the end of her sentence. She drew her hand suddenly across her eyes. "I will conquer this obsession."

A man would have whined and cried and besought and worried his mistress out of her wits. Women behave better than we; only once did her feelings overcome her. She spoke to me of the deception that life is. Again we were standing by the gate at the end of the chestnut avenue, and I remember her telling me how a few years ago life had seemed to hold out its hands to her; her painting and her youth created her enjoyment.

"But now life seems to have shrivelled up," she said; "only a little dust is left."

"Nothing is changed, so far as you and I are concerned. We see each other just the same."

"I am no more to you than any other woman."

She went away again to Italy to paint and returned to Ireland, and one day she came to see me, and remained talking for an hour. I have no memory of what we said to each other, but a very clear memory of our walk through Dublin over Carlisle Bridge and along the quays. I had accompanied her as far the Phœnix Park gates and at the corner of the Conyngham Road, just as I was bidding her good-bye, she said:

"I want to ask your advice on a matter of importance to me."

"And to me, for what is important to you is equally important to me."

"I am thinking," she said, "of being married."

At the news it seems to me that I was unduly elated and tried to assume the interest that a friend should.

XII

It was three years after that the Colonel asked me to go to see some friends who lived in the Clondalkin district, and we followed the quays talking of the woman we were going to see and her sisters in Galway, but when we reached the long road leading to the Moat House, a group of trees (one of Stella's motives) recalled her, and so vividly, that I could not keep myself from speaking of her.

"I have no peace since her death. Not every day," I said, "nor every night, else I should be dead by now, or mad; consciousness is spasmodic, and no warning is given. Any sight or sound is enough. She painted those trees; they hang in my room, feathery against a blue sky that has changed to gray, to everlasting gray." A touch of rhetoric had come into my speech. . . . Yet I was speaking truthfully, and the Colonel tried to soothe me.

"Blame! Of course no blame attaches to me, and yet . . . I may have wronged Florence. But I never felt any remorse on her account, only on Stella's. The question isn't whether I gave her the best advice that might have been given in the circumstances; I gave her the only advice that was possible for me to give. I knew nothing but good of the man; and the advice I gave was the only advice

295

she would have taken. No, I cannot reproach my-self with anything, and yet, and yet—— Why did I speak in his favor? And that is what I am afraid no one will ever be able to tell me. Was it because I wished to free myself from all responsibility? There was none. She took her chance with me and I took mine with her—an equal chance in those days when women desert their lovers as frequently as men desert their mistresses. We were bound by no contract; it was no passing fancy, no infidelity that parted us. Again and again I have given thanks to my stars, to my destiny, to the Providence that watches over me that it is impossible to trace any connection between my confession to her and her announcement to me of her marriage. More than a year intervened."

"I can't see that any blame attaches to you for the advice that you gave."

"Nor can I, yet her death overshadows my life, and for no reason. You see I told her, but not till she had admitted that she was going to be married, or was thinking of being married, that I had gotten a letter from Elizabeth, inviting me to come to see her. She had neglected me for years, ever since her marriage, but she is the only woman of whom I did not weary. A sister-mistress," I said. The Colonel, who does not understand these subtleties, kept si-lence. I had expected him to ask why I had told Stella of the letter, but the Colonel never asks per-sonal questions, and I doubt if he was very much interested in my story. "It may have been to drive her into this marriage that I told her that this other woman had written to me. What do you think?"

"I don't think it at all likely. She was determined on her marriage before she spoke to you about it. You have no reason to suppose that her marriage was not a happy one?"

"On the contrary there are many reasons to think that it was a very happy one."

"I don't see there is any cause for blame."

"Nor do I, but her death is the one thing that I wish had not happened to me."

I waited for the Colonel to continue the inquiry, but he showed no inclination to do so and his indifference exasperated me without shocking me as Edward had done when I had gone to him for sympathy, throwing all the blame upon myself, and he had answered: "Why didn't she mind herself?"—the pure peasant speaking through him; and to escape from the atmosphere of the cabin I looked toward the Colonel. "Any mention," I thought, "of Sarsfield and the Siege of Limerick would rouse him"; but having no desire for a historical disquisition at that moment, I began to think out the whole story again, finding some consolation in remembering that it was not for any mere woman I had crossed two seas, but for her whom I had sought for twenty years, turning from many fallacious forms and vain appearances, till at length I discovered the divine reciprocation of all my instincts and aspirations, the prophetic echo of my eternity, one summer's day among a luncheon party in Auteuil. Certain moments cannot pass behind us, and it does not seem

to me possible that I shall ever outlive that moment, when I rose out of my chair to meet my fate,
unsuspicious, of course. My fate wore that day
the moving tints of a shot-silk gown. I would give
many guineas for those few yards of silk, faded and
torn to-day, but which once held—— My habitual
readers need not be told that they did not cover a
dusky body from Italy or Spain, else writing were
indeed a vain thing; my readers have guessed already
that nobody but Rubens could set forth my natural
affinity. She came to me out of Flanders in all the
fair bloom of her twentieth summer, Rubens and
nothing but Rubens; the full, flower-like eyes, the
round brow, the golden hair and the lilt that carries
her along at the head of a rout of satyrs and fauns
hustling drunken Silenus through a forest glade. If
the dryad in Rubens's picture were to come upon a
traveler's fire in a forest, she would sit by it warm-
ing her shins as long as it lasted, and then depart
for lack of thought to rouse the ashes into flame
again with some dry branches, and the arts are to
my mistress what that casual flame was to her an-
cestress; the arts cheer Elizabeth on a cold evening, but she rises at daybreak, and overtaking the
satyrs and fauns in a mossy dell abandons herself
again to the present moment, the only moment of
worth to her despite her intelligence.

"I can pick up a thread," I had heard her say,
"but I can't stand continuity," and feeling that it
would have been stupid to answer, "You look upon
me as a thread than can be picked up and dropped
with every change of fancy," I had started for a

country; and after journeying many days came to a castle in a hilly country fronting great prospects of pasture in which kine wandered in long herds about the edge of the woods. She was watching for my coming by the balustraded terrace, and she led me into the thick woods that grew about the castle, for only in the woods were we safe from human surprises, and day after day she led me through sunny interspaces for many a pleasant frolic in the warm fragrant grass; and under the tasseled branches of the larches we listened to "the little musicians of the world": the blackbird in the underwood, the thrush on the high branch. The silence of the woods is a book of ancient lore, but at the moment when it seemed about to yield up its secret to us, a yaffle hidden in the branches above us crossed from wood to wood mocking us with insolent laughter.

But all the while of this summer pleasance somebody was dying near us; we were parted for many months, and when we came together again our love story was no longer told in the woods. She seemed so contented and docile in this Michaelmas summer that I said, "There will be no change," for I did not like to think that it was impossible for her to love me always, though I knew very well that in ten years I should be too old even to desire her love, the love that now united us, and any other love was unthinkable to me, so obsessed was I by her soul and body. We like to deceive ourselves; we must deceive ourselves. "I wonder if we shall love each other always, if in ten years' time——" She laughed, for in ten years' time I should be an old man. Nor was my foreseeing far ahead. Three weeks after she took me aside to confide a strange project to me.

"You don't mind, darling, if I don't see you to-night? I prefer to tell you —— has asked me if he might come. I can't well refuse. You don't mind?"

"However much I minded this inconstancy it would be vain for me to try to oppose your wishes, and, moreover, you would hate me if I did."

"How well you know me! How clever you are!"

The pair of shanks and ears that had come into our garden through the underwood disappeared soon after, never to return; and we resumed our love-story; and then another pair of shanks and another pair of ears appeared, and these were succeeded by more shanks and ears, and the thought became clear that the last leaves were falling, and that no renewal of our love would ever happen in my life again. "But is this death of love a thing that I should regret?" I asked myself. Love is for the young and for the middle-aged, and I was growing old, the love of the senses was burning out, and it would be better to quench it by a sudden resolve than to keep blowing upon the ashes, undignified and un-healthy, the folly of fools. By fifty we should have learnt that human life is a lonely thing and can-not be shared; delirious transports do not help us; we are farther from our mistresses when they throw their arms about us than we are when we sit by the fire, elderly men, dreaming of the kisses given and the words said in distant years. Recollection

is the resource of the middle-aged, so says Turgenev
in one of his many beautiful stories. So did I reason
with myself, and for two or three months I believed
that love would never flame up in my life again, but
one evening a lady whom I had known many years
ago crossed a restaurant, and I ran to her for news
of a friend of hers. She had not heard of Doris
for some years, and in reply to my question if Doris
were married she said she had not heard of any
marriage, and becoming suddenly anxious about this
girl I wrote to her relations, who answered that
Doris was not married; my letter had been forwarded to her, and to this letter came a delightful
answer from Florac, a town that will be sought
vainly on the map. It will be discovered, however, in
a story entitled "The Lovers of Orelay," and if the
reader of "Vale" be wishful to know what happened
at Orelay he can do so in a volume entitled "Memoirs
of My Dead Life," but he need not read this novel to
follow adequately the story of "Vale." The difference
between one man and another is so slight that I
could come to no other conclusion than that dear
Edward was right—women cannot be adjudged an
æsthetic sense. "Man," I said to Dujardin, "possesses an æsthetic sense, but he is not an æsthetic
animal like cats, horses, or women," and he had
answered me that woman's point of view is different
from man's, an argument that calls into question
the reality of the visible world. I don't think the
point has ever been fairly argued out; however this
may be, I have never been able to get it out of my
head that women are idealists, and that it is their

natural idealism which enables them to ignore our ugliness. "Extraordinary!" I said, for looking into Doris's face I could see that she was pleased and happy; and the thought came into my mind that if Lewis Marshall were to see us together he would be astonished by it, for it had always been his conviction that no woman could ever love me. I remembered his hardly concealed pity of my ugliness, his sudden inspiration that I should grow a beard for my chin deflected, and how I had been taken to a tailor, and instructed when the clothes came home how I must lean against the doorpost and look through the ballroom. The company should be gazed at with indifference; a nonchalant air, he said, attracted women, and many years of my life were spent trying to imitate him. Traces of Ponsonby Marshall linger in me still, but my deliberate and conscious imitation of him was fruitless. "Time," he said to me, "wears away everything, even ugliness; you will be more interesting after thirty than before." And it was he who told me that Goethe had said, "We had better take care what we desire in youth, for in age we will get it."

The pedant that was in Goethe muddied this utterance. We do not choose our desires; he should have said, "If we desire in youth ardently, our desires will be fulfilled in age." "But what is truth?" the sage has often asked, and the æsthetician in me regretted Doris's taste for elderly men, and, stopping before the *armoire à glace* at Orelay, I had felt intensely that this love story was no frolic of nymph and satyr, but a disgraceful exhibition of

302

Beauty and the Beast. I felt that I did not find the pleasure in Doris's beauty that I should have found if I had met her earlier in my life. "I live," I said, "in a world in which æsthetes rule the roost," and spent much time wondering what kind of punishment would be meted out to me if my morality were accepted generally.

Theories, however, avail us nothing, and it was not till several months after parting with Doris that I began to reconsider the important question—important, for no man lives who can say he is not interested in the question when a man should begin to try—how shall I put it? Well, to avoid unplatonic love encounters. But is an encounter ever platonic? A question for grammarians, for me it is to tell that a few months after my return to Dublin a lady called to see my pictures; the encounter of our lips sent the blood rushing to my head, and so violently that for ten minutes I lay where I had fallen on the sofa, holding my splitting temples. "My time for love encounters is over," I said, reaching out my hand to her sadly. . . . She was too frightened to answer, and after proposing a glass of water was glad to get away out of the house. A sigh escaped me; my head was quieter, and, struggling to my feet, I stood by the window watching the hawthorns blowing. At last words came to me: "Love's period is over for me. Life is forever changing, and very little remains after fifty for a man and still less for a woman. We are forever dying. Woolly bear is succeeded by the cricket bat, the bat is followed by the rod, the gun, the horse,

the girl, and between fifty and sixty we discover
that our love-life is over and done. Our interest in
sex, however, remains the same, but it is an intellectual interest, changed, transformed, lifted out
of the flesh. Our eyes follow the movement of the
body under the silken gown, a well-turned neck and
shapely bosom please us, and we like to look into the
feminine eyes and read the feminine soul; but we do
not kiss the point of white shoulders when thought-
less ladies lead us away after dinner into a corner
of a shadowy drawing-room and cry in our ears,
"No, all is not over yet."

I wandered out into the garden, finding consolation in the thought that one does not grieve for a
lost appetite, for a lost power, for a lost force.
"Horrible," I said, and my eyes wandered over my
garden, for the month was October. The dahlias
were blackening and the Michaelmas daisies were
growing slattern; soon there would be no flowers
left but the flower that never fails to remind me
of the mops with which coachmen wash their carriage
wheels. "The swallows must be by now half way
across the Mediterranean. Soon they will be nesting
among the stones of Cheops' Pyramid," and, my
thoughts returning to myself, I said, "My mother
used to say that I was born with a silver spoon in
my mouth." Celibacy is set above all the other virtues in Ireland, and the Irish people will listen to my
exhortations now that I have become the equal of
the priest, the nun, and the ox. Chastity is the pre-
rogative of the prophet, why no man can tell, and
dear Edward, to whom the virtue of chastity is es-

pecially dear, believes that it was the stories of what the newspapers would call "my unbridled passions" that had caused the Irish people to turn a deaf ear to my exhortations that they should speak Irish and write Irish, and to my prophesying that a new literature would arise out of the new language, or the old language revived.

My thoughts unfolded, and I remembered how strangely I had been moved the night in the Temple when Edward said he would like to write his plays in Irish. "The Tale of a Town" had brought me to Tillyra, and I had caught sight of Cathleen ni Houlihan in the dusk over against the Burran mountains as I returned through the beech-woods and the dank bracken. The rewriting of "The Tale of a Town" had awakened the Irishman that was dormant in me, and the Boer War had turned my love of England to hatred of England, and a voice heard on three different occasions had bidden me pack my portmanteau and return to Ireland. The voice was one that had to be obeyed, but Ireland had not listened to me and until now it seemed that I had misread the signs. "But Nature is not a humorist. She intended to redeem Ireland from Catholicism and has chosen me as her instrument, and has cast chastity upon me so that I may be able to do her work," I said. As soon as my change of life becomes known the women of Ireland will come to me crying, "Master, speak to us, for, at the bidding of our magicians, we have borne children long enough. May we escape from the burden of child-bearing without sin?" they will ask me, and I will answer them:

"Ireland has lain too long under the spell of the magicians, without will, without intellect, useless and shameful, the despised of nations. I have come into the most impersonal country in the world to preach personality—personal love and personal religion, personal art, personality for all except for God"; and I walked across the greensward afraid to leave the garden, and to heighten my inspiration I looked toward the old apple-tree, remembering that many had striven to draw forth the sword that Wotan had struck into the tree about which Hunding had built his hut. Parnell, like Sigmund, had drawn it forth, but Wotan had allowed Hunding to strike him with his spear. And the allegory becoming clearer I asked myself if I were Siegfried, son of Sigmund slain by Hunding, and if it were my fate to reforge the sword that lay broken in halves in Mimi's cave.

It seemed to me that the garden filled with tremendous music, out of which came a phrase glittering like a sword suddenly drawn from its sheath and raised defiantly to the sun.

XIII

Ever since the day that I strayed into my garden
and it had been revealed to me as I walked therein
that Catholics had not written a book worth reading
since the Reformation, my belief had never faltered
that I was an instrument in the hands of the Gods,
and that their mighty purpose was the liberation
of my country from priestcraft. But seemingly
they had forgotten to put a spear in my hand and a
buckler on my arm, and for many months I had
stood perplexed, but never doubting. I knew there
was no preacher in me, and therefore had striven to
fashion a story, and then a play, but the artist in
me could not be suborned. Davitt came with a
project for a newspaper, but he died; and I had
begun to lose patience, to lose spirit, and to mutter,
"I am without hands to smite," and suchlike, until
one day on coming in from the garden, the form
which the book should take was revealed to me.
"But an autobiography," I said, "is an unusual
form for a sacred book." My doubts quenched a
moment after in a memory of Paul, and the next
day the dictation of the rough outline from the
Temple to Moore Hall was begun, and from that
outline, decided upon in a week of inspiration, I
have never strayed. Any straying would have been

fatal, so intricate are the windings of the story I had been chosen to tell. As soon as the sketch of the whole was completed, the text of "Ave" kept steadily rising; and one murk December day the typewritten copy was tied up, sealed, registered, and directed to Heinemann in Bedford Street. But no pause occurred in the composition, for no sooner was "Ave" out of the house than I set myself to the dictation of "Salve," following my memory of a long search for divinity through Meath and Louth, introducing the Colonel into the narrative, never stopping until Heinemann's letter came proposing the May of that year as the best time for the publication of "Ave." And it was his letter that planted the conviction in my mind that "Hail and Farewell" had brought my sojourn in Ireland to a close.

He had written, "Are you coming to live in England?" meaning nothing very probably thereby, but setting me thinking all the same that it would be in bad taste for me to remain in Dublin meeting my friends and acquaintances in the street, my models, and when the letter slipped from my hand to the floor I foresaw how exile would give the book a definite distinction.

The scope of my design was to begin in the Temple and to end at Moore Hall; but I was loath to go to Moore Hall, and often answered Miss Gough, "Of what use for me to go there? I can see the lake with my mind's eye better than I could see it with the physical. All the beautiful curves of the bay are before me, along Kiltoome and Connor Island."

"But if the lake hasn't changed, the country has, and you'll bring back many new impressions and moods."

"You may be right. The gentry have gone and the big houses are in ruins, or empty or sold to nuns and monks, who are the only people who can afford to live in fine houses. Ballinafad is now a monastery."

"You'll see Ballinafad."

"I know it as well as Moore Hall."

"But you haven't seen it as a monastery?"

"He hasn't had time yet to pull down the old house and build cells; and all I shall see is a peasant in a frock and sandaled shoon instead of a peasant in frieze and clouted shoon; merely a difference of garb."

"One never can say what one is going to see."

"You may be right. I'll go. Nature is full of surprises. Prolific mother of detail, I'll go to thee."

And I wrote to the secretary of the Great Western Railway asking him if he would stop the morning mail for me at Balla.

"The road from Balla," I said to Miss Gough, "passes by Lakemount; I shall only have to turn about a mile aside to see the woods of Ballinafad. It may be I shall drive to the house on my way to Moore Hall."

But the secretary wrote saying that he could not stop the train for me at Balla, and his refusal to order the train to my convenience annoyed me very much, for some months before he had stopped the up-train at Kilcock to suit the convenience of a priest.

"No one is cared for in this country but priests. I must write to the Colonel asking him to send a conveyance to meet me at Manulla."

Ballinafad lies away to the left between Balla and Manulla, and on stepping out of the train I said: "To take in Ballinafad would mean a round of four or five miles. I will instead drive over from Moore Hall with the Colonel. But where is the trap?" I asked myself in terror, for there was nothing to see but gray sky and bridge or to hear but the plaint of telegraph wires. The porter himself at that moment seemed an hallucination, and overtaking him swiftly I laid hand on his shoulder and he told me that if the Colonel's trap did not arrive soon, my best chance of getting a car would be in the village. After conference with the station-master, he promised that as soon as his work was finished he would go down and inquire, but he was afraid Johnnie MacCormac had gone to Westport. The village was about a mile and a half away, and if Johnnie wasn't at home the only thing to do would be to wire for a car to Balla. Balla was seven miles away; an hour and a half wait at Manulla Junction would seem like a lifetime, and I had begun to wonder how the station-master and the porters managed to get through the day, when the porter said he thought he heard a "yoke" coming up the road. "He'll cross the bridge over beyant"; and the bridge became at once the object of interest to me. "It's his 'yoke' right enough.

You'll be off now in no time"; and these words were
spoken in a tone that convinced me the man was
conscious of his melancholy lot. But I couldn't
stop at Manulla to keep him company; as soon as I
left he would be as lonely as before; everyone for
himself, especially at Manulla, and the devil gets the
hindmost. Nor could I hear the end of this story,
the Colonel's groom being so anxious to excuse himself for being late that I had to listen to him telling
me he had gone to Derrinanny to sleep with his
family overnight, and the Colonel hadn't told him
that he would be wanting him to go to the train in
the morning.

"I wonder where the station-master and the porters live?"

"Are you after leaving anything behind you,
sir?"

"No, I was merely wondering what they do when
not at work at the station. There are only two
trains in the day." The boy thought there were
three, but he would be able to find out at the
grocer's. "So there is a shop in Manulla?"

"We'll be passing it in a minute, sir; we're just
going into the village now."

It was, perhaps, because of the steep descent in
the road and the trees on either side and between
the houses that Manulla did not seem to me an ugly
village. Nobody was about; we saw neither cat,
nor dog, nor pig in the muddy street; the groom
mentioned, however, that the Colonel knew the
priest, and as soon as we passed his chapel the
fields began again, uneventful little fields, for there

was neither tree nor brook to be seen, nor anyone at work in them; only an occasional sheep, or goat, or mule, or ass, to tell us that the country was not yet a desert. Great stones had rolled down from the walls into the boreens leading from the main road up a landscape that it would be flattering to call hilly; it was merely a little tumbled. Over the hill-side a cabin showed sometimes, and at last a dog bounded out of one, and I said:

"Where there's a dog there's a man, and where there's a man a woman isn't far off—isn't that so?"

The boy did not answer, and, as seemingly he could not be persuaded into talk of any interest, I continued my survey of the country, noticing, for lack of something else to do, that it had flattened out without becoming a plain, and that the clouds were gathering on the horizon in a mass foretelling a downpour. But to mention that we were in for a wetting would only provoke a monosyllable from the boy. On the whole, the better chance of con-versation seemed to be in a comparison between the Manulla and the Balla road.

"The Colonel thinks this is the easier road."

"It doesn't seem to be quite so hilly, but it is treeless, whereas on the Balla road there are trees nearly all the way to Moore Hall. Ballinafad—by the way, Mr. Llewellyn Blake has settled the monks at Ballinafad, hasn't he?"

"So I've heard tell, sir."

"And how do the country people like that, and they going to get the estate divided between them?"

The boy called to the pony, and I had to repeat the question.

"The monks is giving fine wages at Ballinafad."

But how much they were paying he could not tell, and I tried to forget his presence, remembering that there never was any gentry between Balla and Castlebar, and that the only trees in the west are the woods that encircle the Big Houses. On leaving Balla one leaves Athy Valley on the right, and I took pleasure in recalling Sir Robert Blosse and Lady Harriet; their children I never knew. A little farther on was Browne Hall; Edith and Alice had been beautiful girls. The Browne Hall and the Ballinafad estates were contiguous, and Joe Blake going off to Castlebar races with his arm round his serving-maid's waist rose up in my mind as if it had been yesterday. Two miles farther up the road is Ballyglass, our post town; the mail coach used to change horses there, and I remembered my mother reining in her ponies so that we might have a good view of the coach as it came swinging round the bend. The men that clipped horses lived in Ballyglass, in a cottage with a pretty flower garden in front—a rare thing in Mayo; and from the gate of Tower Hill to Carnacun the road is wooded, between Carnacun and Moore Hall the hills are naked, and the Annys River dribbles through the low-lying fields under Annys bridge to Lough Carra.

"We shall turn into the Castlebar road presently, shan't we?"

"Yes, sir, round by Clogher."

Clogher! the name carried my thoughts over the

313

years to the time when it was our delight to go
there to gather cherries—to tear down the branches
unreproved. There were four girls at Clogher—
Helena, Lizzie, Livy, and May. Lizzie was the
merriest, and her inventiveness was my father's admiration, for, needing a hearth-rug for her doll's
house, she had divined one in a mouse. My father
delighted in this association of images—a mouse-
skin rug for a doll's house; and as we drove toward
Moore Hall it seemed to me that I could see Clogher
and its dead girls quite plainly—a little mist had
come between us, that was all. "In another instant
I shall be pondering on life and its meaning," I
said, and looked round for something in the landscape to which I might direct the lad's attention.
"Don't you think we may hope for a fine day after
all?" I asked, and the question seemed legitimate
enough, for at that moment a ray lit the worn field
in which a ewe bleated after her lamb to come at
once to relieve her distended udder.

"The lamb is the first sign of spring. The lamb
comes before the daffodil. Do you know the
flower?"

"Do you mean the daffydowndilly, sir?"

"That's what old Betty MacDonald used to call
them."

"We're just turning into the Clogher road, sir."

"Yes, and yonder is the police-station, and beyond is the cross-road—to the right Castlebar, to
the left Carnacun."

"You've a fine memory, God bless it, yer honor."

The same whitewash of the Clogher police bar-

racks struck through the trees the same as forty
years before, and I began to wonder what answer
the boy would make if I were to tell him that the
trees had not grown a foot within forty years.
"There's no use in wondering," I said. "He would
make none"; but to my surprise he said:

"Them fellows do be too busy oiling their quiffs
to put the comether on the girls."

For a moment this remark was mistaken by me
for Celtic wit, but the sullenness of my companion
stirred me to guess that perhaps one of the police-
man's quiffs had been the means of doing him out
of his own girl and that it would be well to talk to
him of something else.

"As soon as we pass the barracks we shall turn
to the left and there will be hazel bushes and rocks
on both sides of the road, and about two hundred
yards farther on we shall get a blink of Carnacun
Lake where the hill drops."

But the groom was not listening, and I fell to
thinking of the pretty brooks one sees in England,
purling and curling between low green banks, and
shadowed by willow-trees. The willow follows the
brook, and the Irish landscape lacks brooks and
willows. "Lakes are not in my temperament," I
said; and set myself to remembering the many different lakes that we catch sight of from our roads.
"Lake and Hazel" would have been a better title
perhaps than "The Untilled Field." The country
should be redeemed from that disagreeable and useless tree now that iron hoops have superseded
wooden. We used to be able to sell hazel rods to

the coopers, and I remembered their huts in Derrinrush all the summer, and Domnick Browne, who
went away to New Zealand, taking with him a bundle of rods for walking-sticks. That was forty
years ago, and he did not write till he discovered
that he could trace me no farther back than Charles
V., whereas himself went back to Charlemagne. "A
wonderful thing life is," I said, and began to notice
the endless stone walls between Moore Hall and
Manulla, loose walls dividing little fields with a hawthorn growing in one corner and two magpies flying
—whither? "The people and the country are still
savage," I mused. "Ireland is without pleasant
objects to look upon, though why there have never
been wind-mills in Ireland it would be difficult to
say, for there is plenty of wind." In my childhood
there were a few water-mills, and it was pleasing to
recall the day when the governess and the Colonel
and myself had tripped over to Tower Hill to watch
the mill-wheel. But long ago that mill stopped
working; flour is now imported. Yonder is Carnacun Lake, behind a scrubby hillside with the pines
"fornent it," as the groom would say if he could be
persuaded into speech. The lake seemed smaller
than I remembered it, but he could not tell me if it
were drying up. I looked forward to the cross-
roads, and it was pleasant to see that the smith's
forge was still there, and Grayon's house, one of my
tenants, the tenant of Ballintubber, a wealthy man,
even forty years ago, for he could afford to lend me
two hundred pounds . . . money spent during my
minority. The chapel stood up over the village on

VALE

a knoll, and the fringe of trees about it was as
ragged as when our carriage used to turn in the
gateway. The smith's house and three or four
cabins with sagging roofs were still the village of
Carnacun; nothing had been added or taken away,
and I looked out for the house licensed to sell beer
and tobacco. It was there, as dark and as dismal
as of yore, a threshold that any moralist would
approve, and above it was the great wall of the ball
alley denounced by Father James Browne in his
sermons: "You think I don't be hearing your
brogues about the doorways, and after I have gone
up the steps of the altar," he used to say. And
now the rival of his Mass had fallen into ruins, some
of the cut-stone had tumbled out of the high wall,
weeds had sprung up in the alley, and Father James's
house, to which I used to ride my pony for a Latin
lesson, was a ruin too. The present priest lives
higher up the hill, in a two-storied house with plate-
glass windows; but does he read Virgil for his pleasure and drink as good port as Father James? Be
this as it may, it will always seem to me that a great
deal of the character of the village of Carnacun
has gone with the old cottage under the ilex-trees,
the ball alley, and Father James Browne. His image
has nearly faded from my mind, but I can still recall a high-shouldered man with a large hooked nose
and a complexion like a Crofton apple, and whose
wont it was to walk about the parish in a torn cas-
sock seeing that everybody was about his business.
He would hop over the wall down into the road and
out of the road again, on to the path across the

triangular field to the school-house over yonder on the hillside. "Why, Misther School-masther, do you mind being called the school-masther? You are the school-masther just as I am the parish priesht. I don't mind being called the parish priesht. I like being called the parish priesht, so why should you not like being called the school-masther?" "So class distinctions were beginning to jar even then," I said. "And to this school we owe the disappear-ance of the Irish language from this part of the country." I remembered the children returning from this school along the road that winds through damp fields on one side, melting almost into bog about the Annys River; on the other side the land rises, and all the cabins appeared just as I had left them; a little improvement was noticeable in the last one; a style it used to be in old time, amid cess-pools, unfit truly for an animal to live in. Indeed, I used to hope that no human being would come out of its doorway until we had passed it by, and I re-membered, too, the satisfaction with which I learnt one day that this cabin was not on our property, but on the Tower Hill property. I anticipated the elder-bushes a few yards farther on, and could still see my mother and my governess gathering the flowers which were supposed to be good for sun-burn, and myself cutting the stems for pop-guns.

A path leads over the hill to the right and down to the left a boreen runs along one of our woods, to Runnineal, a Tower Hill village by the Annys River, and the house under the pines where the main road strikes through is a wood-ranger's lodge, the dwelling of a man called Murphy, whose welcome I used to dread; for, like a great big dog, he would run out of his house or saw-pit when he heard the wheels of the car, and his bark of welcome followed us until we reached the little bridge that spans the bog drain. In those days a path was a wonderful thing, much more wonderful than a road, and there was a path by the bridge; and one day I succeeded in persuading my governess to wander down it, and we had followed it through some young fir-trees; and yet undaunted I had implored that we should follow the path through a wood, and it had led us at last to a field golden with buttercups and a drain in which wild irises grew. A little farther on we spied another path leading up the hillside, a dark and suspicious path, but a girl who dropped a curt-sey told us that it would lead us right on to the stables of the Big House. We had dared to follow it too; and had come upon dells, open spaces, and copses, and trees of every kind; silver firs in whose vasty heights I was certain there were wood-pigeons' nests; and as we descended the hill on the other side a rowan delayed us; the berries were just beginning to redden, and immediately after we were in the bog road which was well known to us, and at the end of our adventure. Red rowan berries and blue irises are not of the same month; two memories seem to have got mingled. No matter, this wooded hillside was once full of adventure and mystery, and there was a dark place under the turret at the end of the garden into which I did not dare to go, bramble-covered hollows into which I used to peep and then run away, afraid to look back. But the day came when I pushed my way through the dark coverts, and lo! there was nothing.

I was awakened out of my dreams of childhood by the new gateway that the Colonel had brought from Newbrook, and it looked handsomer even than I had expected, though the Colonel's praise had led me to expect a good deal. It had opened upon one of the Newbrook avenues a hundred years ago; cut-stone was not so costly then as it is to-day: even so, money must have been more plentiful in those days, for the gateway obviously represented a great deal of labor. In those times everything came off the land: mutton, beer, butter, bread, jam; the stewards, gardeners, butlers, and huntsmen came from the village, the housemaids too, for feudalism had lasted in Ireland down to 1870. But all that is changed now; the peasants have repossessed themselves of Newbrook and are offering its trees, two hundred years old, at eighteen pence a piece. "And the trees that I am now looking at—the Moore Hall trees—will soon after my death be felled and the gateway will again be offered for sale, and there being no foolish buyer, the cut-stone will be used to build cottages."

A sudden stopping of the pony jerked me forward in my seat, and he began the ascent laboriously while I looked out for the tall laburnum up whose slippery stem I had never succeeded in swarming. It was not there, yet it existed in my memory; some hawthorn-bushes I missed too, and very little was left of the great lilac-bush that used to stand by

another path to the stables . . . one of our land-
marks. We used to look forward to seeing it when
we returned from our walks, and I remembered how
one day in mid-summer, after chasing through the
woods, playing at Red Indians, yelling as we imagined Red Indians yell on the war-path, I had thrown
myself into a haycock just by this lilac-bush, and,
looking up into the blue sky, it had seemed to me
that I had discovered how to be happy, and all night
long I had lain awake, planning for the morrow:
we would bring out whips with louder lashes and
extend our adventure into mysterious places whither
we had never dared to venture. We would penetrate
the tangled coverts despite lurking ghouls and fairies. Children see many things that grown-ups have
lost sight of. But the next day the woods had lost
some of their mystery, and when summer returned
the ghouls and fairies had died out of our imagination. Fairyland had vanished from our vision, and
I went to old Joseph Applely to ask him how it was
that I no longer experienced any desire to crack
my whip, or to hide in the lilac-bush, or to roll in
the hay.

The drive turned round a hawthorn, passed
through a glade, and I looked out for the next lilac-
bush, for it was within its perfume that I had had
my first religious conversation with the Colonel. I
could find no trace of it, but on the left, on the brow
of the lawn, were two holly-trees into which I had
shot many an arrow from the steps. But the labur-
nums that had once decorated the head of the drive,
had they died too, died of old age or for lack of

human companionship, the laburnum being a familiar tree? The last ascent is steep, and the pony
walked every step of it, not consenting to trot till
he reached the gravel sweep in front of the square
Georgian house with the great flight of steps and
big pillars supporting a balcony. On these steps
a couple of red setters were always waiting—a special breed for which the house was famous. Nell
rose up before me in her color, in her shape, in all
her winsome ways. A better dog never drew the
scent of a covey of partridges or pack of grouse,
and she would retrieve a duck far out in the reeds.
My father often beat her for coursing hares, but
despite these beatings she could not bear to be separated from him, and one evening he pulled her out
of the lake into the boat saying that she had been
swimming after us for more than an hour, and that
if the large trout had not delayed us outside the
reeds, she would have gone on swimming till she
sank. Her son, Saddler, the biggest setter ever
known—like a Newfoundland he was, and not a
single white hair in his coat—used to lie in the hall
on the mat. One day my father mentioned that the
dog always snapped if he was stirred out of his
sleep, and looked round with a bewildered air, and
then suddenly seemed to recover himself. Saddler
was suffering all this while from rabies, and as soon
as the veterinary surgeon saw him he ordered him
to be shot. Blush and Ruby were the last setters
that adorned the steps, and the steps were the only
part of the architecture that I ever liked, Moore
Hall not being in my early taste, which was for

brick, and perhaps it is still, for houses that have been added to by different generations rather than for gray square blocks with pillared balconies. That is how I used to speak of Moore Hall. Moore Hall had always seemed a Mansion House to me inferior to Clogher and Tower Hill. But it is superior to either, for it was built in 1780, and it was with a sense of relief that I had heard from the Colonel in Dublin that the roof had been raised by my father after winning some big races. The old roof was fifteen feet lower, and the slates that covered it were the small green Irish slates like tiles mortared together. It appears that it never was completely water-tight and that constant leakage had rotted the beams, so there was some excuse for the high roof and the ugly blue slates and likewise for my antipathy to Moore Hall, justified in a measure by the change. The proportions of the house had been spoilt by the new roof and by the plate-glass that my father had put into the windows of the hall and dining-room and drawing-room, and I felt sure that if I were ever to come to live in Moore Hall, the whole countryside would have to be searched for the old hand-made glass with rings in each pane like blobs of grease in soup.

But I always liked the imposing flight of steps and the hall with its Adams ceiling, and should have liked the rooms on either side better if they had not been decorated in accordance with Victorian taste. It would seem that my father's journey to the East had to expend itself somehow, and being a clever man of many aptitudes he had designed a

Greek room in an interval between racing and politics. His room had filled my childhood with admiration. But the straw color and the blue-gray chosen for the walls had faded in the course of forty years, and the decorators that had come from Dublin when the Colonel went into his residence at Moore Hall had failed to divine the original tints in the faded; the Colonel had warned me that they had failed, but I was not prepared for so complete a failure, and the somewhat coarse, very nearly vulgar appearance that had been given to the room set me thinking that perhaps it would be well to replace all this plaster of Paris with a pretty French paper. "But who could restore the Adams ceiling?" I asked myself, as I crossed a hall of fne proportions, "and absolutely untouched," I muttered, going into the dining-room. My father's pilasters and variegated woods displeased me, and I felt certain that if Moore Hall were to be the end of my life the drawing-room and dining-room would have to be brought into harmony with the hall and the roof lowered some ten or fifteen feet; "my father was too near the Georgian period to appreciate it," I added, and, raising my eyes from the carved merman and mermaid on either side of the fireplace to my ancestor in the red coat, I began to wonder if the painting were Spanish. . . . "Be that as it may, my grandfather is a Wilkie for sure"; and just as I had arrived at this conclusion the Colonel bounced in, fresh and rosy from the farmyard, all breeches and gaiters, and anxious to show me round the house.

The hall opened on to a wide passage with a stair-

case at either end, and off this passage there were
four rooms—our old school-room, the water-closet,
and two more rooms opening one into the other,
and known as the doctor's and the priest's room.
All these rooms the Colonel had thrown into one,
and he had brought down grandfather's book-cases
and set them along the walls, achieving in this way
a fine room, no doubt; but a long narrow room is
un-Georgian, and character in a house is as important as in a man. No one sits in a long, narrow
room. The fireplace is necessarily at one end, so
while our left side is freezing our right is being
roasted. Rooms should be square, there can be no
doubt about it; and the present library is at another disadvantage—it overlooks a back-yard, a
desert place surrounded by high walls, the top of
the walls spiked like a jail. This desert place was
once set round with outhouses; a scullery opened
on to this yard, and the hen-house was next to it.
There was the wood-house, and on the other side of
the gate was a turf-house, and in the right-hand
corner I remembered the great chimney of the brew-
house. William Mullowney's father used to brew
beer there. But that was before my time. We used
to get our beer from Ballinrobe in the sixties; our
beer now comes up to Mayo from Dublin.

The yard had always been considered to be a
drawback, and with the disappearance of the outhouses it had become a very ugly feature. In old
times it was the center of activity. The water for
the house was brought from the lake in a water-
barrel, the cart stood in the yard with the mule-

boy beside it, and when the maids had filled their
cans he put the mule into the shafts and went away
to the lake again, leaving them to exchange words
with the garden-boy, their gossip interrupted by the
voice of the cook or the arrival of the ass from the
bog with creels of turf, which the turf-boy would
carry up the back staircase, emptying his load into
the great barrels that stood on the different landings, filling with special care the barrel in Joseph
Applely's pantry, and I think it was Joseph who
told me that these barrels had come from Spain
filled with port and sherry. And my thoughts passing into dialogue, I said:

"Did Joseph Applely say that they came from
Spain in the days of my grandfather, in the days
of William Mullowney, the father of the valet I took
to Paris with me? Probably. These importations
of wine must have ceased in Ireland some time about
the beginning of the nineteenth century."

The Colonel could not tell me if this were so, and
he seemed much more interested to learn whether I
thought it would be better to rebuild the outhouses
or cover in the yard.

"Cover in the yard!" I said.

"Why not? A series of arches and a terrace on
the top."

"And a flight of steps would serve from the higher
to the lower terrace."

"And on either hand vases——"

"Or rare pieces of sculpture," I said. The
Colonel looked distressed. "But how would the
yard underneath be lighted?"

"By side windows."

"And the drip? The rain would have to go somewhere."

On our way to the bathroom he explained how it might be mitigated, if not altogether avoided.

"Here," he said, "is the bathroom."

"The first," I answered, "that Moore Hall has ever known"; and we talked of the footpans and the bidets that once formed part of the furniture of every bedroom, and the disrepute into which bathing had fallen since Roman times, all through the Middle Ages, until Anglo-Indians reintroduced the habit of the thorough washing of the body into Europe.

From the bathroom window we caught sight of the ruined privy under the beech-trees to which our ancestors were wont to adjourn in the morning, their pipes in their mouths, to talk the news, and the news was always of a racehorse, or a duel, or a hunt.

"We have improved upon those times, yet our neighbors still allow their dogs to deposit ordure upon our doorsteps. Humanity advances slowly," I observed.

The Colonel had chosen my father's dressing-room for the bathroom, the room not being as intimately associated in his mind as it was in mine with our father. I should never have had the courage to make the change, so real is my memory of the room as it stood in my father's lifetime, himself seated at the great bureau full of countless drawers at which he wrote his letters, or standing before the toilet-table between the windows covered with cut-glass phials of macassar oil, pots of bear's grease, many kinds of ivory brushes, tortoiseshell combs of all sorts and sizes, some destined for the hair of the head, some for the whiskers, relics of the days of his dandyhood, for he must have been a great dandy when Anonymous turned a shoe at Liverpool and Corunna won the Chester Cup.

He liked me to come into his dressing-room to talk to him while he lathered his face, and I remembered the lie I told him when he asked me if I had used the top of his silver shaving-pot to knock in a nail, and the day when he asked me to read him Burke's speeches aloud in an edition printed with long s's. I stumbled over these, as I should do now, and in great alarm he opened the baize door that communicated with my mother's room. As she showed little or no alarm the governess was sent for and it was put to them: Had they ever known or heard of a child of seven who could not read Burke's speeches without faltering in an edition printed with the long s's? Before Miss Westby had time to answer my mother said that she didn't believe that any child of seven could read the long s's without faltering, and I can see him, his face covered with lather, telling that he used to read the *Times* aloud to his mother at breakfast when he was three. My mother's incredulity exasperated him, and he ordered my governess and me to the school-room, where for days we sat reading a very indifferent history of England by one Lingard. We dreaded his incursions into the school-room, and

listened with apprehension while Joseph Appleby
brushed the master's silk hats and arranged his
gloves for him in the hall, and we breathed more
freely when we heard the hall-door clang, for we knew
then he had gone to the stables to feel the horses'
legs, and our hope was that the interest in the morning gallops would help him to forget my lessons.

The room in which I had seen him lying dead had
not been in use since mother's death. The Colonel
was with her; he had probably seen her die, and I
supposed that that was why he had chosen the two
rooms at the end of the passage—rooms that I
recollected as grandmother's rooms; and after visiting them he threw open the door of the summer
room, a pretty room opening on to the balcony that
the four great pillars support, and in an instant
the room returned to what it had been forty years
before, and I remembered my father sitting at the
rosewood table in the evening, drinking a large cup
of tea, telling me stories of Egypt and the Dead
Sea, Baghdad, the Euphrates and the Ganges, stories
of monkeys and alligators and hippopotami, stories
that a boy loves. "And I am older now than my
father was when he used to be telling me those
stories," I thought as we left the room and went to
the two rooms at the head of the staircase. My
grandfather's library had been allotted to me during
my stay.

"Grandfather's spirit seems still to animate these
rooms," I said. The Colonel did not answer, and
then I seemed to apprehend something that had
hitherto escaped me: Moore Hall had always seemed

alien and remote to me because it was pervaded by
the minds of those that preceded me. My grand-
fathers and grandmothers were underground, but
along the landings and in the large rooms opening
on the passages one seemed to be aware of mentali-
ties different from one's own. Nor is it strange
that this should be so, Moore Hall not having been
subjected to any new influences after 1870; and
going down to luncheon with my brother I felt I
should never be able to live in this house; I should
always feel my grandfather sitting by me wondering how it was that his grandson should practice
so familiar a style so unlike Gibbon.

"I should be always engaged in imaginary dia-
logues," I said, "telling him that he did not always
write like Gibbon but like me in his preface to the
"French Revolution," and the preface is the best
part of it."

"If you were to say that he would answer, 'But
you haven't read my history of the French Revolution,'" the Colonel answered.

After luncheon, he said he would like to show me
the garden, but I could barely see it, so clear was
my memory of the old eighteenth-century garden
with its rows of espalier apple-trees and four great
walnut-trees, one in each plot. The two great ilex-
trees whose branches leaned in front of the turret
had died; the turret was in ruins, and the Colonel
had felled a good many beeches along the twenty-foot
wall to get light and air for his fruit-trees. I was
sorry for these. "One of the walnut-trees has gone."

"But nothing grows under them," he explained,

and led me round his peach and pear and apple and cherry trees, and while he explained the different varieties, I dreamed of the sweet-briar hedge that divided my mother's flower-garden from the plots in which we had once grown potatoes, cabbages, onions, spinach, chives, parsnips, cauliflowers, beans, asparagus. The asparagus-bed was never a great success, because of the walnut-trees which my father would not allow to be felled, his mother having planted them. Even more distinct in my memory than these trees was a great apple-tree—a very venerable tree, moss-grown and carious. It stood up a little beyond the flower walk, and near it, tucked away in a corner, was a dense growth of raspberry bushes enclosed by a thick hedge, a dangerous place in my imagination, one in which witches and other evil spirits were to be met, but the fruit tempted me, and my governess once boxed my ears for having hidden myself and eaten too many raspberries.

We came upon the ruins of the greenhouse from which we used to steal the grapes, even when the door was kept locked, and my father once beat me with a horse-whip for breaking the panes, and now, elderly men both of us, the Colonel and I stood looking at a large cut-stone chimney that the Colonel had saved in case I should care to rebuild the greenhouse again.

"Cut-stone is very expensive," he added, "but in our grandfather's days labor was cheaper"; and we passed into the stables, none of which had fallen. There was the box in which Croagh Patrick neighed when the boy brought his sieveful of corn. How he plunged his muzzle into it! for he was a greedy feeder and ready to kick anyone that came near him till the last grain was licked up. In the next box I had seen Master George, one of the best horses of his year, only a few pounds behind Croagh Patrick at a mile and a half, and his superior at two miles, a terrible buck-jumper that would have dislodged any cowboy. The little ponies that these horsemen ride have not sufficient strength to throw them out of the high Mexican saddles, but Master George was sixteen hands and a half, and when his head disappeared between his legs it was no easy thing to keep on a six-pound saddle, and the tightest might have been flung out of it as I was three times one morning before breakfast, these falls irritating my father scarcely less than the long s's had done eight years before, compelling him to declare that no horse could unseat him. Joseph Applely smiled and went out of the room, and next morning my father was thrown in front of the house by the holly-trees, breaking his collar-bone, and the doctor had to be sent for.

"Wolf Dog, Anonymous, and Corunna have dragged hay out of those very racks," I said; and the coach-house recalled the coach hung on leather straps, and the great phaeton, likewise on leather straps, which hardly ever went out—a museum piece it was—and the tiny phaeton in which my mother used to drive Primrose and Ivory, a beautiful pair of ponies. The great fir at the back of the stable, in front of the hayrick, reminded me of the day that Joseph Applely took me out for a walk and taught me a little bird-lore. The nest he showed me at the end of the bough was a goldfinch's, and we explored the woods together, and far clearer than to-day is that fragrant morning by the hawthorn-tree all in flower, Joseph lifting me up to see into the blackbird's nest. And I remember his voice: "You mustn't touch the eggs, Master George, or the bird will forsake her nest." "But how will the bird know? Let's try." "We must go back, Master George, and if we return at once we shall get back in time for dinner." "Oh no, Joseph, let's go a little farther and find some more nests," I cried, for it did not seem to me that I should ever want dinner again.

But of what was the Colonel thinking? He is like his father, discreet; therefore not a man of letters, and we talked about the foreign firs which our father had planted in the sixties, and they seemed to me to be out of keeping with the landscape.

"Deodars may be suited to India," I said, "and the Wellingtonia may be well enough in California, but here they are detestable; and far worse than the deodar and the Wellingtonia is that cypress los—— something, a tree of vile habit, sending down branches to take root, creating a little jungle."

The Colonel admitted the habit, which he could not well deny, but he could not be persuaded to send round for a couple of hatchets, urging that felling trees is not the light work that I imagined it to be, the real reason being that he is as averse

as I am from felling a tree, an aversion inherent in
every sensitive nature, one might almost say in every
nature except the wood-cutter's; habit has blunted
his; he has forgotten the original instinct of tree-
worship, and perceives no longer the mystery of the
vasty height sprung out of a single seed.

It was while I was thinking these things that the
great walls of the farmyard rose up through the
beech-trees, eighteen or twenty feet high, enclosing
buildings of all kinds: stables for many cart-horses,
granaries, barns, haggards, byres, smithies. A great
deal of cut-stone had been used in these buildings,
and the Colonel had saved many pieces from the
ruins of the smithy, and these he said would come
in useful when the time came to rebuild the farmyard. I liked to hear him dreaming his dreams
while I meditated the question whether it were
crueller to fell an ox or a tree. Behind that wall I
had seen death for the first time, and with that kind
of morbid pleasure which one feels in wounding oneself, I recalled how the shepherd had come one day
into the yard driving half a dozen sheep before him,
and how, stopping in my play, I asked him why he
had brought them from the fields. He answered
me that Friday was always "killing day," and putting out his crook he caught a sheep by the leg and
felt for the fat; but not being satisfied with the animal, he allowed it to escape from him. Again he
put out his crook and caught another, and again
he was not satisfied; three or four sheep were tried;
it may have been over the fourth that he muttered,
"This one will do," and led it into a corner. He

and his boy stretched it on a slightly raised platform, and I asked why a bucket was placed under
its head. "To catch the blood, Master George,"
the shepherd answered as he sharpened his knife;
and all this ritual was so enticing that I waited
impatiently, perhaps even asked him to hurry, fearing that my governess might come and call me away
before the sheep died. It accepted death without a
bleat, looking at us all the time with round, peace-
ful eyes, in which one could read neither love of
life, nor fear of death, nor reproach; and as I write
this line I can see the blood pouring, pouring, pouring into the bucket. "Why won't he die?" I asked
myself. At last the eyes began to glaze, and I said
to the shepherd, "He has begun to die," and the
shepherd pressed the sheep all over with his great
strong fingers, urging the blood out of the wound
in the neck. And then I remembered how a few
days after the Colonel and I stopped amazed, so terrific were the shrieks we heard. But our governess
would not, or could not, tell us whence they came
or their cause. As if scenting death, we appealed
to a peasant; and he told us the butcher was killing
pigs. We ran from her to see the pigs killed; we
hid from her in a stable, and did not venture out till
she had given up the search. "I'm afraid you're
late; he's a goner by this time," the peasant called
after us, and when we arrived at the farmyard the
carcass was being cut up and salted, and it would
be some time before the butcher would be ready for
another. The Colonel was a little diffident, uncer-
tain whether he should stay to see a pig killed, but

perhaps ashamed to go lest I might laugh at him. If I rightly remember, I took on authoritative airs, and bade the men hurry, returning now and again to the dung-heap to watch the pigs; there were eleven or twelve rooting and rolling, happy, for the warm May sunlight caressed their sides, and apparently the screams of their fellow, now passed away into salt pork, had not disturbed them. Standing by them I picked out the biggest to be taken next, a pig-headed animal that contested every yard of the way, two rustics dragging him, and myself applying an ash-stick as a goad to his rump, and so cruelly that one of the rustics begged me to desist. He was bleeding under the tail when he was hoisted to the platform, and I felt ashamed of my cruelty; but he was a vicious brute that would have bitten the butcher had it not been for the rope about his snout. The butcher worked his knife slowly through the neck; and I plied him with questions: Why was it that pigs squealed when they were being killed and sheep died without uttering a bleat? Was it because it hurt pigs more to die than it did sheep? The butcher answered that pigs were noisy devils; somebody else added that they liked music, the bagpipes especially—answers that perplexed me; and I stood watching the blood, noting that with its flowing the squeals grew fainter and fainter. At last they ceased altogether, and dead he seemed such a stupid thing that I began to wish him alive again. My governess came into the cowyard saying she had been looking for us everywhere; our dinner was ready and we must come at once. "But we haven't got the bladder yet." The butcher put his hand into the pig, tore it out, and handed it to us all stinking; our governess begged us to relinquish it, but we explained to her that we were going to blow it out and tie it to the end of a stick. We followed her to the school-room. "We shall want two more bladders to beat each other with," I explained, and hurried the Colonel through his dinner. Our governess thought that pig-killing was not likely to exercise any softening influence on our characters and resisted firmly our attempt to bring our sister with us. "A young lady," she said, "would be disgraced for ever if it became known that she had seen pigs killed." My sister cried. We were sorry for her, but clean forgot her in the spectacle of the pigs wallowing in the dung-heap outside Fright's stable, each waiting his turn for the great experience of his life—the butcher's knife.

Fright was a very handsome thoroughbred horse. He had won some big races—the Cæsarewitch, I think—and had gone to the stud with a deformed foreleg. My father was sure Fright would get winners if he were given the right mares; he was a great authority on the breeding of thoroughbreds; Croagh Patrick had inspired him to write a work proving—I have forgotten what it was intended to prove—that certain strains died out, but into this intricate subject of heredity it will be perhaps well not to enter.

Whether he was right or wrong in his theory, it is certain that he brought Fright from England determined that he should have his chance, and the horse stood at Moore Hall for many years. Ten pounds for thoroughbred mares, five for half-breds; the groom's fee was, I think, the same in every case, five shillings, and it was a very well earned five shillings, for Fright gave Pat Kelly a great deal of trouble. So indifferent did he seem to his job that at one time my father was thinking seriously of getting rid of him, so Pat Kelly said, and he related to me with some pride how he had discovered the way to manage him. One day when he was bringing him home from walking exercise Fright had neighed at the sight of some cart mares: Pat had spoken in his ear and encouraged him, and then Pat had become suddenly reticent—not to the horse, but to me, and I was left pondering on the mystery of the continuous existence of life in this world. I had been told, as every child is told, that babies were found under gooseberry bushes, and had accepted the explanation for some years, but between the ages of ten and twelve this explanation seemed hardly worthy of a boy's serious credence, and I had accepted the only other possible solution—that the female produced children unaided, and had begun to regret my sex when Pat Kelly's words made life seem again worth living. And not to find myself lacking when my day came, I used to bide in the carpenter's shop (the carpenter's shop being next to Fright's stable) so that I might hear Pat encouraging the horse with all kinds of coaxings: "That's the old boy, that's the old man," and sometimes with so little effect that Pat's mouth would grow dry and he would curse the horse, and after cursing him he would start another set of coaxings, at the end of which, perhaps, the horse would be led out of the stable. It was then time for me to run out of the carpenter's shop and climb into one of the beech-trees overlooking the yard. One day I succeeded in persuading the Colonel to come with me, and that was the very day that Pat pointed us out to our father, who called to us to come down and caned the Colonel severely.

With all these memories flocking through my mind, it was sad to see the carpenter's shop in ruins, for in it I had spent many days with Mickey Murphy trying to learn to use the chisel, the plane, and the saw; but to no purpose did I labor, for I was without handicraft, less gifted than the carpenter's son. The Colonel had never collected hatchets and hammers, saws and chisels, planes and gouges, files and augers and gimlets, and perhaps that is why he had bought an old saw-mill in Ballinrobe and established it in a corner of the haggard where, once upon a time, there used to be great sport ferreting rats in the wheat stacks built upon short stone pillars about three feet from the ground, with a slab on the top to keep out the rats. But a mischievous boy, preferring a rick full of rats to his father's grain, will leave a plank for them to climb; and when threshing-day comes, the rats will scurry before a ferret with the dogs in full tilt after them; and if perchance a curious dog should try to appreciate the smells of rat and ferret and get his nose bitten, he will cry, "You'll know better next time, Towser."

Outside the barn was a curious threshing machine; two horses yoked to a great beam were the motive power; and these set going within a little stone circle all kinds of wheels and cog-wheels, and in response the winnowing machine inside the barn clattered, and the women smiled upon me as they fed it with sheaves and asked me not to come too near, for I might have my fingers snapped off. When the threshing machine went out of gear, the flail was flung, and dodging "the thresher's weary flingin' tree," I would snatch a handful of grain and throw it to the finches that were waiting in the fir-trees on the hillside; not out of kindness of heart, but to entice them to their death; and when they had assembled in sufficient numbers on the ground and were pecking greedily, unmindful of any danger, two barrels of a fowling-piece were loosed upon them, and the ground was covered with blood and feathers. It is thus that a boy learns to shoot, and for some time he fires at every living thing—birds that he would afterwards think it barbarous to harm: tomtits, bullfinches, goldfinches, thrushes, and blackbirds; the jackdaws as they hover about the chimneys, the magpies as they fly from hawthorn to hawthorn. And the gulls flapping about the lake's shore are shot at again and again, for gulls will dive after a wounded gull, and so the sportsman has a chance of shooting fifteen, or twenty, or twenty-five, or thirty birds, as long as he has cartridges in his belt and the massacre does not sicken his heart. A boy will shoot squirrels, he will shoot a badger, a raven, an eagle, and all the hawks, owls, and wood-

pigeons. As we grow older the right to kill seems
more and more doubtful, but a boy will even set
dogs after a cat, and one day a very beautiful white
cat had been hunted out of the laundry into the lofts
and then out of the lofts; it had been driven to
escape by a broken window; the dogs were set after
it, and when it crossed the road, the dogs in hot
pursuit, it was forced to take to one of the trees
growing out of the shelving hillside, the laundry
maids came running down the road pleading for
their cat, but a barbarous boy forced it out of the
branches, and it had been killed by the dogs underneath. And shameful it is to relate that in imitation of the huntsman he pulled out a knife and cut
off the cat's head and distributed the flesh, treating
it as if it had been a wild animal—a hare or a rabbit—whose function it is to provide us with sport
as well as food.

"You would like to see the Stone Park," the
Colonel said, and I prayed that he might not be
tempted to ask me to take the path that led round
by the bog; it once opened on to Fairyland, but it
could not now be else than a wilderness, the cottage
a ruin, and the bog derelict. "The last creel of
turf has been drawn out of it," I said, and a vision
of waste water rose up in my mind. As we come
up the bog-road I shall look through the tall hedge
for the orchard; fifty years ago Joseph Applely
found a bullfinches' nest in one of the apple trees.
"I wonder if the trees have disappeared. The
Colonel can tell me." But loth to ask him, I began
turning over my memories of the hut made of hay

and wattles that an old man used to build there and live in with a savage dog till the crop was gathered. The smoke rising out of his thatch had stirred in me a greater wonder than the hut of a Terra del Fuegian could do to-day, or indeed a settlement of chimpanzees. No, I did not wish to follow the old paths, and prayed that the Colonel might not ask me. By the Bull Park are the Turlough and the Stone Park; and to the Stone Park I had gone one summer's evening long ago with two laundry maids and a stable boy to gather nuts. Perhaps there is nothing that takes as deep a hold on memory as drawing down boughs laden with flowers or fruit. We had gathered till it was dark night under the trees and strange shadows began to move about the fairy-ring. In those days everybody believed in fairies and leprecauns. My father, when he set to work to redeem the Stone Park from the hazel, spared the rath or fairy-ring out of respect for old superstition, or was it because he half believed that bad luck attended the disturbance of these spirit dwellings? Be this as it may, the rath was spared but the sacred hazel was uprooted all around; and a fine sight were the villagers loosing the roots with crowbars, two, three, sometimes four horses yoked to the same tree, and they never gibbing, for they could feel the tree coming all the while.

A great clearing was sown with corn, and in the virgin soil the corn grew to be the tallest and thickest in the country; but when the day came for reaping there was only a fringe, a hundred or more peafowl having encamped in the middle of the field, and the villagers muttered that the master would have done well not to have meddled with the "good people."

" 'The good people' seem to have recovered their holding," I said, and sought for the road that our father had built. But all trace of it had been swallowed up in a jungle of blackthorn, "And by the deer park it must be impenetrable," I said, and we talked of the great deer park that had once extended round Castle Carra. Its wall was our mearing, and while the Colonel narrated his plans for the second ridding of the Stone Park by means of dynamite, I heard him break off in the middle of a sentence. "The goats again!" and away he went with thirty or forty goats trotting in front of him, to return a few minutes afterwards, and so much out of breath that he could barely tell me he had seen them jump the deer park wall. "It is just as I suspected," he added a little later. "During the summer they are in Castle Carra, but just at this time of the year they descend into Moore Hall because they have nothing to eat."

"Why don't you shoot them?"

He had thought of shooting them, but was afraid to raise up hatred against himself in the country, for the goats were not altogether wild; somebody had a claim upon them or their milk. And the goats carried my thoughts back to the days when we used to climb the deer park wall and find our way to Castle Carra, a great stronghold in the fifteenth and sixteenth centuries, abandoned, so it was said, in the seventeenth, or later. The descendants of the great chieftains had gone to live in the modern house, now a ruin like the castle. A herdsman once lived in a corner of it, who would milk his goats for us, bringing us the milk warm from the udders in noggins. The circumstances of the abandonment of the castle must have been wonderful. Or was it abandoned by degrees? All the headland was at one time fortified, but of this vast castle little remains except the central tower or fort, overgrown with thorn. My mother used to repeat verses from "Marmion" as we passed under the gateway, and our tablecloth was laid on the grassy space which we said was the ancient banqueting hall. Above us in the broken wall were glimpses of staircases built between the walls, and despite the protestations of my mother and the governess, I climbed up the wall one day and reached the staircase. But the chieftains had left neither treasure nor pistols nor swords behind them, and I returned . . . disconsolate.

"We might do a little clearing every year," the Colonel broke in, "and all the trees that we get out of the Stone Park can be cut up by the saw-mill, creating a huge provision of fuel for the house, and in ten or twelve years we shall find that we have done a great deal. Aren't you listening?"

"Yes, I'm listening, and I think you're right; in about ten or twelve years Moore Hall would be nearly the same as it was in the time of our father. But about Castle Carra. Tell me, have you been there lately?"

He had visited Castle Carra some three or four months ago, and the castle was crumbling; last Christmas there had been a great downfall; the old gateway had wellnigh disappeared.

"But the castle itself?"

"It won't last more than fifty years, and nobody is living now in the ruins of the modern house; it is even in a worse state of repair than the castle. You remember the great stone fox that stood in the middle of the courtyard and the two hounds on either side? They have been broken; I found the pieces among the brushwood. Another thing. Castle Island needs repair. Michael Malia was out there some time ago and he tells me that the base of the old castle is insecure, but that a few pounds would make it safe."

"My dear friend, it is sad to see all these things going, but one can't rebuild ancient Ireland." And when we regained the lawn and stood viewing the house from the hill, I said: "There isn't enough money left to carry on another generation in Moore Hall. As soon as I am gone the house will be pulled down; the cottages in Derrinanny and Ballyholly will be rebuilt out of the rubble, or the house will become a monkery or a nunnery. Which would you prefer?"

The Colonel sought refuge in silence, and the melancholy that overspread his face suggested to me that the idea of Moore Hall being turned into a monastery had put the thought of Ballinafad into his mind. I knew that the abandoning of family property to strangers was distasteful to him. "Now

345

that Llewellyn has given Ballinafad to the monks, he may," I said to myself, "be more willing than he was some years ago to allow me to bring up one of his children a Protestant, on condition, of course, that I leave him Moore Hall." I had written to him once on this very subject, and his answer had reached me in Paris, where I was staying at the Hotel Continental—a very angry letter, in which he spoke of my proposal as infamous and outrageous. His letter was an amazing one from my point of view. Why should my proposal be looked upon as infamous and disgraceful? I had asked myself, and I began to ask myself again the same question as we walked up the lawn together. "He may," I said, "think differently now; circumstances have changed. Moreover, the proposal might be put to him again in conversation; words pass rapidly; there is no time for anger if they be dealt out skilfully"; and I thought how after dinner, when his wife had gone to bed and we were sitting in two arm-chairs before the turf fire, I might begin by complaining that now that Stella and Walter Osborne and Hughes were gone, Dublin had become a little too small, and he would ask me whether I was going to London or to Paris. Paris would introduce Dujardin's name, and I would tell him that Dujardin's ambitions were to found a new religion in which there was no dogma, only rite. The Colonel would shrug his shoulders and ask how rite could exist independent of dogma, and I would answer that there was no dogma in ancient religions, telling him that it was to the Greek sophists, the hairsplitters of the third and fourth centuries, that we were indebted for dogma. The Colonel would answer "Judaism," and I would explain incidentally that the Jews had never indulged in heresy hunting. It was not permitted to insult Jehovah, and anybody who did so was condemned to death, as Socrates was condemned for insulting the Gods. Dogma and its concomitant, heresy hunting, arose when? What Pope founded the Holy Order? The Reformation would be mentioned, and it would be an easy transition from the Reformation to my proposal.

We make these plans, but very rarely do we adhere to them; and after dinner, when we two were sitting in the drawing-room, without prelude or introductory matter of any kind, I said:

"My dear Maurice, I have a proposal to make to you. I am quite willing to pay for the education of your eldest son, and to leave him any property and pictures that may remain after my death, but I should like to bring him up a Protestant. Our family is a Protestant family; there are one or two apostates, it is true, but it was originally a Protestant family."

"I should never consent to what you are proposing. You needn't go on."

"I'm sorry for that, for of course it is impossible for you to deny that Catholicism makes for illiteracy. As I have pointed out again and again, Catholicism has hardly produced a book worth reading since the Reformation."

"But I deny that completely."

"It doesn't suit you to admit it. But this you will admit, that if Catholicism degrades, corrodes, paralyzes, and stupefies the intelligence, its day is over."

"I admit that, if your premises be correct; but I deny your premises."

"To deny is easy; but if what I say be not true, if Catholics have written as well as Agnostics and Protestants, the books are known. Name them."

At the end of a long waste of argument, I said:

"Well, if you are so convinced that the Catholic is equal to the Protestant, why not bring the matter to the test? You bring up one of your sons a Catholic, I will bring up the other a Protestant, and I will back the Protestant boy to be the superior of the Catholic to the extent of five hundred pounds. You can't afford five hundred; well, I'll be generous. If I win, I will give the five hundred to the Catholic as a sort of consolation prize."

"The proposal you are making to me is utterly inacceptable and horrible. I can't think of anything more detestable than that I should give you one of my children to be brought up in a religion of which I disapprove, and that I should be tempted to do this by a promise that you will leave him money! If, later on, my children were to tell me that they preferred Protestantism to Catholicism, I don't say that I shouldn't be sorry, but I should do nothing to prevent them following the religion which they wished to follow, but if they were to change their religion in order to inherit property, or to get money, I should hate the very sight of them."

"But, my dear Maurice, nobody except Cardinal Newman ever changed his religion for theological reasons. All changes of religion are brought about by pecuniary or sexual reasons."

The Colonel did not answer. He lay back in his arm-chair white with passion, the first time I had ever seen him lose his temper since he was a little boy. It would have been easier to let the matter drop, but I had determined to make a last attempt to save the boy, and could not stop half-way.

"You told me that I libeled my great-grandfather by suggesting he became a Catholic because it was impossible to carry on business in Spain as a Protestant."

"And I say so still; but we're not talking now of our great-grandfather, but of my children. Your proposal is not an honorable one, and if possible it would be less honorable of me to accept it."

"Everybody has his own ideas of honor; there is no fixed standard; but it is a very common thing, as you must know, that when parents are divided in religious beliefs some of the children are brought up in one religion and some in another, and it would be difficult to impugn the fairness of such an arrangement. I am prejudiced in favor of Protestantism for intellectual reasons, and because my life is moulded on facts rather than upon sentimentalities."

To which the Colonel answered that I looked at the world through a narrow tube and could only see one spot at a time, and that my opinions were always as narrow as the tube; and then, getting angrier and angrier, his face bleached with a passion which I could not help admiring, for at all events he was himself in this scene, he reminded me that I had said I would leave Moore Hall to his children, but no sooner had I said that than I began to impose conditions. In the beginning they were to learn Irish, that was the condition; now a new condition was to be imposed, they were to be brought up Protestants.

"Not both, only one; and if I pay for his education you can't expect me to bring up a boy in a religion which I think paralyzes the intelligence, the one thing that I value. Your concern is with the possibility of a future life, the soul's arrival in Purgatory and its subsequent release by means of Masses paid for the Pope's indulgences, and——"

"There's no use discussing this matter any further," the Colonel answered, "and it doesn't seem to me that it would be advisable that we should see each other any more. As for Moore Hall, you have made it impossible for me to live here any longer, and as soon as I can I shall leave."

XIV

An hour later, when my brother told me, in answer to a question, that I had been paying fifty pounds a year to the Jesuits, and subsequently one hundred a year to the Benedictines for the education of my nephew, I uttered the cry or moan of a man taken with a sudden sickness. The sensation the news brought me was, strangely enough, physical, a sort of fainting in the very bowels, or else I cannot describe it. A mistake on his part, or on mine, and no doubt he was right. . . . "A shocking piece of ill-luck," I muttered, and seeing there had been a misunderstanding, he offered at once to repay me; and with the transference of some hundreds of pounds from Cox's to the National Bank, the question of money would be settled between us. "But there is no question of money," I bewailed. "I don't care a fig for the money." I could not answer him further; the shock of the discovery deprived me of any power of reasoning, and I ascended the stairs, thinking as well as I could, that any calamity had been preferable to the one that had befallen me. It rankled like salt in a wound, that I should have been paying for the education of a Catholic while meditating "Hail and Farewell"; "while writing 'Ave' and 'Salve,' " I muttered, and the fact that nobody was

351

to blame did not make the pain easier to bear. "Nobody is to blame, but the worst ill-luck that could have befallen me," I moaned, and a deeper sense of unhappiness than I had ever known before began to steal over me as I dragged my feet along the landing to the room in which I was to sleep.

"I shall get no sleep to-night," I said, raising the blind in the hope that the still night and the moon shining on the lake would calm me and help me to forgive. "But there is nothing to forgive, and as for forgetting, what has happened will rankle for ever. I have been stung to the quick." And while thinking of my inexhaustible loathing of priests, my eyes roved over the dim outlines of the lake into the pearly distances, and I began to wonder whether the moonlight on the lake was blue or gray. A moment after the words "He is a born Catholic" fell from my lips, and the phrase, coming into my mind unexpectedly, seemed to represent a truth that I had hitherto not recognized, or insufficiently. "Quite true," I said. "We do not acquire our religion; we bring it into the world. Every man in this island is a born Catholic or a Protestant. Protestantism and Catholicism are attitudes of mind that will go on for ever"; and I pondered this question for what seemed a long while, awakened suddenly by the thought that if my nephews had any zest of intelligence in them, they would discover themselves to be Protestants sooner or later . . . if they didn't delay too long. "From eighteen to twenty-one is the time when we stick for ever in it, or find a way out. But what matter my nephew?

Every man must choose a religion for himself, and must find it in his own heart; and the money that has been spent will not make Catholics, but that isn't it." And I fell into a long disputation with myself, one side of me pointing out that there was no reason why I should be miserable if my money had not gone to the making of a Catholic, another side of me unable to accept this argument, and crying out, "Not for all the money in the world would I that this thing had happened." I had laughed and jeered at dear Edward because he dreaded lest his money might be applied to the production of heretical plays, yet here was I experiencing the very same anguish. I suppose everybody has noticed how, in moments of great mental excitement, the mind escapes from the strain in observation of some external object. It was the perfect circle of the moon that set me wondering if I could draw one as perfect, and the clarity of the great beam of light falling across the lake into the bay that procured me the vision of the castle as it stood a thousand years ago, the raft being wafted over, the Welshmen looking to their weapons while a hermit prayed by his island altar. But however long our thoughts may wander, we are awakened by the old pain. "All these years the Jesuits and the Benedictines have been getting my money and propagating their poison with it"; and my senses sickened again at the thought. "A judgment upon me for having jeered at dear Edward, the only Catholic in whose society I could ever feel pleasure." My thoughts sped away to Bayreuth, and returned to

my brother and to our childhood which had been
spent about Lough Carra. Hours went by, and I
stood by the window, still thinking. "My mind is
like an ever-veering wind," I said; "and my only
escape from my thoughts is in sleep." Then sleep
I sought vainly, the same thoughts revisiting me,
marching round my brain like prisoners in a yard,
high walls, and no strip of sky above the multi-
tudinous bricks. "Round and round they go," I
cried, and then away went my thoughts again, and
where they ended I do not know.

"Your bath-water is ready, sir."

The hot water seemed to set me thinking on what
terms we should meet at breakfast and how we should
get through the day, and if on the morrow my
brother would drive me over to Ballinafad to see
Llewellyn's monastery. If we could get over the
first half-hour the rest of the day would pass easily
about the lake and in the fields, and to give Evelyn,
my sister-in-law, time to get down before me, I
lingered over my dressing, and so advantageously
that she was dispensing tea and coffee when I entered the dining-room, and after breakfast I thanked
her inly when she said:

"Now, Maurice, won't you take George out and
show him the new gateway which he says he has not
seen sufficiently?"

The Colonel murmured some answer and, while
hustling himself into his old yellow overcoat, he
told me that the part of the ironwork that was
missing had been supplied by the smith at Carnacun, and that he was curious to hear if I should be

able to distinguish the old from the new. The stonework was complete, all except two knobs, these Michael Malia would be able to replace, the cost would not be more than five or ten pounds a knob. His optimism was somewhat dismal, for I never imagined anybody living in Moore Hall again, and after viewing the gateway which had only cost me forty pounds, we turned down the road to the gate lodge, now empty, the Colonel having succeeded in expelling its late tenant, his gardener. "A gate lodge," I said, "is generally beside the gate, but this one is fifty yards away." The Colonel declared it to be an excellent house, and I meditated not its excellency which interested me not at all, but the chestnut-trees all in bloom about it long ago, and the pretty garden in front of it. This gate lodge was associated in my mind with many memories. It had a loft which was reached by a ladder, and I had often thought that I would like to sleep in a loft among the hay; and there was a deep drain beyond the garden at the edge of the wood, and down this drain I had often floated on a raft made out of a plank and the shutters from the windows, into deep water under the bridge. It was a thrilling experience to find oneself on a raft under an arch, but the novelty wore away quickly, and the Colonel reminded me that one day I had undertaken a longer voyage, punting the raft down the drain into the lake. But in the lake the punt pole (a branch torn from a tree) had proved insufficient, and the freshening wind had carried me and the raft out into the open lake, and looking at the Colonel I remembered

355

him crying among the rushes while I debated my chances whether it would be better to remain on the raft trusting it to carry me to some island or to throw myself from it into the lake in the hope that the water was not deep enough to drown me. The waves leaped higher and higher, threatening to wash the shutters from the plank, till at last it became clear that the chance that the water was not deep enough to drown me would have to be accepted. It rose to my chin, lifting me off my feet, and I continued wading, hoping not to stumble into a hole.

"Yes," I said to the Colonel, "I had a near escape that day from drowning, and now I can still see you running along the strand crying for someone to come and save your brother."

"If the accident had happened a few years before," he said, "you would have been drowned, the lake was deeper," and he told me how in the sixties a young engineer had come down from the Board of Works with a project for draining Lough Carra into Lough Mask, but our father had offered such vigorous opposition to the scheme that it had to be abandoned.

"Up to the seventies," I answered, "we were feudal lords, and he was listened to in the House of Commons when he said that he could not allow a small Sahara to be created before his front-door. We controlled our aspects in those days, or it may have been that the shores of Lough Mask were implicated in this drainage scheme. As likely as not it was suddenly discovered that the draining of Lough Carra into Lough Mask would mean an inundation." "A weir was therefore constructed in the river a little beyond Ballinrobe," I heard the Colonel say, and his words revived the day I had brought a boat from Lough Carra to Lough Mask and had put back frightened by the great waves of that gloomy lake.

"Our father saved Lough Carra, but it is for certain many feet lower than it used to be"; and I reminded the Colonel of the great pleasure-boat about whose rotting planks we used to play. It had been allowed to rot under a group of pines, standing some fifty or sixty yards from the lake's edge, by the side of a walled trench, once its' harbor. For to what other purpose could the walled trench have been put? we often asked our governess, our subsequent questions drifting into dim speculation as to how many pounds it would cost to mend the boat; and if Micky Murphy could mend it if he were paid ten pounds. This rotting boat appealed to our imaginations, for its seats would hold a dozen or more ladies and gentlemen, and there were row-locks for eight oars, and the Colonel and I used to imagine the great picnic-parties that had sat under the sail, for there was a hole in one of the seats for a mast. "Was Castle Hag or Castle Island the destination of these picnic-parties?" we asked each other; "and was there a turkey stuffed with chest-nuts in the hamper?" We were certain that there were cakes and fruits and jams, and that the foot-man spread a snowy cloth in the glade under the castle wall. Our governess read while we dreamed. We! Did the Colonel dream? If he did, he never told me his dreams. He is reticent about his dreams, but garrulous about externals, and as we walked round the shores of Lough Carra for the last time, he regretted that he had not brought with him the key of the new boat-house, for he would like to show me his brother-in-law's boats, rowing-boats, skiffs, wherries, a steam launch, and a yacht. A shrunken lake for certain, else the reeds would not have thriven. —— had had to cut a passage through them for his boats, and the Colonel unfolded a project to me whereby the lake might be cleared of reeds, and before he had reached the end of his project we were at the bridge that stretches over the turlough (a turlough in Mayo is a low-lying field, that is flooded in winter), and he pointed out the pump that drew the water from a well out in the middle of the lake—a well that old Betty MacDonald used to say was once up in Kiltoome, but it had suddenly descended and had sprung up in the lake, a ring of grass around it, for it was a holy, or maybe a fairy, well. She was not quite sure which. The pump had cost me two hundred pounds, but I had to admit that if people were to live at Moore Hall, a pump was necessary. "The walls require mending," I remarked, coming upon a cottage that my father had built but had never put a roof on; and I added, "A ruin that will supply excellent material for the building of necessary walls."

But the Colonel said there was plenty of stone, and no need either to pull down the cottage or to roof it. The walls were probably too rotten to bear a roof, and, speaking of the Congested Districts Board, he said, "They even ask for the paddock, the field behind the cottage." The fields beyond the gate were Corrour, the New Gardens, Lough Navadogue, Rochetown, and our father's race-course, on which he had trained Corunna, Wolf Dog, Anonymous, Croagh Patrick, and Master George, to number a few of his famous horses, and all these fields the Congested Districts Board required.

"So that the holdings of three tenants might be extended," the Colonel said; "and if you yield, Moore Hall will be no more than a villa in the midst of a wild country; cottagers within the woods right up against Kiltoome, and who can say that pigsties will not be built? The present cottagers would probably prevent the pigs from rooting in the graveyard, but the cottagers fifty years hence will have no scruples."

"Heavens! has it come to this that a man must consent to the desecration of a family tomb or be made bankrupt!"

"The land right up to Kiltoome, and at their own price, is what they are asking, and must get, else the Board may refuse to buy your other estates, Ballintubber, and those in Galway and Roscommon. A very serious matter for you if the Board refused to buy."

"How is that?"

"The next move would be to stir up all the tenants to combine in a campaign against rent—like putting a stick into a wasp's nest," the Colonel added, with a deep note of anger in his voice. "So far as I understand, the proposal is to leave you Derrinrush."

"But if all the land is to be taken right up to the edge of the wood, of what use?"

"The Board is prepared to reserve a right of way."

"A right of way to my own wood!"

"Coercion is dead in Ireland," he added.

We returned to Moore Hall, and so gloomy were our thoughts that we turned aside instinctively from the Dark Road and ascended the steep lawn together. As soon as the house came into full view I stopped so that I might speak more easily.

"My dear Maurice, Moore Hall was built in feudal times. Read the tablet over the balcony, 1790, and feudalism continued down to 1870; a big square house on a hill, to which the peasants came every morning to work. Do you remember the bell that used to hang over the laundry? It used to ring at seven, and before it ceased clanging our laborers assembled and were bidden to their day's work; a shilling a day was fine wages. Do you remember the women coming from the village with their husbands' and brothers' dinners? Half a dozen boiled potatoes tied in a cloth, and it was a great dinner if they got a noggin of buttermilk from the cook. They ate their potatoes and drank their buttermilk under the hawthorn hedge in the backyard, if it were fine, and, if it were wet, in a byre or stable. The young men wore corduroy trousers and frieze coats, the old men were still in knee breeches and tall hats; the women had a red petticoat to their knees, and a handkerchief tied round their heads. A familiar sight in the sixties was a bare-legged woman digging the bog in a fierce north-east gale. We were kings in those days; little kings, but kings for all that, with power of life and death as has been said and truly, for we often sundered wife and husband, sister from brother; drove away a whole village to America if it pleased us to grow beef and mutton for the English market."

"In those days the peasants were afraid to thatch their cottages lest their rent should be raised," the Colonel said; "nor was there one peasant in our villages or in the Tower Hill villages worth a ten-pound note," and he asked me if I remembered a cabin in the middle of Annys bog, a dwelling hardly suited for an animal, yet a man and woman lived there and children were born in it. "We used to pass it on our walks, you and I and our governess."

"Yes, I remember it," I answered, "and I remember one day up in the mountains while grouse shooting that I stabled my horse in a man's cabin, and it seemed to everybody quite the natural thing to do. But we shall never be able to do it again. The landlords have had their day, and their day is over. We are a disappearing class, our lands are being confiscated, and our houses are decaying or being pulled down to build cottages for the folk. Dialect, idiom, local customs, and character are disappearing, and in a great hurry. I cannot understand how it is that you don't see that Moore Hall represents feudalism. Have a look at it, and tell me, if you can, that it is not an anachronism in the landscape."

"I think that anybody who would like to live in a comfortable house——"

"But the comfort of yesterday is not the comfort of to-day. Square rooms and lofty passages conformed to the ideas of our ascendants, and jerry-built villas, all gables, red tiles, and mock beams, stand for modern taste and modern comfort; hot water on every landing and electric light. Can't you feel that nobody wants a real house unless an American millionaire, and it is not because of its reality that he wants it but for its unreality. It is unreal to him, and having a great deal of money, he indulges in eccentricity. In this way the old world is carried on by Americans; even in England there are very few houses that are the capitals of the estate they stand in as Moore Hall was up to fifty years ago. Moore Hall is out of date, and it astonishes me that you don't feel it. I wish in a way that I could summon sufficient courage to pull it down and sell it; it would make excellent rubble to build laborers' cottages, and if I could I would cut down every tree and lay the hillside bare. Why not, since I know it will be laid bare a few years after my death? The fate that overtook Ashbrook hangs over Muckloon. It will be given over to peasants, like Ashbrook. You remember the piece of tapestry that was woven in Ashbrook by our great grand-aunt or grandmother and which is now on exhibition in South Kensington Museum? I wonder how long it will be before another piece of tapestry like that is woven in Mayo. In the dining-room hangs a portrait of a lady with a dog, painted by a young girl in Galway. Is there one in Galway now who would paint as well? No. With all our so-called culture, sculpture, painting, architecture, and the art of the use of words are disappearing. By the way, Maurice, I don't know whether you have heard my theory that the age of art is over as much as the Stone Age."

"People have always been saying that the age of art is over. I could cite you many passages from Elizabethan writers in which they deplore the decline of art and the English language."

"They were wrong, that is all. But it cannot be denied that there was neither art nor literature in Europe in the Middle Ages, from the sixth, shall we say, to the twelfth century? A pretty long interval."

"During which Europe was overrun by Goths and Visigoths and Huns, not for any other reason. Art cannot flourish in the midst of invasions"; and he began the story of the decline and fall of the Roman Empire: Rome was sacked by Alaric in the fifth century, and in the same century Europe was overrun by the Huns, headed by Attila, and a century later the Saracens invaded Europe and were defeated by the French at the Battle of Tours. The Colonel was of opinion that this defeat was owing entirely to a certain miscalculation on the part of the Moorish general, and as we walked toward the house he explained that if this defeat had not taken place we might all be Mohammedans now.

"But do you think that the sleep of Mohammedanism is a deeper sleep than the sleep of Catholicism? I beg your pardon for introducing the religious question. You are appreciative of the trend of the past, but seem blind to that of the present. I cannot help being sorry for my poor country that has never been able to show a brave face to the world, not because the Irish are less intelligent than another race, but for some extraordinary curse that seems to have been laid upon this land in the tenth century. Ireland was something then; she had a religion of her own—and she was inventing an art of her own. Up to the tenth century God seemed as if he intended to do something for Ireland, and in the tenth or the eleventh century he changed his mind, and ever since the curse seems to have been deepening. In another fifty years Ireland will have lost all the civilization of the eighteenth century; a swamp of peasants with a priest here and there, the exaltation of the rosary and whiskey her lot. A hundred legislators interested only in protecting monkeries and nunneries from secular inquisition."

The Colonel did not agree with me that the gentry were dying out of Mayo. The Brownes of Breaghwy and the Lynches of Partry had been building lately.

"My dear Maurice, you will not see things as they are. Or is it that you don't remember Mayo in the days of the gentry as well as I do? Athy Valley is empty. Browne Hall—you told me that you and an old peasant had searched for traces of the house, but could find none. Ballinafad is a monastery. The Blakes are still in Tower Hill, and a last Lynch lives his lonely life in Clogher. Cornfield is empty, and will be pulled down very soon. The Knoxes have left Creagher. Newbrook is sold, and the masonry distributed—part of it is at the end of the drive. Brownestown House was burnt before our time, but not much before it. How many more? The Lamberts are gone. What was the name of their place? Brook something."

"Every class has its ups and downs, and there is no doubt that ours is going through a crisis."

"No crisis whatsoever. We have outlived our day, that is all; and in thirty years we shall be, as I have said, as extinct as the dodo, unless religion comes to our aid."

"How is that?"

"Haven't you heard of the New French party— the Catholic Atheists? Religion is to be taught again in the hope that man may be persuaded to forego the joy of a woman's bosom for the sake of Abraham's."

The Colonel laughed, but it was clear that he was not pleased, and after an irritating silence he told me that Castle Carra had been sold to the Congested Districts Board, and out of the arch, built during the famine, a row of concrete cottages had been run up according to specifications.

"The old deer park will supply some material," I said. "The jungle will be grubbed up; you will get rid of the goats."

And we talked on in this fashion, and after dinner

resumed the same talk, saying the same things over and over again; and when we ascended the stairs to our beds, about eleven o'clock, the Colonel promised to drive me over to Llewellyn's Monastery next day.

Llewellyn Blake is my uncle, my mother's youngest brother, and he came into the property of Ballinafad on the death of Joe Blake, famous in the county Mayo for many race-horses and a love-story. Joe seems to have been the only one in the family whose soul did not trouble him. His brother Mark, from whom he inherited the property of Ballinafad, was a fine old country rake, leaving samples of his voice and demeanor and appearance in every village, and then going to Dublin to repent of his sins. In the last years of his life he attained to the appearance of Father Christmas, and caused much annoyance in the chapels that he frequented from his incurable habit of interrupting the services with "Oh, Lord; oh, Lord; my unfortunate soul!" Llewellyn is as tall as his brother Mark, two or three inches over six feet, large in proportion, with sloping shoulders, snapping his words out and then relapsing into silence. He used to be much admired at dances in the drawing-rooms of Merrion and Fitzwilliam Squares, and in the old Royalty Theater he patronized the Muse Terpsichore. But those days are over and done with, and, like his brother Mark, he has become uneasy about his soul. His soul died years ago; he was warned of its disease by me, but he paid no heed to my warnings, and convinced of its continuous existence, and that priests can help him to save it, he has founded a monastery. I should do the same if I were a Roman Catholic, but the Colonel, who is one, would have me try to prevent the founding of this monastery by action at law, and I am still trying to understand the Colonel who believes in the efficacy of masses for the dead, but seems to think that Llewellyn's relations should come before his soul—a most impossible Colonelesque argument; and the spirit fumed within me to express my point of view; but I put chains upon my spirit, and Carnacun went by for the last time. We were on the heights of Ballyglass when the struggling spirit sundered its last chains, and I said:

"How is it that you disapprove of this monastery? It seems to me that you should, on the contrary, urge me to found another at Moore Hall. You believe that masses for the dead will get your soul out of Purgatory. If you don't, you are not a Catholic. Now, why shouldn't we have a little plump of monasteries? At Moore Hall we could have Benedictines; at Clogher Franciscans. Lynch is a Roman Catholic: he has got no children, what better could he do? At Tower Hill some arrangements might be come to with the Blakes to put in Trappists. You don't know what order is in Ballinafad?"

The Colonel answered sullenly that he was not sure whether Llewellyn had founded a mission house or a monastery.

"Well, no matter. This little plump of monasteries sending up prayers for your soul, for Llewellyn's soul, for Lynch's soul, and for the souls of

all at Tower Hill; and the prayers bringing down
the archangels constantly, crooks in their hands,
pulling you one after the other out of Purgatory.
The Father and the Son and the Holy Ghost; am-
brosia and nectar perpetually, and aureoles that
never wear out. A rich prospect before you all!"

An ironical smile, deliberately introduced, pervaded the Colonel's face, and it said as plainly as
words: "How very superficial you are, and vulgar,
quite vulgar!"

"My dear friend, I am sorry for bringing up this
question again. It is the fault of Llewellyn Blake."

"Count Llewellyn Blake. He has been made
Count of the Papal States"; and the Colonel
laughed derisively.

"But why laugh? In his eyes the Pope is not
only a spiritual, but a temporal power. His title
is more valid than any other. Don't you think
so?"

The Colonel never answers these questions, and
while wondering at my own detestable character in
thus plaguing him, I looked round the fields. They
seemed very small and dim. "And yet," I said,
"that gleam of light falling across the worn fields
reminds us irresistibly that summer is coming in.
The fine days we meet in January are visionary days
with no promise in them, but the ray that lights
up the dim February landscape is a herald. We
believe in it, and that is the principal thing."

A peasant stood in the roadway in front of the
car, and the Colonel had to pull up.

"Long life to yer honor," cried the old man, and

in his eyes I read the reverence of yore. He was a hairy and boisterous fellow, and we had to listen to his description of his house, which he said was damp enough to give a wild duck rheumatism. I promised to help him, and we bade him godspeed. "A godspeed," I said, "which is probably for eternity."

"We are very late," the Colonel muttered. "It was unlucky meeting him."

"Don't say that. It is pleasant to meet literature on the road from Ballyglass to Ballinafad."

The road looped round the shoulder of a hill, and beyond a long straight bridge or viaduct we spied the gate of Ballinafad.

"But," said the Colonel, "I am afraid that this gate is always kept locked. You'll miss your train."

"If I were to miss a thousand trains, I will see Llewellyn's monastery."

"You'll certainly miss your train. It is two miles round—two Irish miles."

He pulled up before a rusty gate, and bounding out of the trap, I shook it. It was locked, but there was a stile beside it.

"We can send the trap round to the other gate, which is nearer by two miles to the station, and walk up to the house."

"Yes, we can do that," he said.

"Train or no train, I must see Llewellyn's mission-house or monastery. To a very pleasant place they have come to live," I said, surprised by the beauty of the domain, having no remembrance that Ballinafad was as beautifully wooded.

"Before Moore Hall, Ballinafad was," the Colonel

answered, and he told me how the Blakes had kept their property through the Penal Laws by a special charter granted to them by Charles II. The charter he assured me was still preserved, and I asked if all this comely woodland were going to be given over to the monks. "Groves in which," I said, "it would be easy to imagine a rout of nymphs and satyrs. Or Thyrsis praying the goat-herd to seat himself in the shelter of that great oak, and pipe to him. Delightful woods." And I was talking of Amaryllis Silenus and the Zephyrs when twenty or thirty youths passed across the glade; their doleful chant came back to us over the red bracken, and we had need to run to overtake them, so absorbed were they in their desire to escape from a stranger. At last their shepherd called a halt, and he told us that we should find Father —— in the house.

"An insignificant house," I said to the Colonel on our way thither, "if I remember it, without much character or design. A strange porch, out of keeping with the landscape." And the Colonel answered me that the house had been built by our grandfather, Maurice Blake, a soldier who had served in the Peninsular wars, and the porch was probably a memory of one he had seen in Italy on his way home.

"The house may be a memory, but it was not in Italy that he descried that porch. I don't know, though; it may be his memory of a loggia. And the high steps thereto! Where did he get them from? Those panes of yellow and red glass were always my detestation. No attempt has been yet made to give the house an ecclesiastical air."

"The ecclesiastical changes will come later on when Llewellyn has made sure of his title"; and the Colonel entered on the complex question of Llewellyn's rights under his father's will while I looked round the drawing-room in which my mother had practiced certain pieces of music. She and her sisters had played a selection from "Norma" for certain on that piano, and in later years Joe had strummed his memories of "Traviata" and "Il Trovatore" for his own amusement, or for Biddy's. There was no carpet on the floor, but the boards had been scrubbed, and the old pictures were on the walls—pictures that were among my earliest memories—setters creeping up to birds, probably grouse; and I began to peer into the painting like a Bond Street dealer, for the approach of a priest always sets me mumming.

The door opened and a young man of sleek speech and calves begged us to be seated; and choosing the most comfortable chair for himself, and tossing himself till he discovered its easiest corner, he told us that a large number of the last batch of missionaries sent out to West Africa had died, the climate being unhealthy, but another batch was going out shortly, and he hoped not to lose so many.

"And did those that died pray for the soul of Count Llewellyn Blake?"

He hoped that they had done so, for Count Llewellyn Blake had done a great deal for them, and I put it to him that Llewellyn's soul was a heavy tax upon the population of Mayo, something like seventeen out of thirty-six having died. We then spoke of the Seminary's farming operations. A fine price had been gotten for bullocks at the last fair, and I don't know how it was, but his appearance of smug satisfaction drew from me the remark that Count Llewellyn Blake might find that he had not the right to dispose of the domain of Ballinafad. The young man said he had never inquired into these matters; he knew nothing about them, and as it seemed polite not to importune him on this point, we asked him some questions regarding the possibility of converting the savages to a more rational spirituality than that which they practiced in the forest.

"We meet with a great many difficulties; first and foremost the unwillingness of the men to relinquish their wives."

"But what would become of the abandoned wives?"

The young man admitted that they had not thought out that side of the question.

"The children," I answered, "offer you a fairer field."

"Yes, we try to get hold of the children," he answered, and our talk turned on the question of religious heredity, the climate of Africa being answerable for much of the faith of the savages in their superstitions.

The Colonel left me to carry on the conversation, which I did with some difficulty for he was willing to talk; he brightened a little, however, when we rose to go, and it seemed to me that the Colonel answered the young priest not a little dryly when he ventured to express a hope that the Colonel would come over again from Moore Hall to see them and bring his two little boys with him.

"Father Zimmerman, who is at present in Switzerland," he said, "will be back in Ballinafad at the end of the month."

"The whole scheme is intimately associated with Father Zimmerman," the Colonel said on our way to the stables. "A very different man from the one we have seen."

"But how can he be different and continue the traffic he is engaged in? I cannot disassociate a man from his work as you do. A man is his work."

We were met by some of Joe Blake's hirelings, stablemen of old time who had seen the cracks go up to the Curragh, and they lamented the change; a foreign priest, they said, come to take Irishmen away to Africa. Count Llewellyn had met him at Ballinafad some two or three years ago and when he ordered Jimmy Glynn to ready the dining-room for Mass, they began to have a shrewd notion of what was going to happen; so the tenants had collected round the hall door to know how much of the land the Count was going to make over to the Swiss boyo, who told them that he was "up to the height of his ankles in carpets before he took up with religion." "Literature again," I whispered, and listened with glee to the tale of how the Swiss boyo and the Count had escaped through the garden, but they were caught up at Lakemount, brought to bay, and getting round them in a circle, the tenants had "cut the ground from under them," telling them that if any bloody monks came to Ballinafad they would all become Protesants.

"I wonder if any of them will become Protestants?" I said to the Colonel, undeterred by the rain that came toward us aslant over the bog. It was soon in our faces, and with the large drops running down my nose, I continued: "The monks and Llewellyn's anxiety about his soul may well bring about a revival of Christianity. The tenants will rise against the monks. You noticed that they would not admit these Swiss fellows as priests."

"I think the word Protestant was a sop for you," the Colonel answered.

The rain splashed in our faces, making conversation difficult, and when it ceased I heard the Colonel's voice saying from under his mackintosh:

"I should like to outwit Llewellyn."

"It is all very difficult to me," I answered, "for you are not moved by any mean sense of future pecuniary loss to yourself; your fingers do not itch to clutch. Family feeling is very strong in you, stronger than in me. No one could be more shocked than you were when I told you that I had heard the ecclesiastics had gotten Howth Castle, and the disappearance of Ballinafad affects you in the same way. But what I don't understand is how you contrive to reconcile admiration of the cause with detestation of the result. For, of course, as long as priests can persuade people that Masses for the dead will get their souls out of purgatory they will continue to dispoil their relations."

"The rain is coming on again," the Colonel interjected. "We shall only get to Manulla in time"; and he urged the pony to his best pace with whip and voice. As the road was quite unknown to me, it seemed interminable, and at every hill I asked how far we were from the station. "We shall just catch the train," the Colonel answered.

The train was late, and walking up the platform I grew so bitter about Catholicism that he at last said:

"A religion, at all events, that has made more converts than any other."

"But whom does it convert? Not the wise, but the witless and hysterical—ladies who have been through the Divorce Courts and young men with filthy careers behind them."

The train steamed in, and the porter cried, "First class behind! Would you like to have your hat-box in the carriage with you?"

"Yes," I answered mechanically, and jumped into the train, glad to escape from a wrangle that had become unendurable. He had said the night before last that we had better not see each other, and though the words seemed hard I could not resist their truth. It was a relief to get away from him. "Catholics and protestants don't mix; we are never comfortable in their society; we can pick them out—a certain foolishness in their faces difficult to define." At that moment the guard blew his whistle, the train moved up the platform, and the Colonel passed out of my sight. "So this is the end of it all, and there is no help for it. We never knew it before and might never have known it if I hadn't come down to Mayo. So it was while revisiting the scenes of our youth that we discovered how hopeless is our estrangement! He thinks, no doubt, that I have changed: we have both changed, and the fault is neither with him nor with me. He was born a papist. But his children, I'm sorry I wasn't able to slip a file into one of their pockets. No matter, they'll save themselves if they've anything in them, only let them not delay too long. If a boy doesn't file through the chains that Jesuits and Benedictines lay upon him before he is eighteen, he'll wear them to his grave."

Like an unwelcome wind, the thought that my money should have been spent forging these chains went by, and looking out on the great fields of Roscommon, I said aloud, startling a fellow-passenger: "Not for all these would I have wished that mistake to have happened." The thought seemed unendurable, but happily no thought lasts; our thoughts wander like the wind; and between Athlone and Mullingar I sat like a figure in a picture by the side of a brimming lake meditating the suavity of the contours of my life, asking myself, "What new and beautiful curve will it take? My mission in Ireland is over," I said, "and the time has come for me to decide in which town I shall cast my fortune."

My choice seemed to lie between Paris and London. My old friends in Paris were all dead or scattered, and the French are not a sociable people. Their doors are closed in the evening against intruders. There is little casual visiting in Paris. I had not learnt to read, and if I decided to live in Paris it would be impossible for me to escape from reading. "As time goes on I shall write less and read more; and the large book containing the thirty-six plays will never be out of my hand. I shall become another Sir Sidney Lee." At this prospect Paris began to recede a little, and I remember that Steer and Tonks and Sickert lived in London. But even if I settled in London I should have to learn to read. I could not spend every evening with Steers and Tonks. The New English Art Club opens its doors only twice a week, and at the Queen's Hall Saint-Saëns and Dvořák are often played. . . . A private orchestra is beyond my means, but a piano . . . and with a wife who could play Haydn, Mozart, Beethoven, Schumann, Schubert, Wagner, Chopin, and Liszt, but never Brahms, the evenings would go by happily, an excellent cigar in my mouth, my stern in a comfortable arm-chair. . . . An hour-and-a-half of music every evening, and if the rule were maintained for several years, we should get through the vast pile of chamber-music that men have been writing for the last two hundred years. I have a taste for Scarlatti; and if this admirable woman who can play all Bach, not brilliantly, but correctly, were to bear me a child, he would inherit his mother's musical ear, and it is not likely that my son would lack inventive faculty and sense of composition. And while watching the musical instinct developing in him, my heart will be filling with joy, and I shall look forward to hearing all the ridiculous and uncouth strains that have tempted and deceived me reduced to shape, but not in symphonies—my son will write operas, the words as well as the music, for I should like him to inherit as much of my literary gifts as will enable him to construct the poem on which to weave the woof, but not more. The Moore family has produced enough literature. My thoughts were away in a jiffy in France, for the German musical idiom is worn to rags; but there is a musical atmosphere in France, and I remembered a great stone bridge with fishermen sitting on the quays, their legs hanging over the side. I had watched their floats being carried down by the current last year, had seen them lift their floats out of the current and drop them in again, and had waited, pretending to myself that I would like to see a fish rise, but really interested in the adventure that I knew to be at my heels. An empty fly came by, and the driver asked if he might take me to Chinon. It seemed as if I heard the name, and feeling Chinon to be my adventure, I jumped into the carriage, and was driven along a road of which I remember nothing except a steep hill and at the top of it a feudal castle in ruins. Our poor little horse could hardly drag us up the hill, and the coachman turned in his seat and began to relate some history; but at that moment my eyes were taken by a poster representing a house, or castle—I was not sure which—an extravagant painting it was. *"Post Impressionism,"* I said, "at Chinon"; and dismissing the driver, I applied to an old man sitting by the side of the gate, his shaggy dog beside him, for information.

"*C'est le portrait de la maison.*"

"*Laquelle? Pardon, monsieur, mais je ne vois pas une maison ici qui ait pu vous servir de modèle.*"

"*La maison n'est pas encore construite. Je l'ai seulement dessinée pour inspirer l'acheteur de la propriété que voici. Le clos St. Georges.*"

"*Une vraie petite aventure,*" I said to myself, and followed the old man round the little enclosure, amused by the pomp with which he vaunted the excellence of his grapes and the courtesy with which he invited my admiration of the pears and peaches ripening on the southern wall. I admired them, for they were worthy of my admiration. But I had seen fine peaches and pears at home, but never had I seen flowers like silk gathered into a rosette. Did the tree bear fruit? At first he thought I was quizzing him, but seeing that I was genuinely ignorant, he told me the tree in question was a *grenadier*, and trying to remember what a *grenadier* was in English, I stood admiring the roofs of Chinon under the hill.

"*C'est là où naquit notre grand Rabelais.*"

"*Finir mes jours en face de la ville re Rabelais; quelle joie pour un Irlandais!*"

"*Mais, monsieur, vous êtes encore jeune; cinquante et quelques années*"; and he looked at me interrogatively and regretfully, for the old man was seventy *et quelques années.*

"*Ici, je voudrais vivre et mourir,*" I answered mechanically.

"*Rien ne vous empêche, monsieur, d'acheter ma vigne . . . et pas cher. Voyez-vous il y a des avantages*"; and he led me down into a pit which he had digged in the center of the enclosure, and pointed out to me a great many stones and broken arches.

"*Il y a de quoi bâtir une jolie maison*"; and I learnt from him that these stones had once formed part of the castle, and that it was here that Henry of Anjou (Henry II of England) had died on the altar steps. He had excavated the ruin with his own hands, and the house I had in mind to build would not cost me more than a thousand pounds, and the old carvings he had stacked by the hut in which he and his dog lived could be let into the walls. He asked me if I would like to see his pictures, for when he was not spraying his vines he was painting scenes from the life of Joan of Arc in distemper, and spraying vines had become hard work; he was seventy-five, and wished to finish his paintings before he died.

"*Achetez donc ma vigne, monsieur; finissez vos jours en face de la ville où naquit notre grand Rabelais.*"

"Why not?"

And now with the advent of my new idea—that a musician was the legitimate end of my life—the Clos St. Georges began to acquire a new and potent significance. "She and the boy and the vineyard will be the pear and the peach, the apricot, the nectarine, the bottle of wine from my own vineyard. My life will have to end somewhere. Why not in the Clos St. Georges?" "Because 'Hail and Farewell' must be written," a voice answered from within. Before the vineyard could be purchased and the house built "Hail and Farewell" must be finished. "Ave" was in the publisher's hands; a good deal of "Salve" was written; there was a sketch, chapter for chapter, down to the very end. The book could not be abandoned for the vineyard, that I felt and at once. It was between Mullingar and Dublin that I realized, more acutely than I had ever done before, that this book was the cause of my being. "I have been led to write it, by whom I know not, but I have been led by the hand like a little child." It was borne in upon me at the same time that a sacrifice was demanded of me, by whom I knew not, nor for what purpose, but I felt I must leave my native land and my friends for the sake of the book; a work of liberation I divined it to be—liberation from ritual and priests, a book of precept and example. I knew this book to be the turning point in Ireland's destiny and yet I prayed that I might be spared the pain of the writing it and permitted instead to acquire the Clos St. Georges, a wife, and a son. But no man escapes his fate. Something was propelling me out of Ireland, whither I was not yet sure.

"I must yield myself to my instinct," I said to Æ, and he was deeply moved.

"But where shall I spend my evenings when you are gone?"

"It surprises me to hear you talk like this," I answered. "It was you who brought me here, knowing that Ireland needed my help; you voiced the desire of Ireland and I obeyed your bidding, and now it is done, and I must go. 'Ave' is in the printer's hands, after it will come 'Salve,' and after that 'Vale.' It may grieve you to lose me, dear Æ, and it grieves me to lose you. . . . I shall never find anybody like you again. Æ is only found once in a lifetime."

"But you'll not forget me," he said, grasping my hand, and there were almost tears in his eyes.

Next night we met at Bailey's, the Land Commissioner who lives in Earlsfort Terrace, and whose friendship I had gained in the last year of my sojourn in Ireland, and found it so pleasant that it is a matter of regret for me not to have claimed it sooner. An alert and witty mind is always so rare among men that it is a pity ever to let it go by, and I let Bailey go by for many a year. He knows a good picture and buys one occasionally, he reads books and has practiced literature, and will probably practice it again; some day he will write his memoirs. And, better still, he practices life. He goes away every year for long travel, and returns, his mind the richer. He likes to invite clever men and pretty women to his house. He has not influenced me in my life as Æ, or John Eglinton, or Yeats, and to speak of him here is a little outside of my subject, but if I closed this book without mention of him it would seem that I had forgotten the many hours we passed together. Besides, his din-

ner party is fixed in my mind. He assembled all my
friends: Æ, Ernest Longworth, Philip Hanson,
John Healy, John Eglinton, the graceful and witty
Dena Tyrrell, and Susan Mitchell, who sang songs
about the friends I was leaving behind me.

It was very sad leaving those ten years of my
life, and next morning, a gray misty morning in
February, the train took me to Kingstown, a very
different departure from the one that I had long
been meditating. The ideal departure should have
been on an evening in May, and with the golden
west behind me I should have watched from the vessel's stern the beautiful outlines of the coast and
the lovely shapes of Howth, thinking a last farewell. I should have murmured the words of Catullus
when he journeyed over land and sea to burn the
body of his brother, and to fit them to my circumstance a change of a single word would have been
enough:

Atque in Perpetuum, Mater, Ave Atque Vale.

Our dreams and our circumstances are often in
conflict, and never were they in greater opposition
than the day the train took me from Westland Row
to Kingstown—a long, barren tract of sand: a gray
sky hanging low over the gray sea without a ripple
in it, like glass. If the evening had been a golden
evening my heart might have overflowed with fine
sentiments; it is on golden evenings that fine sentiments overflow the heart! then it is like crystal that
the least touch will break; but on a cold, bleak,

February morning the prophet is as uninspired as his humblest fellow, and a very humble fellow, forgetful of Ireland, forgetful of Catholicism, forgetful of literature, went below to think of the friends he had left behind him—Æ and the rest.

(1)

THE END